Essentials of Pure Mathematics

J. R. Irwin

Head of Mathematics
Harrow Weald Sixth Form College

Edward Arnold

© R. Irwin 1981

First published 1981
by Edward Arnold (Publishers) Ltd.
41 Bedford Square, London WCIB 3DQ

ISBN 0 7131 0551 8

British Library Cataloguing in Publication Data

Irwin, J. R.
  Essentials of pure mathematics.
  1. Mathematics – 1961–
  I. Title
  510   QA39.2

Photo Typeset by
Macmillan India Ltd. Bangalore
Printed in Great Britain by
Butler & Tanner Ltd, Frome and London

Preface

This book is intended to cover the pure mathematics content of single subject Advanced level courses in 'Mathematics' and 'Pure Mathematics with Statistics'. When used in conjunction with *Essentials of Applied Mathematics* it will provide a complete course in mathematics. Particular attention has been paid to the SCUE/CNAA Minimal Core Syllabus which seems to be gaining widespread acceptance.

As with *Essentials of Applied Mathematics* the aim has been to produce a book which can be comprehended by the average student and which provides a carefully structured sequence of exercises designed to increase proficiency in easy stages. Important ideas are introduced as simply as possible and interpreted by frequent reference to basic curve shapes. It is hoped that this graphical emphasis will encourage the student to develop a visual image of what he is doing and so increase his understanding.

Most students nowadays have access to electronic calculators and certain sections of the book are designed to make use of these. At the same time, however, the importance of accuracy is stressed repeatedly and, from the first chapter, the student is encouraged to work in surds whenever appropriate.

There is no work on vectors in this volume and only a short section on differential equations has been included. I dislike an abstract approach to these topics and believe they are best understood and appreciated through a study of their applications. Both receive detailed treatment along these lines in *Essentials of Applied Mathematics* so it would seem unnecessary and uneconomical to repeat this material here.

The book contains a vast number of exercises which should give ample routine practice on each topic. For further work many teachers prefer to use the past examination papers of their own particular examining board and for this reason sets of miscellaneous examination questions have not been included.

Note: Questions marked * introduce ideas or techniques which are not specifically mentioned in the text. Many of these will need discussion after the group has attempted them.

Contents

1
Basic Methods

With the possible exception of Section 1.2 most of the ideas in this chapter should already have been encountered at Ordinary Level. The exercises are intended for revision purposes. Explanation is kept to a minimum.

1.1 Indices

Positive powers

$$a^1 = a$$
$$a^2 = a \times a$$
$$a^3 = a \times a \times a$$
$$a^4 = a \times a \times a \times a \quad \text{etc.}$$

Laws of indices

$$\text{Clearly} \quad a^2 \times a^3 = (a \times a) \times (a \times a \times a) \qquad = a^5$$
$$a^6 \div a^2 = \frac{a \times a \times a \times a \times a \times a}{a \times a} \qquad = a^4$$
$$(a^2)^3 \quad = a^2 \times a^2 \times a^2 \qquad = a^6$$

These examples illustrate the three fundamental laws of indices, which may be stated as follows:

$a^m \times a^n = a^{m+n}$	Add indices	(1)
$a^m \div a^n = a^{m-n}$	Subtract indices	(2)
$(a^m)^n = a^{mn}$	Multiply indices	(3)

Negative powers

These are best remembered as 'one over' the corresponding positive power, i.e.

$$a^{-1} = \frac{1}{a} \qquad a^{-2} = \frac{1}{a^2} \qquad a^{-3} = \frac{1}{a^3}$$

This is consistent with law (2) above since, for example, we may write

$$a^{-3} = a^1 \div a^4 = \frac{a}{a \times a \times a \times a} = \frac{1}{a^3}$$

Power zero

$$a^0 = 1$$

Any number raised to power zero gives one. This follows from law (1) since, according to this law,

$$a^n \times a^0 = a^n \qquad \text{(adding indices)}$$

$a^0 = 1$ is the only value consistent with this statement.

Fractional powers

$$a^{\frac{1}{2}} = \sqrt{a} \quad \text{(square root)} \quad \text{since} \quad a^{\frac{1}{2}} \times a^{\frac{1}{2}} = a^1 = a$$
$$a^{\frac{1}{3}} = \sqrt[3]{a} \quad \text{(cube root)} \qquad \text{since} \quad a^{\frac{1}{3}} \times a^{\frac{1}{3}} \times a^{\frac{1}{3}} = a^1 = a$$

In the same way $a^{\frac{2}{3}}$ would be the cube root of a^2 since

$$a^{\frac{2}{3}} \times a^{\frac{2}{3}} \times a^{\frac{2}{3}} = a^{\frac{6}{3}} = a^2$$

Or, alternatively, it may be regarded as the square of the cube root of a

$$a^{\frac{2}{3}} = (a^{\frac{1}{3}})^2 = (\text{cube root})^2$$

Example   1

Evaluate (i) $16^{\frac{1}{4}}$ (ii) $25^{1\frac{1}{2}}$ (iii) $(\frac{3}{4})^{-2}$ (iv) $(0.125)^{-\frac{1}{3}}$

(i) $16^{\frac{1}{4}}$ = fourth root of $16 = \pm 2$

(ii) $25^{1\frac{1}{2}} = 25^{\frac{3}{2}} = (\text{square root of } 25)^3 = (\pm 5)^3 = \pm 125$

For negative powers, work out the corresponding positive power first and then invert. Thus

(iii) $\left(\dfrac{3}{4}\right)^2 = \dfrac{3}{4} \times \dfrac{3}{4} = \dfrac{9}{16}$ so $\left(\dfrac{3}{4}\right)^{-2} = \dfrac{16}{9}$

(iv) $(0.125)^{\frac{1}{3}} = \text{cube root of } \dfrac{1}{8} = \dfrac{1}{2}$ so $(0.125)^{-\frac{1}{3}} = 2$

Exercise 1 (a)

For simplicity, negative roots have been ignored.

1. Write down the values of

(i)	3^4	(ii)	3^{-4}	(iii)	2^5
(iv)	2^{-5}	(v)	10^3	(vi)	10^{-3}
(vii)	$(\frac{1}{2})^3$	(viii)	$(\frac{1}{2})^{-3}$	(ix)	5^0
(x)	$9^{\frac{1}{2}}$	(xi)	$9^{-\frac{1}{2}}$	(xii)	$64^{\frac{1}{3}}$
(xiii)	$64^{-\frac{1}{3}}$	(xiv)	$8^{\frac{2}{3}}$	(xv)	$8^{-\frac{2}{3}}$

2. Simplify

(i) $a^2 \times a^5$ (ii) $b^9 \div b^5$

(iii) $c^3 \times c^{-3}$ (iv) $(d^3)^4$

(v) $3a^2b \times 2a^3b$ (vi) $8pq^4 \div 2pq$

(vii) $(3t^2)^3$ (viii) $2^{-5} \times 2^7$

(ix) $(16a^2)^{\frac{1}{2}}$ (x) $3^{1\frac{1}{2}} \div 3^{\frac{1}{2}}$

(xi) $(\frac{1}{8}r^6)^{\frac{2}{3}}$ (xii) $8^{\frac{1}{3}} \times 2^{-2} \div (\frac{1}{2})^4$

3. Evaluate

(i) $49^{\frac{1}{2}}$ (ii) 3^{-3} (iii) $(0.001)^{\frac{1}{3}}$

(iv) $27^{\frac{2}{3}}$ (v) $16^{1\frac{1}{2}}$ (vi) $(1\frac{1}{2})^{-4}$

(vii) $81^{-\frac{1}{4}}$ (viii) $4^{-2\frac{1}{2}}$ (ix) $(2.5)^{-1}$

(x) $(\frac{9}{16})^{-\frac{1}{2}}$ (xi) $(3\frac{3}{8})^{\frac{1}{3}}$ (xii) $(0.04)^{-1\frac{1}{2}}$

4. State, in each case, the value of x.

(i) $4^x = 64$ (ii) $10^x = 0.01$ (iii) $x^3 = 216$

(iv) $x^{\frac{1}{2}} = 5$ (v) $(\frac{1}{2})^x = 2$ (vi) $x^{0.2} = 3$

(vii) $x^{-2} = \dfrac{1}{25}$ (viii) $(\frac{2}{3})^x = 1$ (ix) $8^x = \frac{1}{2}$

1.2 Approximations and surds

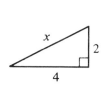

Fig. 1a

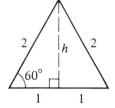

Fig. 1b

By Pythagoras' Theorem it is easily seen that the length x in Fig. 1a is given by $\sqrt{20}$. As soon as we look up this square root, however, our answer becomes approximate. From four figure tables we obtain $x \approx 4.472$ which is correct only to three decimal places. A more accurate answer, perhaps to six decimal places, may be obtained from a calculator, but it will still be an approximation. The only way we can write down the answer *exactly* is to leave it as a square root, i.e. $x = \sqrt{20}$. This is known as leaving the answer in **surd form**.

Similarly when we look up $\sin 60°$ in tables the value we obtain (i.e. 0.8660) is not the exact answer for $\sin 60°$ but an approximation correct to four figures. The *exact* value for $\sin 60°$ may be obtained by considering an equilateral triangle of side 2 units as in Fig. 1b. By Pythagoras, the altitude $h = \sqrt{3}$ so that $\sin 60° = \sqrt{3}/2$. Again, if we wish to be *precise* then we must leave the value in surd form, for the square root of 3 can never be written down exactly.

It is important to remember in 'A' Level Mathematics work that if we are asked to prove a result which is exact then we must not take any values from tables (i.e. sines, cosines, square roots, etc.) since these are *not* exact and cannot help us towards an exact answer. Because of this it is frequently necessary to work in terms of square roots (or **surds**). The purpose of this section is to give some practice in this.

Simplifying answers

(i) When leaving an answer in surd form the square root involved should be the simplest one possible. For example

$$\sqrt{20} = \sqrt{4 \times 5} = 2\sqrt{5}$$

since we may take out the square root of the factor 4. Thus in Fig. 1a the answer $x = 2\sqrt{5}$ is preferable to $x = \sqrt{20}$. Some further examples of this process are

$$\sqrt{18} = \sqrt{2 \times 9} = 3\sqrt{2}$$
$$\sqrt{75} = \sqrt{3 \times 25} = 5\sqrt{3}$$

(ii) When an answer is in the form of a fraction then any square root involved should appear in the numerator (i.e. on top). A fraction where a square root appears in the denominator may be modified to this form by multiplying top and bottom by the same square root, e.g.

$$\frac{2}{\sqrt{6}} = \frac{2\sqrt{6}}{\sqrt{6} \times \sqrt{6}} = \frac{2\sqrt{6}}{6} = \frac{\sqrt{6}}{3}$$

This form is preferred for two reasons. Firstly it is easier to combine surds when they are in this form (see final example below) and secondly it is easier to obtain an approximation to the value of $\sqrt{6}/3$ (i.e. approximately $2.449 \div 3 \approx 0.816$) than it is for $2/\sqrt{6}$ which involves an awkward division.

Combination of surds

Surds may be multiplied together or divided without difficulty in accordance with the following rules:

$$\boxed{\begin{array}{l} \sqrt{a} \times \sqrt{b} = \sqrt{ab} \\ \sqrt{a} \div \sqrt{b} = \sqrt{\dfrac{a}{b}} \end{array}}$$

e.g. $\sqrt{4} \times \sqrt{9} = \sqrt{36} \quad (2 \times 3 = 6)$

e.g. $\sqrt{100} \div \sqrt{4} = \sqrt{25} \quad (10 \div 2 = 5)$

Thus
$$\sqrt{2} \times \sqrt{3} = \sqrt{6}$$
$$\sqrt{10} \div \sqrt{5} = \sqrt{2}$$

With more complicated surds it is better to simplify the individual surds before multiplying. For example

$$\sqrt{18} \times \sqrt{75} = 3\sqrt{2} \times 5\sqrt{3} = 15\sqrt{6}$$

Addition or subtraction of surds is not generally possible. It is clearly not true, for example, that $\sqrt{4} + \sqrt{9} = \sqrt{13}$. In fact addition and subtraction are only possible where simplification of the individual surds leads to a common square root, e.g.

$$\sqrt{20} + \sqrt{5} = 2\sqrt{5} + \sqrt{5} = 3\sqrt{5}$$
$$\sqrt{75} - \sqrt{27} = 5\sqrt{3} - 3\sqrt{3} = 2\sqrt{3}$$

The last example shows how the general rule of keeping surds in the numerators of fractions may sometimes help in achieving a simplification

$$\frac{\sqrt{3}}{\sqrt{2}} - \frac{1}{\sqrt{6}}$$
$$= \frac{\sqrt{3}\sqrt{2}}{\sqrt{2}\sqrt{2}} - \frac{\sqrt{6}}{\sqrt{6}\sqrt{6}}$$
$$= \frac{\sqrt{6}}{2} - \frac{\sqrt{6}}{6} = \frac{1}{3}\sqrt{6}$$

Exercise 1 (b)

1. Simplify the following by leaving the smallest possible square root:
   (i) $\sqrt{12}$ (ii) $\sqrt{28}$ (iii) $\sqrt{45}$
   (iv) $\sqrt{8}$ (v) $\sqrt{48}$ (vi) $\sqrt{40}$
   (vii) $\sqrt{80}$ (viii) $\sqrt{98}$ (ix) $\sqrt{117}$
2. Express each of the following as the square root of a single number:
   (i) $3\sqrt{3}$ (ii) $5\sqrt{2}$ (iii) $2\sqrt{6}$
   (iv) $2\sqrt{11}$ (v) $3\sqrt{10}$ (vi) $4\sqrt{7}$
3. Obtain in each case a fraction in which any surd present is in the numerator.
   (i) $\dfrac{2}{\sqrt{2}}$ (ii) $\dfrac{2}{\sqrt{3}}$ (iii) $\dfrac{3}{\sqrt{6}}$
   (iv) $\dfrac{1}{\sqrt{5}}$ (v) $\dfrac{2}{\sqrt{10}}$ (vi) $\dfrac{\sqrt{3}}{\sqrt{5}}$
4. Find the lengths of a, b, c and d giving answers in surd form as simply as possible.

(i)   (ii)

(iii)   (iv)

5. Simplify

(i) $\sqrt{3} \times \sqrt{12}$ (ii) $\sqrt{5} \times \sqrt{10}$

(iii) $\sqrt{27} \times \sqrt{32}$ (iv) $\sqrt{72} \div \sqrt{8}$

(v) $\sqrt{180} \div \sqrt{15}$ (vi) $(\sqrt{5})^3$

(vii) $(2\sqrt{6})^2$ (viii) $(\sqrt{2})^7$

(ix) $\sqrt{10} \times \sqrt{12} \times \sqrt{15}$ (x) $\sqrt{60} \div \sqrt{90}$

(xi) $\sqrt{3} + \sqrt{12}$ (xii) $\sqrt{45} + 3\sqrt{20}$

(xiii) $\sqrt{99} - \sqrt{44}$ (xiv) $\sqrt{8} + \sqrt{50} - \sqrt{32}$

(xv) $\dfrac{\sqrt{3}}{2} + \dfrac{1}{\sqrt{3}}$ (xvi) $\sqrt{40} - \dfrac{5}{\sqrt{10}}$

1.3 Basic algebraic processes

Factors

An expression is said to be **factorized** when it is expressed as a product of quantities which are **multiplied** together. These quantities are called **factors**. Thus the number 12 may be written as the product of factors 3 and 4 or of factors 2 and 6, i.e.

$$12 = 3 \times 4 \qquad 12 = 2 \times 6$$

In the same way an expression such as $x^2 + 2x$ may be written as the product of two factors, these being x and the bracket $(x + 2)$, i.e.

$$x^2 + 2x = x(x + 2)$$

A quadratic function (see Section 5.2) may sometimes be factorized as the product of two brackets. For example, the factors of $x^2 - 3x - 10$ are $(x - 5)$ and $(x + 2)$ since we may write

$$x^2 - 3x - 10 = (x - 5)(x + 2)$$

Another common type of factorization is that known as the **difference of two squares**. Examples are

$$a^2 - b^2 = (a + b)(a - b)$$
$$x^2 - 4 = (x + 2)(x - 2)$$

Reduction of fractions to lowest terms

The cancellation of a simple fraction to lowest terms, e.g. $\frac{8}{12} = \frac{2}{3}$, involves the cancelling of a common factor (in this case 4) from both numerator and denominator. A similar process may be performed with algebraic fractions but to ensure that we only cancel factors it is vital to begin by factorizing both the numerator and the denominator, e.g.

$$\frac{a^2}{a^2 + 5a} = \frac{a^2}{a(a + 5)} = \frac{a}{(a + 5)}$$

$$\frac{3x - xy}{y^2 - 9} = \frac{x(3 - y)}{(y + 3)(y - 3)} = \frac{-x}{(y + 3)}$$

Notice, in the second example, the introduction of the minus sign after the cancellation of $(3-y)$ and $(y-3)$. This is because when two numbers are subtracted in opposite orders the results are opposite in sign, e.g. $(8-5)=3$ but $(5-8)=-3$.

Exercise 1(c)

1. Multiply out
   (i) $3(2x-5)$ (ii) $a(a-4)$ (iii) $2x(x+y)$
   (iv) $4p(2p+3q)$ (v) $3p^2(2p-1)$ (vi) $ab(ab+c)$
2. Factorize
   (i) $6x+4$ (ii) $ab-4a$ (iii) $3x^2+x$
   (iv) $xy-y^2$ (v) $6r^2+9r$ (vi) $4pq-8p^2$
3. Multiply out
   (i) $(x+2)(x+3)$ (ii) $(x+6)(x-2)$
   (iii) $(a-2)(a-7)$ (iv) $(b-5)(b+4)$
   (v) $(2x-1)(x+1)$ (vi) $(y+3)(3y+2)$
   (vii) $(a-2)(4a-1)$ (viii) $(p-5)(2p+3)$
   (ix) $(2x-3)(3x-2)$ (x) $(x+2y)(x-y)$
4. Factorize
   (i) x^2+3x+2 (ii) x^2+2x-8
   (iii) $p^2+2p-15$ (iv) $a^2-7a+12$
   (v) y^2-y-30 (vi) $r^2-10r+9$
   (vii) $2x^2+5x+3$ (viii) $3a^2-7a+2$
   (ix) $2y^2+y-6$ (x) $4x^2-16x-9$
5. Multiply out the following **perfect squares**:
   (i) $(x+1)^2$ (ii) $(x+7)^2$
   (iii) $(a-4)^2$ (iv) $(y+\frac{1}{2})^2$
   (v) $(x-\frac{3}{4})^2$ (vi) $(a+\frac{2}{5})^2$
*6. Which number must be added to each of the following expressions in order to make them into perfect squares? (This is sometimes called **completing the square**.)
   (i) x^2+4x (ii) x^2-6x
   (iii) a^2+10a (iv) x^2-x
   (v) p^2+5p (vi) $a^2-\frac{4}{3}a$
   (vii) $x^2-\frac{1}{2}x$ (viii) r^2+9r
7. Multiply out
   (i) $(p+q)(p-q)$ (ii) $(x+4)(x-4)$
   (iii) $(5+y)(5-y)$ (iv) $(2a+1)(2a-1)$
8. Factorize
   (i) x^2-y^2 (ii) p^2-1
   (iii) a^2-49 (iv) $16-y^2$
   (v) $9x^2-1$ (vi) $4a^2-9b^2$
9. Cancel to lowest terms
   (i) $\dfrac{4ab}{6a^2}$ (ii) $\dfrac{3m+3}{5m+5}$
   (iii) $\dfrac{2xy}{3x^2-x}$ (iv) $\dfrac{a^2-b^2}{3a+3b}$

(v) $\dfrac{a + a^2}{ab + b}$ (vi) $\dfrac{3x - 3}{x^2 + x - 2}$

(vii) $\dfrac{2a - a^2}{a^2 - 4}$ (viii) $\dfrac{y^2 + 3y}{y^2 + y - 6}$

1.4 Solution of quadratic equations

Solution by factors

This method is used whenever possible, e.g. to solve $2x^2 - x - 10 = 0$

$(2x - 5)(x + 2) = 0$ factorizing

$\Rightarrow 2x - 5 = 0$ or $x + 2 = 0$

$x = 2\tfrac{1}{2}$ or $x = -2$

Solution by 'completing the square'

The basic method for dealing with equations which cannot be solved by factors, e.g. to solve $x^2 + 6x - 3 = 0$

$x^2 + 6x \quad\ = 3$

$x^2 + 6x + 9 = 3 + 9$

Here 9 is added to both sides, making the l.h.s. a perfect square, i.e.

$(x + 3)^2 = 12$

$x + 3 \ = \pm \sqrt{12} = \pm 2\sqrt{3}$

$x = -3 + 2\sqrt{3}$ or $-3 - 2\sqrt{3}$ (in surd form)

or $x \approx 0.46$ or -6.46

In practice this method is only used for fairly simple equations such as the example considered here. It is more usual to use the formula given below, but it should be appreciated that the derivation of this formula (which will not be given here) is by the method of completing the square.

Solution by formula

The solutions of the equation $ax^2 + bx + c = 0$ are given by the formula

$$x = \frac{-b \pm \sqrt{b^2 - 4ac}}{2a}$$

e.g. to solve $3x^2 - 4x - 2 = 0$ we have $a = 3$, $b = -4$, $c = -2$ so that

$$x = \frac{4 \pm \sqrt{16 + 24}}{6} = \frac{4 \pm \sqrt{40}}{6}$$

Approximate solutions may be obtained by looking up $\sqrt{40}$ in tables, i.e.

$$x \approx \frac{4 \pm 6.325}{6} = \frac{10.325}{6} \quad \text{or} \quad \frac{-2.325}{6}$$

$$x \approx 1.72 \quad \text{or} \quad -0.39$$

Alternatively the exact answers may be left in surd form (after simplification), i.e.

$$x = \frac{1}{6}(4 \pm \sqrt{40}) = \frac{1}{6}(4 \pm 2\sqrt{10})$$

$$x = \frac{1}{3}(2 + \sqrt{10}) \quad \text{or} \quad \frac{1}{3}(2 - \sqrt{10})$$

Exercise 1(d)

1. Solve by factors
   (i) $x^2 - 5x + 6 = 0$ (ii) $x^2 + x - 12 = 0$
   (iii) $x^2 - 7x - 18 = 0$ (iv) $2x^2 + 5x + 3 = 0$
   (v) $3x^2 - 4x + 1 = 0$ (vi) $2x^2 - 7x + 6 = 0$
   (vii) $4x^2 + 7x - 2 = 0$ (viii) $6x^2 - 5x - 4 = 0$

2. Solve by completing the square. Leave your answers in surd form, simplifying where possible.
   (i) $x^2 + 4x + 1 = 0$ (ii) $x^2 - 10x + 20 = 0$
   (iii) $x^2 - 2x - 19 = 0$ (iv) $x^2 + 8x - 2 = 0$
   (v) $x^2 - x - 1 = 0$ (vi) $x^2 + 3x - 1 = 0$

3. Solve by using the formula. Give answers correct to two decimal places.
   (i) $x^2 + 3x + 1 = 0$ (ii) $x^2 = 3x + 11$
   (iii) $2x^2 - 7x - 3 = 0$ (iv) $5x^2 + 8x - 2 = 0$
   (v) $3x^2 + 7x + 3 = 0$ (vi) $3x^2 = 6x + 2$
   (vii) $4x^2 = 8x - 1$ (viii) $2x^2 + 8x = 13$

4. Solve by using the formula but leave your answers in surd form, simplifying where possible.
   (i) $x^2 - 6x + 4 = 0$ (ii) $2x^2 + 2x = 1$
   (iii) $3x^2 - 4x - 3 = 0$ (iv) $x^2 - 3x - 9 = 0$

1.5 Fractions

It is vital for the student to be able to manipulate fractions correctly. The methods are essentially the same as those used with ordinary fractions. A detailed explanation is not given here but some examples follow.

Multiplication and division

Cancel any common factors and then multiply together the factors which remain, e.g.

$$\frac{p^2 - pq}{3q} \div \frac{p^2 - q^2}{6p} = \frac{p(p - q)}{3q} \times \frac{\overset{2}{6p}}{(p+q)(p-q)}$$

$$= \frac{2p^2}{q(p+q)}$$

Addition and subtraction

The fractions can only be combined by the usual method of obtaining a common denominator, e.g.

$$\frac{3}{x+y} - \frac{2}{x-y} = \frac{3(x-y)}{(x+y)(x-y)} - \frac{2(x+y)}{(x+y)(x-y)}$$

$$= \frac{3x - 3y - 2x - 2y}{(x+y)(x-y)}$$

$$= \frac{x - 5y}{(x+y)(x-y)} \quad \text{or} \quad \frac{x - 5y}{x^2 - y^2}$$

$$\frac{b}{a^2 - ab} + \frac{1}{a} = \frac{b}{a(a-b)} + \frac{(a-b)}{a(a-b)}$$

$$= \frac{b + a - b}{a(a-b)}$$

$$= \frac{a}{a(a-b)} \quad \text{or} \quad \frac{1}{a-b}$$

The answer should be reduced to lowest terms (as in the last example above).

Exercise 1(e)

Express each of the following as a single fraction in lowest terms:

1. $\dfrac{3a}{bc} \div \dfrac{6b}{ac}$

2. $\dfrac{s}{r} + \dfrac{r^2 - s^2}{rs}$

3. $\dfrac{x+y}{3} - \dfrac{x-y}{4}$

4. $\dfrac{m+n}{m} \times \dfrac{m^2}{2m+2n}$

5. $\dfrac{2+a}{a} + \dfrac{3-b}{b}$

6. $\dfrac{1}{x-3} + \dfrac{1}{x+3}$

7. $\dfrac{a^2 - ab}{2b} \div \dfrac{a^2 - b^2}{6b}$

8. $\dfrac{1}{m} - \dfrac{n}{m^2 + mn}$

9. $1 - \dfrac{p-q}{p+q}$

10. $\dfrac{r^2-4}{r^2-3r+2} \times \dfrac{r-1}{r}$

11. $\dfrac{xy}{x^2-y^2} - \dfrac{y}{x+y}$

12. $\dfrac{1}{y} + \dfrac{1}{z} - \dfrac{2}{(y+z)}$

1.6 Coordinates

To illustrate the ideas of this section we shall use Fig. 2 on which the points $A(2,0)$, $B(3,4)$, $C(-3,2)$ and $D(-2,-3)$ have been plotted.

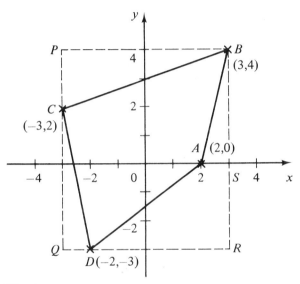

Fig. 2

Midpoints

The midpoint of two points is found by taking the average of the x coordinates and of the y coordinates, e.g.

the midpoint of $A(2,0)$ and $B(3,4)$ is $(2\frac{1}{2}, 2)$
the midpoint of $C(-3,2)$ and $D(-2,-3)$ is $(-2\frac{1}{2}, -\frac{1}{2})$

In general the midpoint of (x_1, y_1) and (x_2, y_2) is

$$\left(\frac{x_1 + x_2}{2}, \frac{y_1 + y_2}{2} \right)$$

Distances

The distance between two points is found by Pythagoras' Theorem, using the horizontal and vertical distances between the points. (These are obtained by comparing the x coordinates and the y coordinates respectively.) For example, to find the distance CB we have

horizontal distance (PB) from -3 to $+3 = 6$ units
vertical distance (CP) from 2 to $4 = 2$ units

so $BC^2 = 6^2 + 2^2 = 40$

           $BC = \sqrt{40}$ or $2\sqrt{10}$ units

In general the distance between (x_1, y_1) and (x_2, y_2) is given by

$$\sqrt{(x_1 - x_2)^2 + (y_1 - y_2)^2}$$

Plane areas

An area, such as that of the quadrilateral $ABCD$, may be found by enclosing the figure in a rectangle and then subtracting the unwanted triangles and trapezia. Thus, in Fig. 2

Area of rectangle	$BPQR$	$= 6 \times 7$	$= 42$ sq. units.
Area of triangle	PBC	$= \frac{1}{2} \times 6 \times 2$	$= 6$ sq. units.
Area of triangle	CQD	$= \frac{1}{2} \times 5 \times 1$	$= 2\frac{1}{2}$ sq. units.
Area of triangle	ABS	$= \frac{1}{2} \times 4 \times 1$	$= 2$ sq. units.
Area of trapezium	$ADRS$	$= \frac{1}{2}(1 + 5) \times 3$	$= 9$ sq. units.
Area of quadrilateral	$ABCD$	$= 42 - 19\frac{1}{2}$	$= 22\frac{1}{2}$ sq. units.

Exercise 1 (f)

1. In each case find the distance between the points given and the coordinates of their midpoint.

   (i) $(1, 4)$ and $(5, 5)$ (ii) $(-2, 1)$ and $(10, 6)$
   (iii) $(-2, -3)$ and $(4, 0)$ (iv) $(-8, -3)$ and $(-1, 4)$

2. Plot the points $A(2, 7)$, $B(-5, 5)$, $C(0, -3)$ and $D(7, -4)$ on squared paper. Find the area of the quadrilateral $ABCD$ and calculate the distance between the midpoints of BC and AD.

3. Find, in surd form, the lengths of the sides of the triangle formed by $R(4, 4)$, $S(-3, 0)$ and $T(1, -2)$. Using these results
   (i) prove that the triangle is right-angled
   (ii) find the area of the triangle.
   Verify your answer to part (ii) by a separate method.

4. Use the method of the above section to find the area of the triangle formed by the points $A(5, 3)$, $B(-3, -1)$ and $C(1, -4)$. Calculate the length of the side BC and hence find the distance of A from the line BC. Show also that the triangle BCM, where M is the midpoint of AB, is isosceles.

5. If the distances from the point $P(x, y)$ to the points $A(-1, 2)$ and $B(3, 1)$ are equal, prove that the coordinates x and y must satisfy the relation $8x - 2y = 5$.

1.7 Graphs and intersections

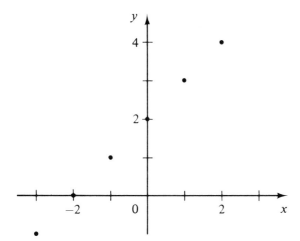

Fig. 3a

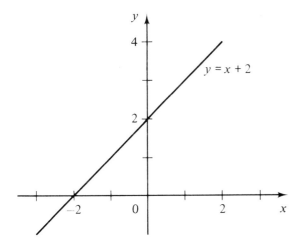

Fig. 3b

Graphs

The graph of an equation involving x and y may be defined as the set of all points (x, y) in $\mathbb{R}^2$ whose coordinates satisfy the given equation.

Consider for example the equation $y = x + 2$. Some points whose coordinates satisfy this relation (i.e. the y coordinate exceeds the x coordinate by 2) are $(2, 4)$, $(1, 3)$, $(0, 2)$, $(-1, 1)$ etc. When plotted these points are found to lie along a line (Fig. 3a). If we could imagine *all* such points to be plotted then we would obtain the straight line of Fig. 3b.

In the same way we may regard the graph of $y = x^2$ as the collection of all points for which the y coordinate is the square of the x coordinate and, to take a more complicated example, the graph of $y = x^2 + 4x$ consists of all points satisfying the relation

$$(y \text{ coord.}) = (x \text{ coord.})^2 - 4(x \text{ coord.})$$

Example　2

Find the points on the curve $y = x^2 + 4x$, where
   (i)　the y coordinate is 5
   (ii)　the curve crosses the x-axis.

(i)　All points on the curve must satisfy the relation $y = x^2 + 4x$. When $y = 5$ we therefore have

$$
\begin{aligned}
5 &= x^2 + 4x \\
\Rightarrow 0 &= x^2 + 4x - 5 \\
0 &= (x + 5)(x - 1) \\
\Rightarrow x &= -5 \quad \text{or} \quad x = 1
\end{aligned}
$$

   The points are $(-5, 5)$ and $(1, 5)$

(ii)　Where the curve crosses the x-axis the y coordinate must be zero. Putting $y = 0$ into the equation we obtain

$$
\begin{aligned}
0 &= x^2 + 4x \\
0 &= x(x + 4) \\
\Rightarrow x &= 0 \quad \text{or} \quad x = -4
\end{aligned}
$$

   The intersections are therefore at $(0, 0)$ and $(-4, 0)$

Intersections

Example　3

Find the points of intersection of the line $y = 2x + 3$ with the curve $y = x^2 + 4x$.

At the intersections we must have (see note below)

$$
\begin{aligned}
x^2 + 4x &= 2x + 3 & \text{(1)} \\
\Rightarrow x^2 + 2x - 3 &= 0 \\
(x + 3)(x - 1) &= 0 \\
\Rightarrow x = -3 \quad &\text{or} \quad x = 1
\end{aligned}
$$

These are the x coordinates of the intersections. The y coordinates are found by substituting in either $y = 2x + 3$ or $y = x^2 + 4x$. Hence the points of intersection are $(-3, -3)$ and $(1, 5)$.

Note: The y coordinate of an intersection point must be given by both $2x + 3$

and $x^2 + 4x$ (since the point lies on both graphs). So at such a point these functions must take the same value, i.e. line (1) is obtained.

Exercise 1 (g)

1. Which of the following points are on the line $y = 3x + 1$?
   $A(2, 7)$, $B(4, 11)$, $C(1, 0)$, $D(-2, -5)$
   Find also the intersection with the x-axis.
2. Which of the following points are on the curve $y = x^2 + x$?
   $P(3, 15)$, $Q(6, 42)$, $R(-2, 2)$, $S(-5, 20)$
   Find also the intersections with the x-axis.
3. How far apart are the points on the line $y = 3x - 2$ whose x coordinates are -1 and 2 respectively?
4. How far apart are the points on $y = x^2 + 5x - 3$ which have y coordinate 11?
5. Find the points of intersection of
   (i) $y = x^2$ and $y = x + 2$
   (ii) $y = 2x^2 - 1$ and $y = 1 - 3x$
6. Fig. 4 shows sketches of four graphs. Two of these are sketched incorrectly. Find the coordinates of the intersections $A, B, C, D, E, F, G, H, I, J$ and hence re-sketch where appropriate.

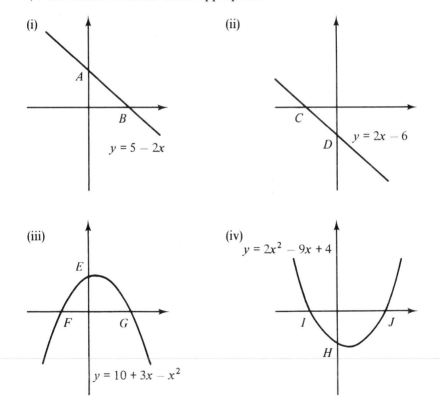

(i)

A

B

$y = 5 - 2x$

(ii)

C

D

$y = 2x - 6$

(iii)

E

F G

$y = 10 + 3x - x^2$

(iv)

$y = 2x^2 - 9x + 4$

I J

H

Fig. 4

7. If the line $y = Ax + B$ (where A and B are constants) passes through the points $(3, 12)$ and $(-1, -8)$, find the values of A and B.

*8. The points P and Q are the intersections of $y = x^2 - x$ and $y = 3x - 2$. Find, in surd form, the x coordinates of P and Q. Hence find *exactly* the coordinates of the midpoint of P and Q.

Exercise 1(h) (Graphical work)

The object of this exercise is to familiarise the student with the shapes of certain basic types of graphs.

1. *Linear (or straight line) graphs*
   Use axes $-3 \leqslant x \leqslant 5$ and $-5 \leqslant y \leqslant 5$. Plot a few points which satisfy each of the following relations and hence obtain their graphs.
   (i) $y = x - 1$ (ii) $y = 3 - 2x$ (iii) $2y + x = 6$
2. *Quadratic graphs*   (equations involving x^2, x and constant terms)
   Use axes $-4 \leqslant x \leqslant 5$ and $-10 \leqslant y \leqslant 20$. Draw the following graphs. (Tables of values may help for (ii) and (iii).)
   (i) $y = x^2$: plot points from $x = -4$ to $+4$
   (ii) $y = 2x^2 - 3x$: plot points from $x = -2$ to $+4$
   (iii) $y = 7 + 2x - x^2$: plot points from $x = -3$ to $+5$

   Notice that the basic shape of these graphs is the same (i.e. a single symmetrical curve) and that this shape is inverted for equation (iii) where the x^2 term is negative.
3. $1/x$ *and* $1/x^2$ *graphs*
   Use axes $-6 \leqslant x \leqslant 6$ and $-12 \leqslant y \leqslant 12$. Plot the graphs of (i) $y = 12/x$ and (ii) $y = 12/x^2$ considering negative values of x also. Notice in particular the behaviour of these graphs as x increases and as x gets close to zero.

2

The Straight Line

2.1 The equation $y = mx + c$

We shall see shortly that the equation $y = mx + c$ represents a straight line with **gradient** m and **intercept** c on the y axis. First it is necessary to explain the word **gradient**.

Fig. 1a   Fig. 1b

The gradient of a line

Naturally enough the gradient of a line is a measure of its steepness. One method by which this may be represented is that used on road signs where a gradient of 1 in 3 indicates that the road rises vertically by 1 unit of distance for every 3 units covered horizontally (Fig. 1a). (On the Continent, road gradients are frequently given as percentages; thus a 1 in 3 gradient is given as $\frac{1}{3} \times 100 = 33\frac{1}{3}\%$.)

Mathematically we write our gradients as fractions, i.e. the gradient of the line in Fig. 1a is taken to be $\frac{1}{3}$. To make this more precise consider Fig. 1b, where an increase in x coordinate, as we pass along the line from A to B, results in a corresponding increase in y coordinate as shown. The gradient is defined by

$$\text{gradient} = \frac{\text{increase in } y}{\text{increase in } x} \quad \text{or} \quad \frac{\text{vertical increase}}{\text{horizontal increase}}$$

Example 4

Find the gradients of the lines through
   (i) $(2, -1)$ and $(5, 4)$ (ii) $(-2, 3)$ and $(4, 1)$

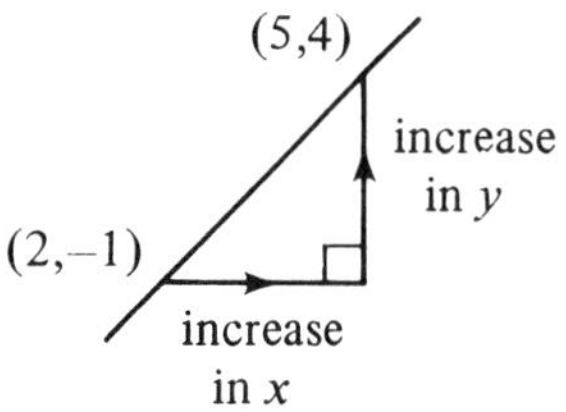

(5,4)

increase
in y

(2,−1)

increase
in x

increase in x

(−2,3)   decrease
in y

(4,1)

Fig. 2a 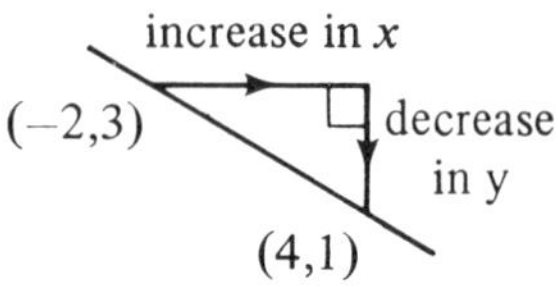   Fig. 2b

(i)   A sketch as in Fig. 2a shows that as x increases by 3 units (from 2 to 5) y increases by 5 units (from -1 to 4). Thus

$$\text{gradient} = \frac{\text{increase in } y}{\text{increase in } x} = \frac{5}{3}$$

(ii) Here as x increases by 6 units (from -2 to 4) the value of y *decreases* (Fig. 2b). In cases such as this the gradient of the line is negative.

$$\text{gradient} = \frac{\text{increase in } y}{\text{increase in } x} = \frac{-2}{6} = -\frac{1}{3}$$

Note: If the two points are (x_1, y_1) and (x_2, y_2) then the gradient is given in all cases by

$$\frac{\text{difference in } y \text{ coordinates}}{\text{difference in } x \text{ coordinates}} = \frac{y_2 - y_1}{x_2 - x_1}$$

where the same order of subtraction is employed for both x and y coordinates.

The equation $y = mx + c$

We now show that this equation represents a straight line with gradient m and intercept c on the y axis (i.e. passing through the y axis at c).

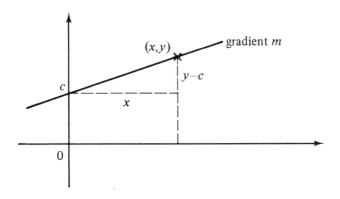

Fig. 3

Let (x, y) be any point on a line with gradient m and intercept c on the y-axis. Then from Fig. 3 we see that

$$\text{gradient } m = \frac{\text{increase in } y}{\text{increase in } x} = \frac{y - c}{x}$$

$$\Rightarrow mx = y - c$$

$$y = mx + c$$

Since this must be true for all points (x, y) on the line, it follows that $y = mx + c$ is the equation of the line.

Thus the equation $y = 2x + 3$ represents a line with gradient 2 and y intercept 3 (Fig. 4a) and the equation $y = 5 - \frac{1}{4}x$ a line with gradient $-\frac{1}{4}$ and y intercept 5 (Fig. 4b).

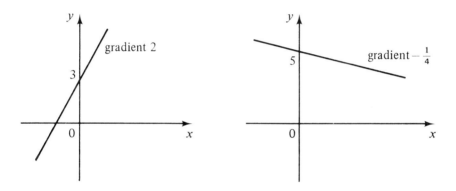

Fig. 4a   Fig. 4b

Example 5

Interpret the characteristics of the line $2y + x = 5$ and find the intercept of this line on the x-axis. Write down also the equation of a parallel line cutting the y-axis at 3.

We first rearrange $2y + x = 5$ to obtain an equation of the form $y = mx + c$

$$2y + x = 5 \quad \Rightarrow 2y = -x + 5$$

$$\text{or} \quad y = -\tfrac{1}{2}x + \tfrac{5}{2}$$

Comparing with $y = mx + c$ we see that $m = -\frac{1}{2}$ and $c = \frac{5}{2}$ or $2\frac{1}{2}$. Thus the line has gradient $-\frac{1}{2}$ and y intercept $2\frac{1}{2}$.

The line crosses the x-axis when $y = 0 \Rightarrow x = 5$ (using the equation $2y + x = 5$). The intercept on the x-axis is therefore 5.

A parallel line will have the same gradient (i.e. $-\frac{1}{2}$). The line required must also have y intercept 3. Its equation is therefore $y = -\frac{1}{2}x + 3$ or $2y + x = 6$.

Exercise 2(a)

1. Find the gradients of the lines through the following pairs of points:
   (i) $(3, 2)$ and $(5, 8)$ (ii) $(2, 1)$ and $(8, -3)$
   (iii) $(-1, 5)$ and $(3, 7)$ (iv) $(-3, -5)$ and $(-1, 4)$.

2. Write down the gradients of PQ and QR where the coordinates are $P(-3, 1)$, $Q(1, 4)$ and $R(9, 10)$. What can be said about the points P, Q and R?

3. Find the gradient of the chord AB on $y = x^2$ where A and B are the points with x coordinates (i) a and $2a$ (ii) a and b (iii) a and $2b$. Give your answers in the simplest possible form.

4. The quadrilateral $ABCD$ has vertices $A(-2, 7)$, $B(3, 2)$, $C(2, -3)$ and $D(-3, 2)$. Find the gradients of AB, BC, CD and DA. What can be deduced about the quadrilateral?

5. Write down the gradient, the y intercept and the x intercept for each of the following lines. Make a simple sketch of each line.
   (i) $y = 3x - 7$ (ii) $y = 3x$
   (iii) $y = 5 - 2x$ (iv) $y = \frac{1}{2}x - 3$
   (v) $y = x + 1$ (vi) $y = \frac{1}{4}(x - 2)$

6. Rearrange the following equations into the form $y = mx + c$ and hence state the gradient and the y intercept of each.

   (i) $5 - y = 3x$ (ii) $3y + 2x = 0$ (iii) $2y - x + 1 = 0$
   (iv) $1 - 3y = 6x$ (v) $4y + 2x = 3$ (vi) $ay - a^2x = 1$

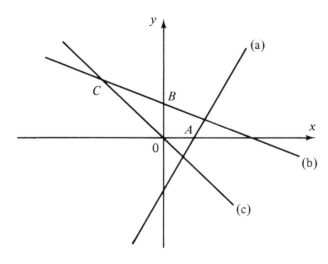

Fig. 5

7. Fig. 5 shows sketches of $x + y = 0$, $4y + x = 6$, $2y - 3x + 6 = 0$. State which of these equations is appropriate to each of the lines (a), (b) and (c). Find the coordinates of the points A, B and C.

8. What is the gradient of the line $4y = 3x$? Write down the equation of the line parallel to $4y = 3x$ whose y intercept is 3. Find
   (i) the x intercept of the second line
   (ii) the perpendicular distance between the two lines.

2.2 Linear laws

It is often useful in experimental work if an algebraic law can be found connecting the values of two variables under observation. The simplest case of this is when the values concerned are found to lie on (or close to) a straight line graph. The two variables are then said to obey a **linear law** and a formula analogous to $y = mx + c$ may be found relating them.

Example 6

The following values of a quantity Q are observed at certain times (t mins) after the start of an experiment

Time t mins	25	35	45	60	70
Quantity Q	61.8	64.5	67.6	72.3	75.1

By plotting Q against t, show that there is an approximate law of the form $Q = a + bt$ and find the best values of the constants a and b. Predict the value of Q at time 90 mins.

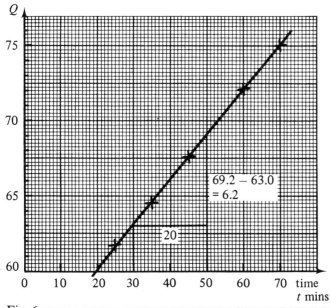

Fig. 6

When required to plot Q *against* t it is important that we put values of Q on the vertical (or y) axis and values of t on the horizontal (or x) axis. This has been done in Fig. 6 and the points obtained are found to lie very close to a straight line. The equation of this line will be of the form $y = mx + c$ but here, replacing y by Q and x by t, we will have

$$Q = mt + c$$

(or $Q = a + bt$ where the constant b is the gradient and a is the intercept on the vertical axis).

To find the gradient of the line choose two points *on the graph* which are at a convenient horizontal separation. (Remember that the points *plotted* may not be exactly on the line.) Read off their vertical coordinates to obtain the vertical separation. Hence, from Fig. 6

$$\text{gradient} = \frac{\text{vertical increase}}{\text{horizontal increase}} = \frac{6.2}{20} = 0.31$$

Thus constant $b = 0.31$. The constant a may be found from the intercept on the vertical axis but where this is off the scale (as in Fig. 6) an alternative method is to substitute the coordinates of a convenient point into the equation. Such a point is the point $t = 30$, $Q = 63.0$ (see Fig. 6) and substituting these values into the equation $Q = a + 0.31t$ we obtain

$$63 = a + 9.3 \qquad a = 53.7$$

So the law we have obtained is

$$Q \approx 53.7 + 0.31t$$

Substituting $t = 90$ into this result we obtain the following prediction for the value of Q at time 90 mins:

$$Q \approx 53.7 + 27.9 \qquad \text{i.e.} \quad Q \approx 81.6$$

Exercise 2(b)

1. By plotting P against T show that there is a law of the form $P = a + bT$ and find the values of a and b.

T	20	35	50	60	75	100
P	160	250	340	400	490	640

2. The effort needed to raise various loads with a certain type of jack was measured and the following results were obtained:

Load W Newtons	100	150	200	300	400	500
Effort P Newtons	39	51	64	87	112	136

Plot P against W and hence obtain an approximate law of the form $P = a + bW$. Estimate the effort needed to raise a load of 250 Newtons.

3. The table shows the length of a certain wire when used to support various loads.

Load m kg	10	15	20	25	30	35
Length l cm	89.8	92.5	95.2	97.8	100.5	103.1

Obtain an approximate law of the form $l = a + bm$. Estimate the unstretched length of the wire and the length when supporting a load of 22 kg.

4. In an experiment the following results were obtained when the length of a rod was measured at different temperatures:

Temperature $T\,^\circ$C	25	40	60	75	90	100
Length l mm	252.3	253.4	255.0	256.2	257.5	258.2

Plot l against T and find an approximate relation of the form $l = a + bT$. Hence
(i) Estimate the length of the rod at $50\,^\circ$C
(ii) Estimate the laboratory temperature at the time of the experiment if the length of the rod before the experiment started was 251.7 mm.

*5. The following table shows values of the resistance experienced by a train at certain speeds:

Speed V (km hr^{-1})	20	30	40	50	60	70	80
Resistance R (Newtons per tonne)	76	94	125	160	204	255	316

By plotting R against V^2 show that there is an approximate law of the form $R = a + bV^2$. Obtain this law and estimate the resistance at 45 km hr^{-1}.

6. By plotting y against $1/x$ test the following data for a relationship of the form $y = a + \dfrac{b}{x}$

x	10	15	20	25	30	35	40
y	2.50	3.02	3.25	3.41	3.49	3.58	3.63

7. The Highway Code gives the following stopping distances for a car travelling on dry road:

Speed v (m.p.h.)	30	40	50	60	70
Stopping distance d (ft)		75	120	175	240	315

It is thought that there is a law of the form $d = av + bv^2$. By drawing a graph of d/v against v confirm that this is the case. Obtain values for a and b and predict the stopping distance at 45 m.p.h.

2.3 Line through a given point with a given gradient

Imagine that we wish to find the equation of the line through $(-2, 3)$ with gradient $\frac{3}{5}$. We may, of course, write the equation as $y = \frac{3}{5}x + c$ (from $y = mx + c$) and then find the constant c by substituting the coordinates $(-2, 3)$ into the equation, i.e.

$$3 = \tfrac{3}{5}(-2) + c \qquad \Rightarrow c = 4.2$$

The equation is therefore $y = 0.6x + 4.2$

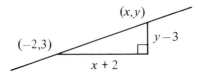

Fig. 7

A more satisfactory method (since it avoids the manipulation of fractions) is the following. Take any point (x, y) on the line (Fig. 7) and write down the gradient by considering the differences in the x and y coordinates

$$\text{gradient} = \frac{y-3}{x-(-2)} = \frac{y-3}{x+2}$$

thus
$$\frac{y-3}{x+2} = \frac{3}{5}$$

$$\Rightarrow 5y - 15 = 3x + 6$$

or
$$5y = 3x + 21$$

In effect we use the result

$$\frac{\text{difference in } y \text{ coordinates}}{\text{difference in } x \text{ coordinates}} = \text{gradient}$$

and no diagram is needed once the basic idea has been understood.

2.4 Line through two given points

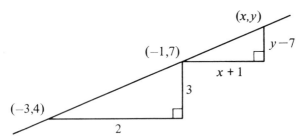

Fig. 8

The method used in the previous section may be adapted easily to situations where the equation of a line through two given points is required. Suppose the two points concerned are $(-3, 4)$ and $(-1, 7)$ and that (x, y) is any other point on the line (Fig. 8). Then using the points (x, y) and $(-1, 7)$ we have

$$\text{gradient} = \frac{y-7}{x-(-1)} = \frac{y-7}{x+1}$$

The value of this gradient is found from the differences in coordinates of the points $(-3, 4)$ and $(-1, 7)$, i.e.

$$\frac{y-7}{x+1} = \frac{7-4}{-1-(-3)} = \frac{3}{2}$$
$$\Rightarrow 2y - 14 = 3x + 3$$

or $\qquad\qquad 2y = 3x + 17$

Example 7

The triangle ABC has vertices $A(-3, 2)$, $B(4, 4)$ and $C(-2, -1)$. Find the equations of (i) the median AM (ii) the line through C parallel to AM.

M is the midpoint of BC and its coordinates are therefore

$$\left(\frac{4+(-2)}{2}, \frac{4+(-1)}{2}\right) \qquad \text{i.e. } (1, 1\tfrac{1}{2})$$

(i) The median AM is the line through $A(-3, 2)$ and $M(1, 1\tfrac{1}{2})$. Its equation is therefore

$$\frac{y-2}{x-(-3)} = \frac{2-1\tfrac{1}{2}}{-3-1}$$
$$\frac{y-2}{x+3} = \frac{\tfrac{1}{2}}{-4} = -\frac{1}{8}$$
$$\Rightarrow 8y - 16 = -x - 3$$
$$8y + x = 13$$

(ii) The gradient of AM is $-\tfrac{1}{8}$ so we now require a line with the same gradient through the point $C(-2, -1)$. The equation is

$$\frac{y-(-1)}{x-(-2)} = -\frac{1}{8}$$
$$\frac{y+1}{x+2} = -\frac{1}{8}$$
$$\Rightarrow 8y + 8 = -x - 2$$
$$8y + x = -10$$

Exercise 2(c)

1. Find the equations of the following lines:
   (i)   through $(-1, 4)$ with gradient 3
   (ii) through $(5, 2)$ with gradient $-\tfrac{1}{2}$
   (iii) through $(-2, -3)$ with gradient $\tfrac{3}{4}$
   (iv) through $(4, -5)$ with gradient $2\tfrac{1}{2}$

2. Find the equations of the lines through the following pairs of points:
   (i) $(1, 3)$ and $(3, 6)$ (ii) $(0, 7)$ and $(2, -2)$
   (iii) $(-1, 4)$ and $(4, 6)$ (iv) $(-5, 9)$ and $(-3, 3)$

3. Find the equation of the line
   (i)   through   (0, 1) parallel to $y = 3x - 1$.
   (ii) through   (3, 5) parallel to $y = 7 - 2x$.
   (iii) through   (2, 1) parallel to $2y = x + 1$.
   (iv) through $(-1, 4)$ parallel to $3y + 4x = 7$.
4. Given the points $A(3, 4)$, $B(4, 0)$ and $C(-2, 3)$ find the coordinates of the point where the line through A with gradient 3 crosses the line BC.
5. In triangle ABC the vertices A and B have coordinates $A(-2, 2)$ and $B(1, -3)$. If the gradients of AC and BC are 1 and 3 respectively find the coordinates of C and the equation of the line through C parallel to AB.
6. The vertices of a quadrilateral are $P(-3, 1)$, $Q(0, 4)$, $R(5, 3)$ and $S(3, -2)$. Find the coordinates of Z, the intersection of the diagonals PR and QS. Show also that Z is the midpoint of PR.
7. Triangle ABC has vertices $A(3, 5)$, $B(-3, 2)$ and $C(3, 0)$.
   (i)   Find the equations of the medians AM and BN
   (ii) Find the coordinates of P, the intersection of AM and BN
   (iii) Verify that the third median also passes through P.
8. A straight line with gradient -2 is a chord to the curve $y = 2x^2 + 3x - 2$. If one intersection is at $x = -3$, find the equation of the line and the coordinates of the second intersection.

2.5 Perpendicular lines

It is evident that two lines are parallel if they have the same gradient. It would be convenient if we could find an equally simple method for determining when two lines are perpendicular.

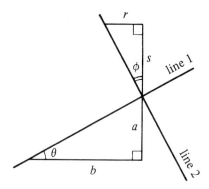

Fig. 9

Consider Fig. 9 in which the gradients m_1 and m_2 of the two lines are given by

$$m_1 = \frac{a}{b} \qquad m_2 = \frac{-s}{r}$$

If the lines are perpendicular then the angles θ and ϕ are equal. Equating the tangents of these two angles we obtain

$$\frac{a}{b} = \frac{r}{s} \qquad \Rightarrow \qquad m_1 = \frac{-1}{m_2}$$

i.e.

> TWO LINES ARE PERPENDICULAR IF THEIR
> GRADIENTS m_1 AND m_2 ARE SUCH THAT $m_1 = -\dfrac{1}{m_2}$

The nature of this rule should be made clear by the following examples.

Gradient	Perpendicular gradient
2	$-\frac{1}{2}$
-3	$+\frac{1}{3}$
$\frac{1}{4}$	-4
$-\frac{2}{3}$	$+\frac{3}{2}$

(To obtain the perpendicular gradient the sign is reversed and the fraction inverted.)

Example 8

Find the equation of the perpendicular bisector of the points $A(-2, 3)$ and $B(4, 6)$. Hence find a point on the y-axis which is equidistant from A and B.

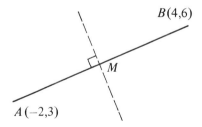

$B(4,6)$

M

$A(-2,3)$

Fig. 10

The perpendicular bisector of AB passes through the midpoint M of AB and is perpendicular to AB (Fig. 10).

coordinates of midpoint are $M(1, 4\frac{1}{2})$

gradient of AB is $\dfrac{6-3}{4-(-2)} = \dfrac{3}{6} = \dfrac{1}{2}$

So the perpendicular gradient is -2 and the equation of the perpendicular bisector is therefore

$$\frac{y-4\frac{1}{2}}{x-1} = \text{gradient} = -2$$
$$\Rightarrow y-4\frac{1}{2} = -2x+2$$
$$2y-9 = -4x+4$$
$$2y+4x = 13$$

Since all points on the perpendicular bisector are equidistant from A and B the point required in the last part of the question is the intercept of $2y+4x = 13$ with the y-axis. Substituting $x = 0$ we see that this is the point $(0, 6\frac{1}{2})$.

Exercise 2(d)

1. State the gradient which would be perpendicular to each of the following lines:
   (i) $y = 4x - 1$
   (ii) $x = 3y$
   (iii) $y = 3 - x$
   (iv) $5y = 2 - x$
   (v) $2y + x = 4$
   (vi) $3y - 4x = 5$
2. Determine which of the following pairs of lines are parallel and which are perpendicular. (Some may be neither.)
   (i) $2y = x + 1$ and $y = 2x - 1$
   (ii) $2y = 4x + 5$ and $2y = 5 - x$
   (iii) $3y + x = 2$ and $y = 3x + 1$
   (iv) $y = 3x$ and $2y + 6x = 3$
   (v) $y = \frac{1}{2}(x - 3)$ and $2y - x = 1$
3. Find the equations of the lines through $(-2, 5)$ which are (i) parallel to $3y = x + 7$ (ii) perpendicular to $3y = x + 7$.
4. Given the points $A(2, -3)$, $B(5, 1)$ and $C(0, 3)$ find the equations of the lines
   (i) through C parallel to AB
   (ii) through B perpendicular to AC
5. The lines $ay = 2x - 3$ and $y + 4x = b$ are perpendicular and they intersect on the x-axis. Find the values of the constants a and b.
6. Find the equation of the perpendicular bisector of the points $P(-2, 1)$ and $Q(3, 3)$. Hence find a point on the x-axis which is equidistant from P and Q.
7. Find the equation of the perpendicular from the origin onto the line $y + 3x = 5$. Find also the coordinates of the foot of this perpendicular and hence determine the distance of the line $y + 3x = 5$ from the origin.
8. A quadrilateral $ABCD$ is such that AD is parallel to BC and angle $BCD = 90°$. Given the vertices $A(-1, 3)$, $B(-2, -3)$ and $C(4, -1)$ find the coordinates of D.
9. The vertices of triangle ABC are $A(-1\frac{1}{2}, 5)$, $B(4, 0)$ and $C(-2, -4)$. Find
   (i)   the equation of the altitude AN.
   (ii) the coordinates of N.
   (iii) the area of the triangle ABC.
10. Find the coordinates of the point which is equidistant from $(-1, 0)$, $(-1, 5)$ and $(5, 2)$.

3

Introduction to Calculus

3.1 Average gradient

In the previous chapter we dealt with the gradient of a straight line. One of the most important branches of Mathematics, that known as Calculus, is concerned primarily with the gradients of curved lines.

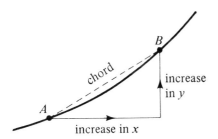

Fig. 1

Consider the curve shown in Fig. 1. If we imagine this to be the section of a hillside then the steepness or gradient of the hill increases as it is ascended. At point B, for example, we are rising more steeply than at point A. The gradient therefore changes as we move along the curve.

The way in which we shall define the gradient *at a particular point* on a curve will be discussed in the next section. For the moment we introduce only the idea of the *average gradient* between two points. A person rising from A to B on our hillside gains the same vertical height (increase in y coordinate) in travelling the same horizontal distance (increase in x coordinate) as someone ascending at a uniform gradient along the straight line or chord AB. The average gradient of the curve between the points A and B is therefore taken to be that of the straight line joining A and B and may be defined by

$$\text{average gradient} = \frac{\text{increase in } y}{\text{increase in } x}$$

The average gradient will be negative if an increase in x coordinate results in a decrease in the y coordinate (i.e. if the curve is falling).

Example 9

Find the average gradient of
(i) $y = x^2 - x$ between $x = 3$ and $x = 5$
(ii) $y = 16/x^2$ between $x = 4$ and $x = 8$

(i) For $y = x^2 - x$ the y coordinates at $x = 3$ and $x = 5$ are found to be 6 and 20 respectively.

$$\text{average gradient} = \frac{\text{increase in } y}{\text{increase in } x} = \frac{20 - 6}{5 - 3} = \frac{14}{2} = \underline{7}$$

(ii) For $y = 16/x^2$ the y coordinates at $x = 4$ and $x = 8$ are $16/16 = 1$ and $16/64 = \frac{1}{4}$. So as x increases from 4 to 8, y *decreases* from 1 to $\frac{1}{4}$.

$$\text{average gradient} = \frac{\text{increase in } y}{\text{increase in } x} = \frac{-3/4}{4} = \underline{\frac{-3}{16}}$$

Exercise 3(a)

In each of the following questions find the average gradient between the two points whose x coordinates are given:

1. $y = x^2$ (a) $x = 2$, $x = 5$ (b) $x = 3$, $x = 3\frac{1}{2}$
2. $y = x^3$ (a) $x = 1$, $x = 4$ (b) $x = -2$, $x = 3$
3. $y = 1/x$ (a) $x = 2$, $x = 6$ (b) $x = \frac{1}{2}$, $x = 2$
4. $y = x^2 - 5x$ (a) $x = 3$, $x = 6$ (b) $x = 1$, $x = 4$
5. $y = x^2$ (a) $x = 2$, $x = 2.2$ (b) $x = 2$, $x = 2.1$
                    (c) $x = 2$, $x = 2.01$ (d) $x = 2$, $x = 2.001$

3.2 Gradient at a given point

We have seen how to calculate the average gradient between two points on a curve. We turn now to the concept of gradient at a particular point on a curve. Our first problem is to decide how this should be defined.

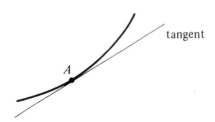

Fig. 2

In Fig. 2 we shall again imagine the curved line to represent a hillside. Consider a walker passing through the point A. It would seem reasonable to suppose that the gradient he experiences at this point is the same as that of the tangent to the curve at the point A. Certainly over a small section of the curve from just before A to just after A his ascent is not greatly different from that of the tangent. (A more powerful justification is provided by the following argument in which we demonstrate that the gradient at the point A *cannot* be given by any line *different* from the tangent. For any line through A different from the tangent must necessarily intersect the curve a second time and our diagram, on magnification, would then resemble Fig. 1 with point B as the second intersection. But the gradient at A in Fig. 1 cannot be identical with that of the chord AB, so the argument is complete.)

We therefore define the gradient at a particular point on a curve as being equal to the gradient of the tangent at that point. Our problem now is to find a method by which such gradients may be calculated quickly and precisely. It will take most of this chapter to develop such a method – in this section we introduce the basic idea on which the method is based.

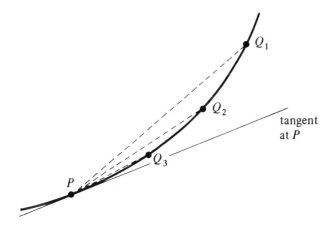

Fig. 3

Imagine that Fig. 3 shows a section of a curve whose equation is known and that from this equation we are required to find the gradient at a particular point P. At present there is no direct way we can do this. All we can do is select a series of points on the curve $Q_1, Q_2, Q_3 \ldots$ which lie progressively closer to P and obtain results for the gradients of the lines $PQ_1, PQ_2, PQ_3 \ldots$ etc.

We see from Fig. 3 that these lines get progressively closer in gradient to the tangent, so that we may hope from our results to get an indication of what the gradient of the tangent should be. In fact by choosing positions of Q which are only very slightly removed from P we may expect to obtain results which are very close to the gradient of the tangent.

To illustrate this further, consider the results of Exercise 3(a) question 5 concerning the curve $y = x^2$.

average gradient from $x = 2$ to $x = 2.2$ is   4.2
average gradient from $x = 2$ to $x = 2.1$ is   4.1
average gradient from $x = 2$ to $x = 2.01$ is   4.01
average gradient from $x = 2$ to $x = 2.001$ is   4.001

Here as we bring the second point closer to $x = 2$ our result for the average gradient appears to approach the value 4. This would suggest that the gradient of $y = x^2$ at the point $x = 2$ is 4.

Note: In the above example 4 is the **limiting value** or **limit** of the sequence of results 4.2, 4.1, 4.01, 4.001, ... , i.e. the final value which these results would appear to be approaching. We cannot at present be sure, however, that 4 (rather than some number close to 4, e.g. 3.999) is the correct limit in this instance.

Exercise 3(b)

1. Draw the graph of $y = 12/x$ for $1 \leqslant x \leqslant 6$ and by drawing in tangents by eye estimate the gradient of the curve at (i) $x = 2$ (ii) $x = 4$.
2. Draw the graph of $y = x^2 - 2x$ for $-2 \leqslant x \leqslant 4$ and estimate, by drawing, the gradient of the curve at (i) $x = 3$ (ii) $x = -1\frac{1}{2}$
3. Find the average gradient of $y = x^2$ between the following pairs of points:
   (i) $x = 3$ and $x = 3.1$ (ii) $x = 3$ and $x = 3.01$ (iii) $x = 3$ and $x = 3.001$.
   What value is suggested for the gradient of $y = x^2$ at the point $x = 3$?
4. Use a calculator to find the average gradient of $y = x^3$ between the following pairs of points:
   (i) $x = 2$ and $x = 2.1$ (ii) $x = 2$ and $x = 2.01$ (iii) $x = 2$ and $x = 2.001$.
   Suggest a value for the gradient of $y = x^3$ at the point $x = 2$.
5. Repeat question 4 for the curve $y = 12/x$ and compare your result with that obtained in question 1(i).
6. Use the method of questions 3, 4 and 5 to check your answer to question 2(i).

3.3 A more sophisticated method

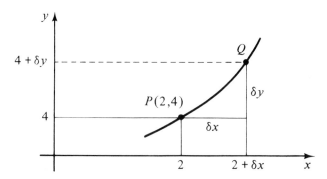

Fig. 4

We return to the calculation of the gradient of $y = x^2$ at the point $x = 2$. In Fig. 4 this is the point P whose coordinates are $(2, 4)$. Suppose we take a point Q on the curve whose x and y coordinates are slightly greater than those of P by amounts δx and δy respectively.

Note: δ is almost invariably used to indicate the idea of a small increase in a variable. Thus δx is a small increase in x and δy a small increase in y.

As in the previous section we shall be interested in the gradient of the line PQ. This is given by $\delta y/\delta x$. To determine the relation between the increases δy and δx we use the fact that the point Q lies on the curve so that its coordinates $(2 + \delta x, 4 + \delta y)$ must satisfy the equation $y = x^2$ i.e. y coord. $= (x$ coord.$)^2$

Thus
$$4 + \delta y = (2 + \delta x)^2$$
$$4 + \delta y = 4 + 4 \cdot \delta x + \delta x^2$$
$$\Rightarrow \quad \delta y = 4 \cdot \delta x + \delta x^2$$
Hence gradient $PQ = \dfrac{\delta y}{\delta x} = 4 + \delta x$

(The last line follows on dividing each term by δx).

We have said that the gradient of PQ will approach that of the tangent at P when Q is brought sufficiently close to P. We see from Fig. 4 that this occurs if the increase δx is made progressively closer to zero and it then follows from the above result that the gradient of PQ (i.e. $4 + \delta x$) approaches the value 4. So the gradient of $y = x^2$ at the point $x = 2$ is 4 (exactly).

Note: The last steps in this argument are more conveniently written out using the symbol $\rightarrow$ which means 'approaches' or 'tends to'

as $Q \rightarrow P$, $\delta x \rightarrow 0$ and so gradient $PQ \rightarrow 4$

Hence gradient of $y = x^2$ at the point $x = 2$ is 4.

Exercise 3(c)

1. Use the method of the above section to find the gradient of $y = x^2$ at the points (i) $x = 3$ (ii) $x = 4$ (iii) $x = 5$. What do you notice?
2. Draw a diagram similar to Fig. 4 to represent the curve $y = x^2 - 2x$. Take the point P at $x = 3$ and write down the coordinates of a second point Q on the curve whose coordinates are greater by δx and δy respectively. Use the fact that the coordinates of Q must satisfy the relation $y = x^2 - 2x$ to obtain a relation between δy and δx. Hence find the gradient of $y = x^2 - 2x$ at the point $x = 3$.
3. Find the gradient of $y = x^2 - 2x$ at the points (i) $x = 4$ (ii) $x = 5$.
4. Find the gradient of $y = 2x^2 + x$ at the points (i) $x = 1$ (ii) $x = 2$.
*5. Find the gradient of $y = x^3$ at the points (i) $x = 2$ (ii) $x = 3$.

3.4 The derived function

Although the method of the previous section is satisfactory it is tedious to have to consider each point on a particular curve as a separate calculation. It would be far more convenient if we could derive by a single calculation a formula valid for any point on the curve concerned. For example, in question 1 of Exercise 3(c) the reader will have noticed that the gradient is always given by twice the x coordinate. This suggests that for the curve $y = x^2$ the gradient is always given by the simple formula $2x$. This formula (which we shall prove shortly to be correct) is called the **derived function** or **derivative** of $y = x^2$; it enables the gradient at any point on $y = x^2$ to be written down immediately, e.g.

at $x = 1\frac{1}{2}$ gradient $= 3$
at $x = -4$ gradient $= -8$

The method by which the derived function for a particular curve is obtained differs only slightly from that of the previous section. Two examples follow.

To find the derived function of $y = x^2$

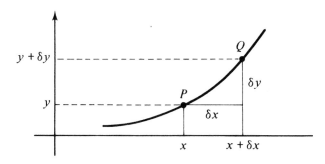

Fig. 5

Let $P(x, y)$ be *any* point on the curve $y = x^2$ and take a second point $Q(x + \delta x, y + \delta y)$ (see Fig. 5).
Since Q is also on the curve $y = x^2$ we have

$$y + \delta y = (x + \delta x)^2$$
$$y + \delta y = x^2 + 2x \cdot \delta x + \delta x^2$$
$$\Rightarrow \quad \delta y = 2x \cdot \delta x + \delta x^2 \quad \text{(since } y = x^2 \text{)}$$

$$\text{gradient } PQ = \frac{\delta y}{\delta x} = 2x + \delta x$$

As $Q \to P$, $\delta x \to 0$ and gradient $PQ \to 2x$. Hence the gradient at the point (x, y) is $2x$.

To find the derived function of $y = 2x^2 + x$

Referring again to Fig. 5, if $Q(x + \delta x, y + \delta y)$ is on the curve $y = 2x^2 + x$ then we must have

$$y + \delta y = 2(x + \delta x)^2 + (x + \delta x)$$
$$y + \delta y = 2x^2 + 4x \cdot \delta x + 2 \cdot \delta x^2 + x + \delta x$$
$$\Rightarrow \quad \delta y = 4x \cdot \delta x + 2 \cdot \delta x^2 + \delta x \quad \text{(since } y = 2x^2 + x \text{)}$$

$$\text{gradient } PQ = \frac{\delta y}{\delta x} = 4x + 1 + 2\delta x$$

As $Q \rightarrow P$, $\delta x \rightarrow 0$ and gradient $PQ \rightarrow 4x + 1$. Hence the derived function for the curve $y = 2x^2 + x$ is $4x + 1$. The reader may verify that this formula gives the correct results for question 4 of Exercise 3(c).

Exercise 3(d)

Enter the results of questions 1–5 in a table and try to see if any pattern emerges.

1. Find the derived functions for the curves
   (i) $y = x^2 - 2x$ (ii) $y = x^2 + 3x$ (iii) $y = 4x - x^2$
2. Find the derived functions for the curves
   (i) $y = 3x^2$ (ii) $y = 2x^2 - x$ (iii) $y = 5x - 2x^2$
3. Find the derived functions for the curves
   (i) $y = x^2 + 7$ (ii) $y = x^2 + 3x - 5$ (iii) $y = 1 + 2x - 3x^2$
4. What are the gradients of the lines (i) $y = 4x - 1$ (ii) $y = 7 - 3x$? Obtain the derived functions for these equations.
5. Find the derived function of (i) $y = x^3$ (ii) $y = 2x^3$
*6. If $P(x, y)$ and $Q(x + \delta x, y + \delta y)$ are points on the curve $y = 1/x$ then we have

$$y = \frac{1}{x} \quad \text{and} \quad y + \delta y = \frac{1}{(x + \delta x)}$$

so that $\qquad \delta y = \dfrac{1}{(x + \delta x)} - \dfrac{1}{x}$

Subtract the two fractions using a common denominator, and hence obtain an expression for $\delta y/\delta x$. What is the derived function for the curve $y = 1/x$?
7. Use the same method as in question 6 to find the derived function for $y = 1/x^2$.

3.5 Notation

The notation $\dfrac{dy}{dx}$ is often used for the derived function.

Thus $\qquad$ for $y = x^2 \qquad \dfrac{dy}{dx} = 2x$

$\qquad\qquad\quad y = x^3 \qquad \dfrac{dy}{dx} = 3x^2 \qquad$ etc.

There is a very important distinction between the derived function, $\dfrac{dy}{dx}$, and the quantity $\dfrac{\delta y}{\delta x}$ which we have encountered in previous sections. It should be remembered that δy and δx are small increases (or **increments**) in the y and x coordinates. The ratio of these, $\dfrac{\delta y}{\delta x}$, is the average gradient between two neighbouring points on a curve (i.e. the gradient of the chord PQ in Fig. 5).

The derived function, $\dfrac{dy}{dx}$, tells us the true gradient of the curve at a particular point (i.e. the gradient of the tangent).

We know that if P and Q are very close together in Fig. 5 (i.e. if $\delta x \approx 0$) then the gradient of the chord will approximate to that of the tangent, i.e.

$$\text{If}\quad \delta x \approx 0 \quad\text{then}\quad \frac{\delta y}{\delta x} \approx \frac{dy}{dx}$$

Furthermore, as Q approaches P, so the gradient of the chord PQ will approach that of the tangent, i.e.

$$\text{as}\quad \delta x \to 0 \qquad \frac{\delta y}{\delta x} \to \frac{dy}{dx}$$

In fact the derived function $\dfrac{dy}{dx}$ may be defined as the limiting value to which the average gradient $\dfrac{\delta y}{\delta x}$ tends as the increment δx is reduced towards zero. This is sometimes written as follows

$$\operatorname*{Lim}_{\delta x \to 0} \frac{\delta y}{\delta x} = \frac{dy}{dx}$$

(Thus in the example given in Section 3.2 values of $\dfrac{\delta y}{\delta x}$ are 4.2, 4.1, 4.01, 4.001 etc. and the value of $\dfrac{dy}{dx}$ at the point considered is the limiting value 4.)

3.6 Differentiation by rule

The principal results obtained in Section 3.4 may be tabulated as follows:

Function y	Derived function $\dfrac{dy}{dx}$
x^3	$3x^2$
x^2	$2x$
x	1
Constant number	—
$\dfrac{1}{x}$ or x^{-1}	$-\dfrac{1}{x^2}$ or $-1.x^{-2}$
$\dfrac{1}{x^2}$ or x^{-2}	$-\dfrac{2}{x^3}$ or $-2.x^{-3}$

The student who has worked through Exercise 3(d) will have noticed:
(i) that multiples of these basic functions have the corresponding multiples for their derived functions, and
(ii) that the results for functions involving several terms may be written down term by term.

Thus (i) for $y = 4x^2$ $\qquad \dfrac{dy}{dx} = 4(2x) = 8x$

$\qquad\qquad\quad y = 2x^3 \qquad\qquad \dfrac{dy}{dx} = 2(3x^2) = 6x^2$

$\qquad\qquad\quad y = -\dfrac{5}{x} \qquad\qquad \dfrac{dy}{dx} = -5\left(-\dfrac{1}{x^2}\right) = +\dfrac{5}{x^2}$

and (ii) for $y = 4x^2 + 2x^3 \qquad \dfrac{dy}{dx} = 8x + 6x^2$

$\qquad\qquad\quad y = 2x^3 - \dfrac{5}{x} + 7 \quad \dfrac{dy}{dx} = 6x^2 + \dfrac{5}{x^2}$

Note: A constant number, such as the 7 in the last example, gives no contribution to the derived function.

We have therefore arrived at a process by which the derived function of a particular curve may be written down quickly. This process is called **differentiation** and once familiarity with this method is attained the longer methods of earlier sections need no longer be used.

Finally, to complete this work, we notice that the results tabulated at the head of this section obey an interesting rule of indices, i.e.

$\qquad$ if $y = x^n \qquad$ then $\qquad \dfrac{dy}{dx} = n \cdot x^{n-1}$

We shall not attempt the proof of this rule here. It does, however, enable us to obtain the derived functions of more complicated functions than those we have considered so far. A few examples are given in Example 11.

Example 10

Differentiate the following functions:

(i) $y = 2x^3 - 3x + 4 + \dfrac{3}{x^2}$ (ii) $y = (x^2 + 1)\left(\dfrac{1}{x} - 1\right)$ (iii) $y = \dfrac{2x^2 - 1}{x}$

Function (i) may be treated term by term

$\qquad y = 2x^3 - 3x + 4 + \dfrac{3}{x^2}$

$\qquad \dfrac{dy}{dx} = 2(3x^2) - 3(1) + 3\left(-\dfrac{2}{x^3}\right) = 6x^2 - 3 - \dfrac{6}{x^3}$

Functions (ii) and (iii) must first be expressed as the sums or differences of *separate* terms, i.e.

(ii) $\quad y = (x^2 + 1)\left(\dfrac{1}{x} - 1\right) = x - x^2 + \dfrac{1}{x} - 1$ (multiplying)

$\qquad\qquad\qquad \dfrac{dy}{dx} = 1 - 2x - \dfrac{1}{x^2}$

(iii) $\quad y = \dfrac{2x^2 - 1}{x} = 2x - \dfrac{1}{x}$ (dividing)

$\qquad\qquad\qquad \dfrac{dy}{dx} = 2 + \dfrac{1}{x^2}$

Example 11

Find the derived functions for (i) x^8 (ii) $\dfrac{1}{x^5}$ (iii) $\sqrt{x}$

The functions (ii) and (iii) may be written as x^{-5} and $x^{\frac{1}{2}}$ respectively. Using the rule of indices noted above the derived functions are therefore

(i) $8x^7$ (ii) $-5x^{-6}$ $\left(\text{or } -\dfrac{5}{x^6}\right)$ (iii) $\frac{1}{2}x^{-\frac{1}{2}}$ $\left(\text{or } \dfrac{1}{2\sqrt{x}}\right)$

Exercise 3(e)

In questions 1–4 write down the derived function for each of the functions given.

1. (i) $y = 2x^2$ (ii) $y = 5x^2$ (iii) $y = 3x^3$ (iv) $y = -4x^3$

     (v) $y = \dfrac{3}{x}$ (vi) $y = 6x$ (vii) $y = 5$ (viii) $y = \dfrac{2}{x^2}$

2. (i) $y = 3x^2 - 2x$ (ii) $y = x^2 + 5x$ (iii) $y = x + \dfrac{1}{x}$

     (iv) $y = x^3 - 5x^2$ (v) $y = 4x - 7$ (vi) $y = \dfrac{3}{x^2} - x^2$

     (vii) $y = 5 - \dfrac{2}{x}$ (viii) $y = \dfrac{x^2}{2} - \dfrac{2}{x^2}$ (ix) $y = \dfrac{x}{3} - \dfrac{x^4}{2}$

3. (i) $y = 2x^3 - x^2 + 1$ (ii) $y = 5 - 4x + x^3$

     (iii) $y = 3x^2 + 1 + \dfrac{3}{x^2}$ (iv) $y = x^2 - x - \dfrac{4}{x}$

     (v) $y = 3x^4 - 4x^2 + 7x - 2$ (vi) $y = 1 + \dfrac{2}{x} - \dfrac{3}{x^2}$

     (vii) $y = 5 + 2x - x^3 - \dfrac{1}{x}$ (viii) $y = \dfrac{1}{2x^2} - \dfrac{1}{3x}$

4. (i) $y = x^7$ (ii) $y = 3x^7$ (iii) $y = 2x^5$ (iv) $y = 5x^4$

     (v) $y = \dfrac{1}{x^4}$ (vi) $y = \dfrac{2}{x^5}$ (vii) $y = \sqrt[3]{x}$ (viii) $y = \dfrac{1}{\sqrt{x}}$

5. Multiply out each of the following functions and hence obtain the derived functions:
     (i) $y = (x + 2)(2x - 1)$ (ii) $y = (x^2 + 1)(2x + 1)$
     (iii) $y = (x^3 - 1)\left(2 + \dfrac{1}{x}\right)$ (iv) $y = \left(1 - \dfrac{1}{x}\right)^2$

6. Differentiate each of the following functions:

     (i) $\dfrac{x^2 + 3}{x}$ (ii) $\dfrac{1 - x}{x^2}$ (iii) $\dfrac{(x - 1)^2}{x}$ (iv) $\dfrac{3x^3 - 1}{x^2}$

3.7 Some problems on gradients

In the work of the previous sections it is perhaps easy to forget that our initial objective in this chapter was to find a method by which the gradient of a curve could be calculated at particular points. This has now been achieved. To take a simple example: suppose we require the gradient of $y = x^3 - 2x$ at the point where $x = 2$. We first write down the derived function $\dfrac{dy}{dx} = 3x^2 - 2$. This gives us the gradient at any point on the curve in terms of its x coordinate. So at the point $x = 2$ the gradient is $12 - 2 = 10$.

Two slightly harder problems are now considered.

Example 12

Find the gradient of the curve $y = 2x^2 + 5x - 3$ at the points where it crosses the x-axis.

At the intersections with the x-axis we have $y = 0$.
Hence from the equation of curve

$$0 = 2x^2 + 5x - 3$$
$$0 = (2x - 1)(x + 3)$$
$$x = \tfrac{1}{2} \quad \text{or} \quad x = -3$$

These are the x coordinates of the required intersections. The gradient at each point is now found from the derived function $\dfrac{dy}{dx} = 4x + 5$, i.e.

at $x = \tfrac{1}{2}$ gradient $= 7$
    $x = -3$ gradient $= -7$

Example 13

Find two points on the curve $y = x^3 + x^2 + x$ where the gradient is equal to 2.

For this curve the gradient is given by the derived function $3x^2 + 2x + 1$ and we must find values of x for which this function takes the value 2, i.e.

$$3x^2 + 2x + 1 = 2$$
$$3x^2 + 2x - 1 = 0$$
$$(3x - 1)(x + 1) = 0$$
$$x = \frac{1}{3} \quad \text{or} \quad x = -1$$

These are the x coordinates of the points required. The corresponding y coordinates may be found from the equation of the curve, i.e. $y = \dfrac{13}{27}$ and $y = -1$.

The points are therefore

$$\left(\frac{1}{3}, \frac{13}{27}\right) \quad \text{and} \quad (-1, -1)$$

Exercise 3(f)

1. Find the gradient of $y = 2x^2 - 7x$ at the point $x = 3$.
2. Find the gradient of $y = 3x + \dfrac{1}{x}$ at the point $x = 2$.
3. Find the coordinates of the point on $y = 3x^2 - 6x$ where the gradient is equal to -3.
4. Find the gradient of $y = x^2 - 2$ at the points where $y = 7$.
5. Find the point on the curve $y = 5 + 6x - x^2$ where the tangent is horizontal.
6. Find the gradient of $y = 2x^2 + x - 6$ at the points where it crosses the x axis.
7. Find two points on the curve $y = x^2 - 3x - 6$ at which the y coordinate is double the x coordinate. What is the gradient at each point?
8. Find two points on $y = x^3 + 4x^2 + x$ where the gradient is equal to 4.
9. Find the coordinates of the point on $y = 11 + \dfrac{4}{x} + 2x^2$ where the gradient is zero.
10. The curve $y = Ax^2 - 2x$ (where A is a constant) has gradient 3 when $x = 2$. Find the value of A.
11. Where does the curve $y = x^2 + x + 8$ cut the y-axis? What is the gradient of the tangent to the curve at this point? Deduce the equation of this tangent.
12. Find the coordinates of two points on the curve $y = x^3 - 3x^2 - 2x$ where the tangents are parallel to the line $y = 7x + 1$. Obtain the equations of these tangents.
13. Find the equations of the tangent to each of the following curves at the point specified:
    (i) $y = x^2 - 3x$ at the point $(5, 10)$
    (ii) $y = 8/x^2$ at the point $x = 2$
    (iii) $y = (2x + 1)^2$ at the point $x = \frac{1}{4}$
14. In question 13 find the equation of the normal to each curve at the point specified. (The normal is the line perpendicular to the curve at the point concerned, i.e. perpendicular to the tangent.)
15. Find the gradients of the following curves at the points specified:
    (i) $y = \sqrt{x}$ at $(9, 3)$
    (ii) $y = (\sqrt{x} + 1)^2$ at $(4, 9)$
16. The curve $y = Ax^2 + Bx$ (where A and B are constants) passes through the point $(3, 6)$ and the tangent to the curve at the point where $x = 1$ is parallel to the x-axis. Find the values of A and B.

3.8 Rates of change

Steady rate of increase

If water is poured into a container at a steady rate then the graph of the volume V against time t is linear and the gradient gives the rate at which the volume of water in the tank is increasing. In Fig. 6a, for example, there are

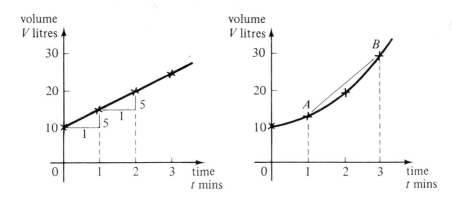

Fig. 6a   Fig. 6b

initially 10 litres of water in the tank and this increases at a steady rate of 5 litres per minute.

Average rate of increase

In Fig. 6b the volume of water in the tank is governed by the formula $V = 10 + 3t + t^2$. It can be seen from the following values that the volume is not increasing steadily:

Time t mins	0	1	2	3
Volume V litres	10	14	20	28

The **average** rate of increase over any given interval of time is given by the rule

$$\text{average rate of increase} = \frac{\text{increase in volume}}{\text{time}}$$

Thus in the 2 minute interval from $t = 1$ to $t = 3$ the volume increases by 14 litres, so that the average rate of increase in this time is $\frac{14}{2}$ or 7 litres per minute. (This is the gradient of the line AB in Fig. 6b.)

Rate of increase at an instant

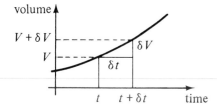

Fig. 7

To find the instantaneous rate of increase at time t we find the average rate of increase from t to $(t + \delta t)$ and then take the limit of this result as $\delta t \to 0$. Thus if the volume increases from V to $V + \delta V$ (Fig. 7) we have

$$\text{average rate of increase} \atop \text{from time } t \text{ to } t + \delta t = \frac{\text{increase in volume}}{\text{time}} = \frac{\delta V}{\delta t}$$

As $\delta t \to 0$ the value of $\delta V / \delta t$ approaches the gradient of the tangent to the curve at time t (Fig. 7), i.e.

$$\text{rate of increase} \atop \text{of } V \text{ at time } t = \frac{\text{gradient of}}{V/t \text{ graph}} = \frac{dV}{dt}$$

In the example considered above, where $V = 10 + 3t + t^2$, we have $\dfrac{dV}{dt} = 3 + 2t$

so that the volume is increasing at 5 litres/min when $t = 1$ and 7 litres/min when $t = 2$ etc.

General result

If Q is any quantity which changes with time t then $\dfrac{dQ}{dt}$ gives the rate at which Q is increasing at any instant of time t.

Note: If $\dfrac{dQ}{dt}$ is negative then Q is *decreasing*.

One particular case of importance is the motion of a body along a straight line. Here the statement that the velocity of the body is 5 ms^{-1} is equivalent to saying that the displacement of the body from a fixed origin is increasing by 5 metres each second, i.e.

$$\text{velocity} = \frac{\text{rate of increase}}{\text{of displacement } s} \quad \left(v = \frac{ds}{dt} \right)$$

In the same way,

$$\text{acceleration} = \frac{\text{rate of increase}}{\text{of velocity } v} \quad \left(a = \frac{dv}{dt} \right)$$

Exercise 3(g)

1. The volume of liquid V cm^3 in a certain container at time t secs is given by $V = \frac{1}{2}t^3 + 10t + 75$. Find the average rate of increase in volume (i) over the first 4 seconds (ii) from $t = 1$ to $t = 3$. Find also the instantaneous rate of increase at $t = 1$ and $t = 3$.

2. The temperature $T\,°C$ of a cold body placed in warmer surroundings is found to rise in accordance with the formula $T = 20 - (10/t^2)$ where t is the time in minutes. Find
   (i)   the rise in temperature from $t = 2$ to $t = 5$.
   (ii) the average rate at which the temperature rises from $t = 2$ to $t = 5$ and from $t = 5$ to $t = 10$.
   (iii) the instantaneous rate at which the temperature is rising at times $t = 2$, $t = 5$ and $t = 10$.

3. Over a certain period of time the depth of water in a tank, d cm, is given by the formula $d = (2t - 9)^2$ where t is the time in minutes.
   (i) Show that the depth at $t = 2$ is less than the initial depth and find the average rate at which the level falls during this time.
   (ii) Find the rate at which the level is falling initially (i.e. at $t = 0$) and at the instant $t = 3$.
   (iii) Find the time at which the level ceases to fall. What happens next?
   (iv) Find the rate at which the level is rising or falling at the instant when the depth is 1 metre.

4. A quantity Q varies with time t in accordance with the law $Q = (t - 1)(t^2 - 16)$.
   (i) By finding the rate of change of Q at time $t = 0$ show that, to begin with, Q decreases.
   (ii) Find the first time $(t > 0)$ at which Q becomes zero. What is the rate of change of Q at this instant?
   (iii) Find the time at which Q stops decreasing and begins to increase again. Hence find the least value taken by Q $(t > 0)$.
   (iv) Find the instant at which Q is increasing at a rate of 17 units per unit time $(t > 0)$.

5. The displacement, s metres, of a body from a fixed origin at time t seconds is given by $s = t^2 + 2t + 5$. Find how far the body moves between (i) $t = 0$ and $t = 3$ (ii) $t = 3$ and $t = 5$. Hence state the average velocity of the body over each of these periods of time. Find also the instantaneous velocity of the body at times $t = 0$, $t = 3$ and $t = 5$.

6. The displacement, s metres, of a body at time t secs is given by $s = t^3 + t^2 + 10$. Find the average velocity of the body during (i) the first second (ii) in the fifth second. Find also the true velocity of the body at times $t = 2$, $t = 4$ and $t = 6$.

7. Write down expressions for the velocity v ms^{-1} at time t secs for each of the bodies in questions 5 and 6.
   (i) Show that the velocity of the body in question 5 is increasing uniformly (i.e. it is accelerating uniformly). By how much does the velocity increase each second?
   (ii) For the body in question 6, find the rate at which the velocity is increasing (i.e. the acceleration) at times $t = 1$ and $t = 3$.

8. A stone is thrown vertically upwards. After t secs its height, h metres, above the ground is given by $h = 32t - 5t^2$.
   (i) Find the velocity of the stone at times 2, 3 and 4 secs. What is the meaning of negative velocity here?
   (ii) Find the instant when the velocity is zero and hence find the greatest height reached.
   (iii) Find the speed with which the stone strikes the ground.

9. The displacement, s metres, of a body at time t secs is given by $s = (2t + 5)^2/t$ $(t > 0)$.
   (i) Find the velocity at times $t = 2$, $t = 5$, $t = 10$.
   (ii) Find the acceleration at times $t = 2$, $t = 5$, $t = 10$.
   (iii) Find the time at which the velocity is zero.
   (iv) What limiting velocity is approached as $t \to \infty$?

*10. Fig. 8 shows a graph of the area A of a circle against the radius r. δA is the increase in area when the radius is increased by δr. If the increase δr is

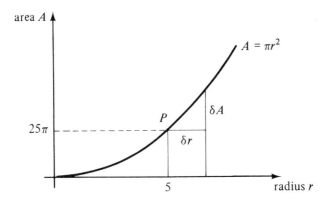

Fig. 8

small then the value of $\delta A/\delta r$ is approximately equal to the gradient of the curve at the point P. Find (in terms of π) the gradients at the points $r = 5$ and $r = 8$ and hence obtain approximate values for the increase in area δA when the radius of a circle is increased (i) from 5 to 5.05 units (ii) from 8 to 8.15 units.

11. Use a method similar to question 10 to find the approximate increase in volume of a sphere when the radius is increased from 10 cm to 10.025 cm.

Note: Some further work on small changes is given in section 22.5.

4

Basic Trigonometry

4.1 The sine and cosine wave functions

Measurement of angles

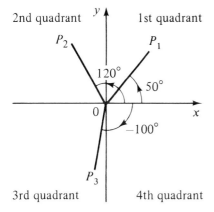

Fig. 1

In the work that follows it is usual to measure all angles from the positive x-axis and to take the positive direction of turn as anticlockwise. Thus if we imagine an arm OP to rotate about the origin O, then Fig. 1 shows positions of this 'rotating arm' corresponding to angles of turn $+50°$, $+120°$ and $-100°$. It is customary also to talk of the four **quadrants** of the complete circle, the first quadrant containing angles from $0°$ to $90°$, the second quadrant angles from $90°$ to $180°$ and so on.

Notice that a given position of the rotating arm may be achieved in more than one way. Thus in Fig. 1, the position OP_1 for $+50°$ could equally represent rotations of $-310°$ (taking the negative direction of turn from the x-axis) or $+410°$ (one complete turn of $360°$ together with a further $+50°$) etc. In the same way, position OP_3 for $-100°$ could represent $+260°$, $+620°$, $+980°$ etc.

Definitions of sine, cosine, tangent

The definitions we make for these important functions must be applicable for positive and negative angles of any magnitude.

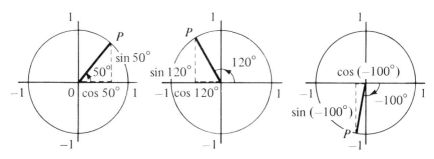

Fig. 2

If the rotating arm OP is of unit length (i.e. of length 1 unit) then P describes a circle of unit radius centred on the origin and for all angles of turn both the x and y coordinates of P will lie between $+1$ and -1. For a given angle of turn θ we define

$$\sin \theta = y \text{ coordinate of } P$$
$$\cos \theta = x \text{ coordinate of } P$$

$$\tan \theta = \frac{y \text{ coordinate}}{x \text{ coordinate}} \quad \text{or} \quad \frac{\sin \theta}{\cos \theta}$$

Note: The usual abbreviations for sine, cosine and tangent are used here. Fig. 2 illustrates the sines and cosines of the angles $50°$, $120°$ and $-100°$ (or $+260°$). We see that the cosine of $120°$ lies on the negative part of the x-axis and is therefore negative in value. Both the sine and the cosine of $-100°$ are negative. The values of all sines and cosines lie between $+1$ and -1.

Exercise 4(a)

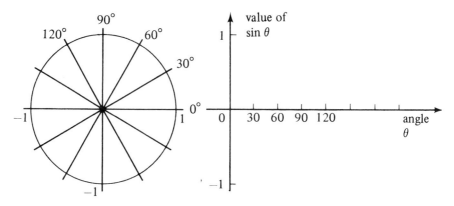

Fig. 3a   Fig. 3b

1. (i) Draw a circle of unit radius and use compasses or a protractor to divide it into $30°$ intervals, as in Fig. 3a. It may help to take a large

scale, e.g. 1 unit = 5 cm. Mark the vertical and horizontal axes from
−1 to 1.
(ii) Read off the values of sin 30°, sin 60°, sin 90° etc. from the vertical
scale (see Fig. 2). Plot these values carefully on axes like those in Fig.
3b. Continue your graph as far as 720°.
(iii) Repeat for the cosine values, taking these from the horizontal scale on
your circle. Continue the cosine graph back from 0° to −90°.
2. (i) What are the maximum and minimum values taken by $\sin \theta$ and for
what angles θ do these occur?
(ii) What are the maximum and minimum values of $\cos \theta$ and for
what angles θ do these occur?
3. Using the results of question 2 write down the greatest and least values
taken by each of the following functions, and state also the angles θ for
which they occur, (between 0° and 360°).
(i) $4 \cos \theta$ (ii) $3 + 2 \sin \theta$
(iii) $1 - 3 \cos \theta$ (iv) $1/(2 + \sin \theta)$
(v) $\cos^2 \theta$ – this means $(\cos \theta)^2$
*4. Draw an equilateral triangle of side 2 units and divide the triangle in two
by drawing an axis of symmetry. Use Pythagoras' theorem to obtain in
surd form the sine, cosine and tangent for (i) 60° (ii) 30°.
*5. Use a suitable isosceles triangle to find the sine, cosine and tangent for 45°
in surd form.

Sine and cosine graphs

Fig. 4 shows the graphs which the student should have obtained in question
1 of Exercise 4(a). Both $\sin \theta$ and $\cos \theta$ are **periodic** functions, i.e. the values
taken by the functions are repeated over a fixed period: in both cases 360°. We
say that the **period** of each function is 360°. Each complete period or cycle of
the function starts at zero, takes in a 'peak' then a 'trough' and finishes again at
zero.

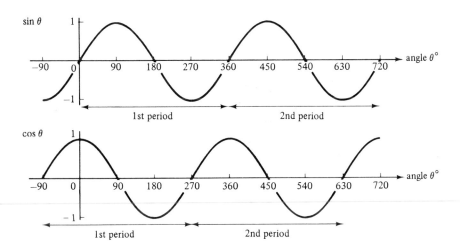

Fig. 4

We see that the general shape of the graphs is identical except that each cosine period starts 90° ahead of the corresponding sine period. The functions are sometimes said to be 90° *out of phase*.

The graph of tan θ is altogether different in character. This is considered in question 3 of Exercise 4(b).

4.2 Use of tables

Mathematical tables give sines, cosines and tangents only for first quadrant angles, i.e. angles from 0° to 90°. We need to know how to use these tables for angles in the other quadrants.

The student should study Fig. 5 carefully. It shows that the sines and cosines of 160°, 200° and 340° are the same *in value* (i.e. ignoring for the moment whether they are positive or negative) as those of 20°, since the triangles from which these values are taken are identical (congruent). We notice that these angles are all 20° from the **horizontal axis** or, alternatively, they differ by 20° from 180° or 360°. In the same way the *values* of sin 35° and cos 35° will be repeated for the angles 145° (180° − 35°), 215° (180° + 35°), 325° (360° − 35°), 395° (360° + 35°) and so on. The same is true of the tangent values since these have been defined in the previous section as sin θ/cos θ.

We now consider the question of sign. Fig. 5 also serves to show that the sine (or y coordinate) is positive in the 1st and 2nd quadrants and the cosine (or

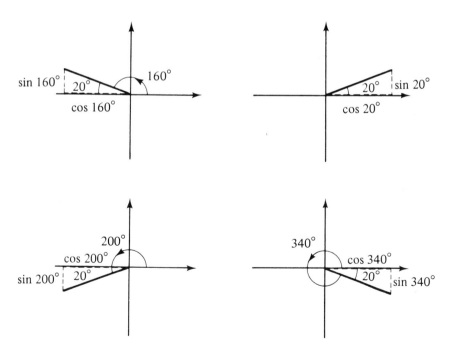

Fig. 5

x coordinate) is positive in the 1st and 4th. The following table may therefore be completed:

Quadrant

	1st	2nd	3rd	4th
Sine	+	+	−	−
Cosine	+	−	−	+
Tangent	+	−	+	−

(The signs for the tangent are obtained by remembering that $\tan \theta = \sin \theta / \cos \theta$). A more convenient way of remembering these results is the diagram of Fig. 6 which shows which of the ratios are *positive* in each quadrant. It can be seen that a useful aid to memory is the word CAST

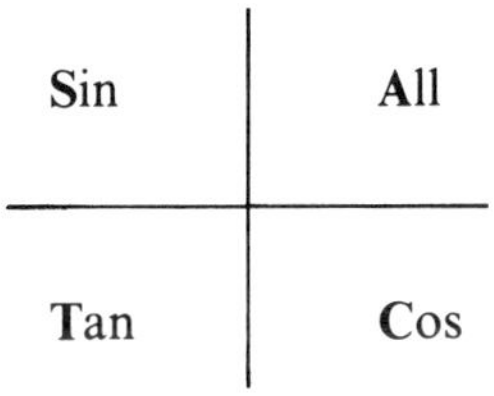

Sin	All
Tan	Cos

Fig. 6 Positive ratios

Example 14

Find from tables the values of
(i) $\cos 250°$ (ii) $\tan 304°$ (iii) $\sin(-230°)$ (iv) $\cos 428°$

First consider the signs

$250°$ is in the 3rd quadrant where the cosine is negative
$304°$ is in the 4th quadrant where the tangent is negative
$-230°$ is in the 2nd quadrant where the sine is positive
$428°$ is in the 1st quadrant where the cosine is positive

For the value of $\cos 250°$ we look up $\cos 70°$; for that of $\tan 304°$ we look up $\tan 56°$ etc. (considering in each case by how much the angle differs from $180°$ or $360°$). Thus

$$\cos 250° \quad = -\cos 70° = -0.3420$$
$$\tan 304° \quad = -\tan 56° = -1.4826$$
$$\sin(-230°) = +\sin 50° = +0.7660$$
$$\cos 428° \quad = +\cos 68° = +0.3746$$

Example 15

(i) Given that $\cos \theta = 0.606$, find the angle θ
(ii) Given that $\sin \phi = -0.410$, find the angle ϕ

(i) Here we are reversing the process of the previous example. A glance at the cosine tables will show that $\theta = 52.7°$ satisfies the required condition. There is, however, a further solution in the 4th quadrant where the cosine again takes positive values. This solution is $360° - 52.7° = 307.3°$. (By considering angles larger than $360°$ we may find further possibilities but it is usual to give only those answers in the range $0°-360°$.)

Thus $\underline{\theta = 52.7°\quad \text{or}\quad 307.3°}$

(ii)   The sine is negative in the 3rd and 4th quadrants so we look for solutions in these quadrants. If we ignore the negative sign the 1st quadrant angle whose sine is 0.410 is $24.2°$. Our 3rd and 4th quadrant solutions are therefore $180° + 24.2° = 204.2°$ and $360° - 24.2° = 335.8°$.

Thus $\underline{\phi = 204.2°\quad \text{or}\quad 335.8°}$

The inverse trigonometric functions

The notation arc cos (0.606) is used to mean *the angle whose cosine is 0.606*, and in the same way arc sin (-0.410) means *the angle whose sine is -0.410.* It follows, as in the above example, that

$$\text{arccos}\,(0.606)\ =\ 52.7°\quad \text{or}\quad 307.3°$$
$$\text{arcsin}\,(-0.410) = 204.2°\quad \text{or}\quad 335.8°$$

The functions **arccos, arcsin, arctan** are often called **inverse trigonometric functions** since they perform the inverse operations to the cosine, sine and tangent functions respectively, i.e.

cosine: $\theta \rightarrow \cos \theta$
arccos: $\cos \theta \rightarrow \theta$

The inverse functions are *not* uniquely defined. For a given cosine value many possible angles may be found, e.g. arccos $(0.606) = 52.7°$ or $307.3°$ and further values outside the range $0°-360°$. (It is assumed here that the term **inverse function** is already familiar to the student.)

Exercise 4(b)

1. Obtain from tables the values of
   (i) $\sin 122°$ (ii) $\cos 216°$ (iii) $\tan 105°$
   (iv) $\cos 305°$ (v) $\tan 280°$ (vi) $\sin(-40°)$
   (vii) $\sin 412°$ (viii) $\tan(-165°)$ (ix) $\cos 109.2°$
   (x) $\cos 605°$ (xi) $\sin(-400.4°)$ (xii) $\tan 199.8°$

2. Find values of θ between $0°$ and $360°$ such that
   (i) $\sin \theta = 0.454$ (ii) $\cos \theta = 0.788$
   (iii) $\tan \theta = 2.246$ (iv) $\sin \theta = -0.910$
   (v) $\cos \theta = 0.632$ (vi) $\tan \theta = -0.3$
   (vii) $\cos \theta = -0.061$ (viii) $\sin \theta = \cos \theta$

*3. Use tangent tables to plot the graph of $\tan \theta$ for $0° \leqslant \theta \leqslant 360°$. Suggested scales are 1 cm $= 20°$ horizontally and 1 cm $= 1$ unit vertically (from 6 to

-6). Plot values at $10°$ intervals. Consider carefully the sign of the function in each quadrant and the behaviour close to $90°$ and $270°$.

4. Do not use tables for this question. Use the results of Exercise 4(a) questions 4 and 5 to obtain the following values. (Leave answers in surd form.)

(i) $\cos 300°$	(ii) $\sin 150°$	(iii) $\tan 120°$
(iv) $\sin 240°$	(v) $\tan 225°$	(vi) $\cos 135°$
(vii) $\tan 330°$	(viii) $\sin 405°$	(ix) $\cos(-120°)$

5. Find values between $0°$ and $360°$ for

(i)	$\arcsin(0.515)$	(ii)	$\arctan(0.364)$
(iii)	$\arccos(\frac{1}{2})$	(iv)	$\arcsin(-0.809)$
(v)	$\arccos(-0.23)$	(vi)	$\arctan(-1)$
(vii)	$\arccos(0)$	(viii)	$\arctan(\sqrt{3})$

6. Draw the graph of $\sin\theta$ from 0 to $360°$. Using the same axes carefully superimpose the following graphs and state briefly what you notice.
   (i) $\sin 2\theta$ (The sine of the angle twice as large as θ: thus if $\theta = 20°$ look up $\sin 40°$ etc.)
   (ii) $\sin^2\theta$ (The square of $\sin\theta$.)

4.3 Secant, cosecant and cotangent

These three ratios, which are abbreviated to sec, cosec and cot respectively, are defined as follows:

For any angle θ

$$\sec\theta = \frac{1}{\cos\theta} \qquad \csc\theta = \frac{1}{\sin\theta} \qquad \cot\theta = \frac{1}{\tan\theta}$$

Since sines and cosines are always less than (or equal to) 1 in magnitude it follows that secants and cosecants are always greater than (or equal to) 1 and in fact become infinite as the values of $\cos\theta$ or $\sin\theta$ approach zero.

Tables of secants, cosecants and cotangents are included in most sets of four figure tables but where this is not the case it is always possible to convert to cosines, sines or tangents respectively, using reciprocals if necessary. For example

If $\cot\theta = 3$ then $\tan\theta = \frac{1}{3} = 0.3333$
   hence $\theta =$ $18.4°$ (1st quadrant)
      or $198.4°$ (3rd quadrant)

If $\sec\theta = -1.28$ then $\cos\theta = \dfrac{-1}{1.28} = -0.7813$ (reciprocals)
   hence $\theta = 180° - 38.6° = 141.4°$ (2nd quadrant)
      or $180° + 38.6° = 218.6°$ (3rd quadrant)

It is important to realise that the sign of the secant is negative in the same quadrants as the cosine is negative and that the cosecant is negative when the sine is negative, etc.

Example   16

Find $\sec 210°$ without using tables.

We begin by finding $\cos 210°$ which is related to $\cos 30°$.

In fact $\cos 210° = -\cos 30° = -\dfrac{\sqrt{3}}{2}$ (3rd quadrant)

Hence $\sec 210° = \dfrac{1}{\cos 210°} = \dfrac{-2}{\sqrt{3}}$ or $-\dfrac{2}{3}\sqrt{3}$

Example   17

If θ is a first quadrant angle and $\cos\theta = \frac{5}{13}$ find, without using tables, the values of $\tan\theta$, $\mathrm{cosec}\,\theta$.

Draw a right-angled triangle with the cosine measurement as $\frac{5}{13}$ and consider a 13 times enlargement of this triangle, as in Fig. 7. By Pythagoras, the missing measurement in the enlarged triangle is 12 units. Hence it can be seen that

$\tan\theta = \dfrac{12}{5}$

$\sin\theta = \dfrac{12}{13}$ $\Rightarrow$ $\mathrm{cosec}\,\theta = \dfrac{1}{\sin\theta} = \dfrac{13}{12}$

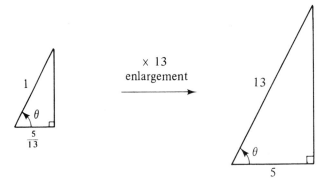

Fig. 7

Example   18

Simplify the expressions (i) $\tan\theta\cos\theta$ (ii) $\dfrac{\mathrm{cosec}\,\theta}{\cot\theta}$

(i) Since $\tan\theta = \sin\theta/\cos\theta$ (for any angle θ) it will always be true that

$\tan\theta\cos\theta = \dfrac{\sin\theta}{\cos\theta}\cos\theta = \sin\theta$

i.e. no matter what angle θ is considered, the value obtained for $\tan\theta \cos\theta$ will always be identical to that for $\sin\theta$.

(ii) Here we use the definitions $\operatorname{cosec}\theta = 1/\sin\theta$ and $\cot\theta = 1/\tan\theta = \cos\theta/\sin\theta$. Thus

$$\frac{\operatorname{cosec}\theta}{\cot\theta} = \operatorname{cosec}\theta \div \cot\theta$$

$$= \frac{1}{\sin\theta} \div \frac{\cos\theta}{\sin\theta} = \frac{1}{\sin\theta} \times \frac{\sin\theta}{\cos\theta}$$

$$= \frac{1}{\cos\theta} \quad \text{or} \quad \sec\theta$$

A simpler form for this expression is therefore $\sec\theta$.

Exercise 4(c)

1. Find values of θ from $0°$ to $360°$ such that
   (i) $\operatorname{cosec}\theta = 4$ (ii) $\sec\theta = 2$
   (iii) $\cot\theta = -2$ (iv) $\operatorname{cosec}\theta = -2.044$
   (v) $\sec\theta = -4.89$ (vi) $\cot\theta = \sqrt{3}$
   (vii) $\operatorname{cosec}\theta = -1$ (viii) $\sec\theta = \sqrt{2}$

2. Without using tables, write down the values of
   (i) $\operatorname{cosec}30°$ (ii) $\cot 60°$ (iii) $\sec 330°$ (iv) $\operatorname{cosec}90°$
   (v) $\sec 225°$ (vi) $\cot 135°$ (vii) $\sec 180°$ (viii) $\cot 270°$

3. If θ is a first quadrant angle and $\sin\theta = \frac{3}{5}$ find, without using tables, the values of $\sec\theta$, $\tan\theta$.
4. If θ is a first quadrant angle and $\cot\theta = \frac{8}{15}$ find, without using tables, the values of $\sin\theta$, $\sec\theta$.
5. If θ is a second quadrant angle and $\sin\theta = \frac{7}{25}$ find, without using tables, the values of $\cos\theta$, $\cot\theta$.
6. Simplify the following expressions:
   (i) $\operatorname{cosec}\theta \tan\theta$ (ii) $\cos\theta \sec\theta$
   (iii) $\dfrac{\cot\theta}{\cos\theta}$ (iv) $\dfrac{\sec\theta}{\operatorname{cosec}\theta}$

*7. Find possible values of θ between $0°$ and $360°$ such that
   (i) $3\sin\theta = 1$ (ii) $4\cot\theta = 3$
   (iii) $2\sin\theta = \cos\theta$ (iv) $\sec\theta = 4\cos\theta$
   (v) $3\operatorname{cosec}\theta = \sec\theta$

4.4 Two basic identities

An **identity** is a result which is *always* true. Thus in algebra the following results are identities since they are true *for all values of* x.

$$(x+1)(x-1) = x^2 - 1 \qquad (x-1)^2 = x^2 - 2x + 1$$

e.g. $x = 10$	$11 \times 9 = 100 - 1$	$9^2 = 100 - 20 + 1$
$x = 5$	$6 \times 4 = 25 - 1$	$4^2 = 25 - 10 + 1$
$x = 1$	$2 \times 0 = 1 - 1$	$0^2 = 1 - 2 + 1$
$x = -2$	$-1 \times -3 = 4 - 1$	$(-3)^2 = 4 + 4 + 1$

It is important not to confuse **identities** with **equations** which are true for certain values of x only. For example $2(x-1) = 2x - 2$ is always true and is therefore an identitiy whereas $2(x-1) = x$ is an equation satisfied by the single value $x = 2$ only.

The sign $\equiv$ is sometimes used for identities. So we could write $(x+1)(x-1) \equiv x^2 - 1$ or $2(x-1) \equiv 2x - 2$. This sign may be read in words as '*is identical to*', i.e. is an alternative form for the same expression.

Two important trigonometric identities

The following results are true *for all angles* θ and are therefore identities:

$$\boxed{\begin{array}{c} \tan\theta = \dfrac{\sin\theta}{\cos\theta} \\[2mm] \sin^2\theta + \cos^2\theta = 1 \end{array}}$$

Note: $\sin^2\theta$ is a shorthand for $(\sin\theta)^2$. Similarly $\cos^2\theta$ means $(\cos\theta)^2$

The first of these results is true by our definition for $\tan\theta$ in Section 4.1. The second follows from our definitions of $\sin\theta$ and $\cos\theta$ by applying Pythagoras' Theorem (see Fig. 8a).

The result holds for angles in any quadrant. Fig. 8b shows the situation for a 2nd quadrant angle. Although $\cos\theta$ is negative $\cos^2\theta$ will be positive and the result $\sin^2\theta + \cos^2\theta = 1$ still holds.

These two identities are useful for simplifying more complicated expressions and for proving further identities, as the following examples illustrate.

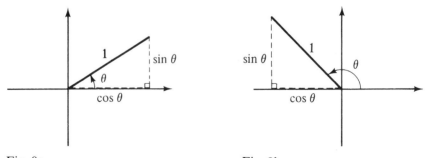

Fig. 8a   Fig. 8b

The student should notice that the identity $\sin^2\theta + \cos^2\theta = 1$ may be written in the alternative forms

$$\sin^2\theta = 1 - \cos^2\theta$$
$$\cos^2\theta = 1 - \sin^2\theta$$

Example 19

Simplify the expression $\dfrac{\cos\theta}{1-\sin^2\theta}$

Since $1-\sin^2\theta = \cos^2\theta$ we may write

$$\frac{\cos\theta}{1-\sin^2\theta} = \frac{\cos\theta}{\cos^2\theta} = \frac{1}{\cos\theta} \quad \text{or} \quad \sec\theta$$

A simpler form is therefore $\sec\theta$.

Example 20

Prove that $\sec\theta - \cos\theta = \tan\theta\sin\theta$

Here we are asked to prove an identity, i.e. that the left-hand side (l.h.s.) is simply an alternative way of writing the right-hand side (r.h.s.) so that both expressions will always take the same value. To prove a result such as this, take either the l.h.s. or the r.h.s. and, using known results, try to change it step by step into the other side. In this example we can achieve this as follows:

$$\begin{aligned}
\text{l.h.s.} \quad \sec\theta - \cos\theta &= \frac{1}{\cos\theta} - \cos\theta \\
&= \frac{1-\cos^2\theta}{\cos\theta} \\
&= \frac{\sin^2\theta}{\cos\theta} = \frac{\sin\theta}{\cos\theta}\sin\theta \\
&= \tan\theta\sin\theta \quad \text{r.h.s.}
\end{aligned}$$

Exercise 4(d)

1. Obtain simpler forms for

   (i) $\dfrac{\cos^2\theta + \sin^2\theta}{\sin^2\theta}$ (ii) $\sqrt{1-\sin^2\theta}$

   (iii) $\dfrac{1-\cos^2\theta}{1-\sin^2\theta}$ (iv) $\sin^3\theta + \sin\theta\cos^2\theta$

2. Simplify

   (i) $\dfrac{\sin\theta\cos\theta}{1-\sin^2\theta}$ (ii) $(1+\cos\theta)(1-\cos\theta)$

   (iii) $\dfrac{\tan\theta}{\sqrt{1-\cos^2\theta}}$ (iv) $1+\tan^2\theta$

3. Prove the identities
   (i) $\operatorname{cosec}^2\theta - 1 = \cot^2\theta$
   (ii) $\tan\theta + \cot\theta = \operatorname{cosec}\theta\sec\theta$
   (iii) $\cos^4\theta - \sin^4\theta = \cos^2\theta - \sin^2\theta$

4. Prove that
   (i) $2\cos^2\theta - 1 = 1 - 2\sin^2\theta$
   (ii) $\sec^2\theta + \text{cosec}^2\theta = \sec^2\theta\,\text{cosec}^2\theta$
   (iii) $(1 + \tan\theta)^2 = \sec^2\theta + 2\tan\theta$

5. Prove that $(\sin\theta + \cos\theta)^2 + (\sin\theta - \cos\theta)^2 = 2$

6. Prove that $\dfrac{\sin\theta}{1 + \cos\theta} = \dfrac{1 - \cos\theta}{\sin\theta}$ and hence show that

$$\left(\frac{\sin\theta}{1 + \cos\theta}\right)^2 = \frac{1 - \cos\theta}{1 + \cos\theta}$$

4.5 Trigonometric equations

Some simple equations were encountered in Exercise 4(c), question 7. Here the object is to find which angles θ satisfy the given relation. Answers are usually restricted to those between $0°$ and $360°$. In this section we consider some of the simpler types of these equations.

Example   21

Solve the following equations, giving all answers in the range $0 \leqslant \theta \leqslant 360°$:

(i) $2\sec\theta = \text{cosec}\,\theta$ (ii) $3\sec\theta = 4\cos\theta$
(iii) $3\sin^2\theta = 1 - 2\sin\theta$ (iv) $2\cos^2\theta + 5\sin\theta = 4$

(i) $2\sec\theta = \text{cosec}\,\theta \Rightarrow \dfrac{2}{\cos\theta} = \dfrac{1}{\sin\theta}$

$$\Rightarrow \tan\theta = \tfrac{1}{2}$$

$$\underline{\theta = 26.6°\quad \text{or}\quad 206.6°}$$

(ii) $3\sec\theta = 4\cos\theta \Rightarrow \dfrac{3}{\cos\theta} = 4\cos\theta$

$$\cos^2\theta = \tfrac{3}{4}$$

$$\cos\theta = \frac{\sqrt{3}}{2}\quad\text{or}\quad\frac{-\sqrt{3}}{2}\quad\text{taking both roots}$$

$$\underline{\theta = 30°\quad\text{or}\quad 330°, 150°\quad\text{or}\quad 210°}$$

In this example we avoid using tables for the square root of $\tfrac{3}{4}$ (i.e. $\sqrt{0.75} = \pm\,0.866$) since $\sqrt{3}/2$ is recognised as the cosine of $30°$.

(iii) This example is solved as a quadratic equation in $\sin\theta$.

$$3\sin^2\theta = 1 - 2\sin\theta \Rightarrow 3\sin^2\theta + 2\sin\theta - 1 = 0 \quad\text{rearranging}$$
$$(3\sin\theta - 1)(\sin\theta + 1) = 0 \quad\text{factorizing}$$
$$\sin\theta = \tfrac{1}{3}\text{ or }\sin\theta = -1$$
$$\underline{\theta = 19.5°\quad\text{or}\quad 160.5°, 270°}$$

(iv) By first using the identity $\cos^2\theta = 1 - \sin^2\theta$ we may solve this equation also as a quadratic in $\sin\theta$.

$$2\cos^2\theta + 5\sin\theta = 4 \Rightarrow 2(1 - \sin^2\theta) + 5\sin\theta = 4$$
$$0 = 2\sin^2\theta - 5\sin\theta + 2$$
$$0 = (2\sin\theta - 1)(\sin\theta - 2)$$
$$\sin\theta = \tfrac{1}{2} \quad \text{or} \quad \sin\theta = 2$$
$$\underline{\theta = 30° \quad \text{or} \quad 150°}$$

$\sin\theta = 2$ is, of course, impossible so that only two solutions are obtained.

Exercise 4(e)

Solve the following equations, giving all answers between $0°$ and $360°$.

1. (i) $3\sin\theta = 4\cos\theta$ (ii) $2\sin\theta = \operatorname{cosec}\theta$
   (iii) $3\cos^2\theta + \cos\theta = 2$ *(iv) $2\sin^2\theta + \sin\theta = 0$
2. (i) $5\sin\theta - 3\cos\theta = \sin\theta + 2\cos\theta$ (ii) $\sec\theta + 4\operatorname{cosec}\theta = 0$
   (iii) $6\sin^2\theta = 5\sin\theta + 1$ *(iv) $3\cos^2\theta = 2\sin\theta\cos\theta$
3. (i) $\tan^2\theta - 2\tan\theta = 3$ (ii) $1 + \cos\theta = 2\sin^2\theta$
   (iii) $\cos^2\theta + \sin^2\theta = 4\sin\theta$ *(iv) $16\sin^4\theta - 16\sin^2\theta + 3 = 0$
4. (i) $\cos^2\theta - \sin^2\theta = \sin\theta$ (ii) $6\cos^2\theta - \sin\theta = 5$
   (iii) $6\sin^2\theta + 4\cos^2\theta = 5$ *(iv) $\tan\theta + 2\cot\theta = 3$

Note: In questions such as 1(iv) the common factor $\sin\theta$ should not be cancelled out to leave $2\sin\theta + 1 = 0$. It is preferable to factorize the equation as $\sin\theta\,(2\sin\theta + 1) = 0$, for otherwise the solution $\sin\theta = 0$ may be overlooked.

4.6 Two further identities

The following identities are often of use:

$$\boxed{\begin{array}{c} \sec^2\theta = 1 + \tan^2\theta \\ \operatorname{cosec}^2\theta = 1 + \cot^2\theta \end{array}}$$

Both are proved from the result $\sin^2\theta + \cos^2\theta = 1$.
To obtain the first, divide each term by $\cos^2\theta$

$$\frac{\sin^2\theta}{\cos^2\theta} + \frac{\cos^2\theta}{\cos^2\theta} = \frac{1}{\cos^2\theta}$$

i.e. $\tan^2\theta + 1 = \sec^2\theta$

The second is obtained on division of each term by $\sin^2\theta$

Example 22

Prove the identity $\sec^2\theta - \operatorname{cosec}^2\theta = \tan^2\theta - \cot^2\theta$

l.h.s. $\sec^2\theta - \cos^2\theta = (1 + \tan^2\theta) - (1 + \cot^2\theta)$
               $= \tan^2\theta - \cot^2\theta$ r.h.s.

Example   23

Solve the equation $4\tan^2\theta + 4\sec\theta + 1 = 0$

Again we may obtain a quadratic equation, this time in $\sec\theta$.

$$4\tan^2\theta + 4\sec\theta + 1 = 0 \;\Rightarrow\; 4(\sec^2\theta - 1) + 4\sec\theta + 1 = 0$$
$$4\sec^2\theta + 4\sec\theta - 3 = 0$$
$$(2\sec\theta + 3)(2\sec\theta - 1) = 0$$
$$\sec\theta = -\tfrac{3}{2} \text{ or } \sec\theta = \tfrac{1}{2}$$
$$\Rightarrow \cos\theta = -\tfrac{2}{3} \text{ or } \cos\theta = 2$$
$$\theta = 131.8° \text{ or } 228.2°$$

Exercise 4(f)

1. Simplify

   (i) $\sqrt{1 + \cot^2\theta}$ (ii) $\dfrac{\tan^2\theta}{1 + \tan^2\theta}$

   (iii) $(1 + \operatorname{cosec}\theta)(1 - \operatorname{cosec}\theta)$ (iv) $\operatorname{cosec}\theta\sqrt{\sec^2\theta - 1}$

2. Solve the equations, giving all answers from $0°$ to $360°$.
   (i) $3\tan\theta = \sec^2\theta - 1$
   (ii) $\operatorname{cosec}^2\theta = 3 + \cot\theta$
   (iii) $5\sec\theta - 2\sec^2\theta = \tan^2\theta - 1$

3. Prove that
   (i) $(\tan\theta + \cot\theta)^2 = \sec^2\theta + \operatorname{cosec}^2\theta$
   (ii) $(\operatorname{cosec}^2\theta - 1)(\sec^2\theta - 1) = 1$
   (iii) $(\sec\theta - \cos\theta)^2 = \tan^2\theta - \sin^2\theta = \tan^2\theta\sin^2\theta$

4. Some miscellaneous equations. As usual give all answers from $0°$ to $360°$.
   (i) $3\tan\theta = \cot\theta$ (ii) $\cot\theta = 5\cos\theta$
   (iii) $3\cos^2\theta = 7\cos\theta + 6$ (iv) $7\sec\theta = 3\tan^2\theta + 5$
   (v) $4\sin\theta + \operatorname{cosec}\theta = 4$ (vi) $3\cos^2\theta - \cos\theta = 0$
   (vii) $4\cos^3\theta = \cos\theta$ (viii) $\tan\theta + 3\cot\theta = 5\sec\theta$

5

Functions and Equations

5.1 Functions and their notation

A **function** is a process by which values of a variable x are transformed into new values; these being called the values of the function. Thus the function $3x + 2$ transforms the values $x = 1$, $x = 2$, $x = 3$ into new values 5, 8, 11 respectively.

The notation $f(x)$ is used to denote the value of the function corresponding to a certain value x; in particular $f(1), f(2), f(3)$ etc. would be the values of the function obtained for $x = 1$, $x = 2$, $x = 3$ respectively. Thus

$$\text{If } f(x) = 3x + 2 \quad \text{then } f(1) = 5, \quad f(2) = 8, \quad f(3) = 11$$
$$\text{If } f(x) = x^2 \quad \text{then } f(1) = 1, \quad f(2) = 4, \quad f(3) = 9$$

A function f may frequently be defined as follows:

$$f : x \to 3x + 2$$
$$\text{or} \quad f : x \to f(x) \quad \text{where} \quad f(x) = 3x + 2$$

This method has the advantage of stressing the idea of a transformation from a value x to a new value.

Domain and range

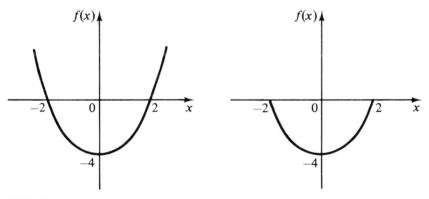

Fig. 1a   Fig. 1b

Fig. 1a sketches the graph of the function $f(x) = x^2 - 4$ (values taken by the function $f(x)$ being plotted on the vertical axis). It is seen from the graph that the function $f(x)$ can take any value from -4 upwards i.e. $f(x) \geqslant -4$. This is often called the **range** of the function.

Sometimes a function may be defined for certain values of x only (occasionally called the **domain**). If, for example, the function $x^2 - 4$ is restricted to the domain $-2 \leqslant x \leqslant 2$ then the graph of Fig. 1b is obtained and the range of the function is now $-4 \leqslant f(x) \leqslant 0$.

For many functions it is essential to restrict the domain in this way. For example, to avoid introducing the square roots of negative numbers the function $\sqrt{x}$ can be restricted to the domain $x \geqslant 0$ and the function $\sqrt{2x-3}$ to $x \geqslant 1\frac{1}{2}$.

Note: When the domain of a function is not restricted in any way we may make this clear by defining the function for $x \in \mathbb{R}$ (i.e. x may take any real value).

The derived function

The gradient or derived function of a function $f(x)$ is denoted $f'(x)$. It follows that $f'(1), f'(2)$ etc. would represent the values taken by the derived function (i.e. the gradients) at $x = 1$, $x = 2$ respectively. For example

If $\quad f(x) = x^3 - 2x$
then $\quad f'(x) = 3x^2 - 2$

and the gradient at the point $x = 2$ is given by

$$f'(2) = 12 - 2 = 10$$

Example 24

Sketch the function $f: x \to \dfrac{6}{x}$ $\quad (x \geqslant 2)$. State the range of the function f and of the derived function f'.

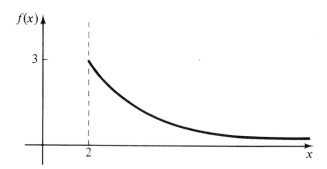

Fig. 2

The sketch is shown in Fig. 2. When $x = 2, f(x) = 3$ and as x increases $f(x)$ gets progressively closer to zero. But $f(x)$ *never equals zero exactly*. So the range of f is $0 < f(x) \leqslant 3$.

The derived function is $f'(x) = -6/x^2$ $(x \geqslant 2)$. When $x = 2$ $f'(x) = -1\frac{1}{2}$ and we see from Fig. 2 that as x increases the gradient also gets closer to zero but again never equals zero exactly. So the range of f' is $-1\frac{1}{2} \leqslant f'(x) < 0$.

Exercise 5(a)

1. If $f(x) = 3x^2 - 5x$ find $f(3)$, $f(-2)$, $f'(x)$, $f'(0)$, $f'(1)$.
2. If $f(x) = x^3 - 3x + 2$ find $f(1)$, $f(3)$, $f'(x)$, $f'(2)$, $f'(-1)$.
3. If $f(t) = 2t^2 + \dfrac{1}{t}$ find $f(2)$, $f(-3)$, $f'(t)$, $f'(1)$, $f'(\frac{1}{2})$.
4. If $f(x) = 3x^2 - x - 2$ find values of x such that (i) $f(x) = 0$ (ii) $f'(x) = 2$
5. If $f(x) = 3x - \dfrac{2}{x}$ find a value K such that $f(K) = -5$.
6. Sketch the graphs of the following functions and state the range of the function in each case:
   (i) $x \to x^3$
   (ii) $x \to 2^x$
   (iii) $x \to \sin x°$ $(0 \leqslant x \leqslant 180)$
   (iv) $x \to \tan x°$ $(0 \leqslant x \leqslant 45)$
   (v) $x \to 6 - 2x$ $(x \geqslant 0)$
   (vi) $x \to 9 - x^2$ $(-3 \leqslant x \leqslant 3)$
   (vii) $x \to \dfrac{1}{x^2}$
   (viii) $x \to 1 - \dfrac{1}{x}$ $(x \geqslant 1)$

   (All values of x are to be considered except where otherwise stated.)
7. State the range of the derived function in question 6, parts (v)–(viii).
*8. Explain the following statement, with the help of a diagram:

$$f'(x) = \lim_{\delta x \to 0} \frac{f(x + \delta x) - f(x)}{\delta x}$$

5.2 The quadratic function

A function containing terms in x^2, x and a constant is known as a **quadratic function**. The general quadratic function may be written as

$$ax^2 + bx + c \qquad (a, b, c \text{ constants})$$

For the moment we shall consider only those functions in which the x^2 term is positive (i.e. $a > 0$). The graphs of all such functions are similar in shape to

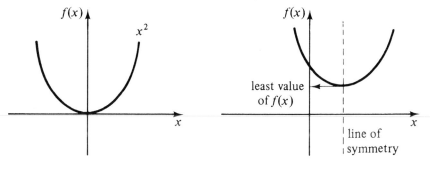

Fig. 3a   Fig. 3b

the graph of x^2 itself (Fig. 3a), i.e. they exhibit a single continuous curve symmetrical about the lowest point. At this point the function takes its least possible value (Fig. 3b).

To demonstrate this we first notice that

(i) the addition of a constant term to the function x^2 simply moves the graph vertically up or down (Fig. 4a).

(ii) perfect squares such as $(x-2)^2$, $(x+3)^2$ etc. are identical in shape to x^2 except that they take their least value (zero) not when $x = 0$ but when $x = +2$, $x = -3$ . . . respectively (Fig. 4b).

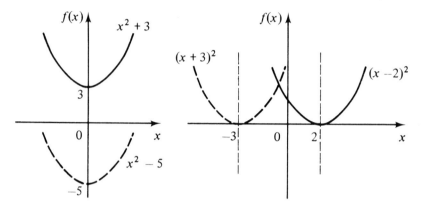

Fig. 4a   Fig. 4b

Any quadratic function may be expressed in terms of a perfect square and a constant term. Consider, for example, the function $x^2 - 4x + 9$.

$$x^2 - 4x + 9 = (x^2 - 4x + 4) + 5$$
$$= (x - 2)^2 + 5$$

This function will have a graph identical in shape to $(x-2)^2$ but raised 5 units vertically. The zero value of the perfect square occurs when $x = 2$ so that the least value of the function itself is 5, also at $x = 2$ (Fig. 5).

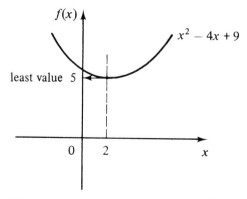

Fig. 5

A further, more difficult, case is considered in the following example.

Example 25

Express the function $3x^2 - 4x + 2$ in the form $p(x - q)^2 + r$ where p, q and r are constants. Hence show that the function is always positive and state the least value taken by the function.

We begin by taking out a factor 3 (so as to obtain a function whose x^2 coefficient is 1). The second step is to complete the square on $x^2 - \frac{4}{3}x$ and then ensure that the constants combine to $\frac{2}{3}$. Thus

$$3x^2 - 4x + 2 = 3\left[x^2 - \frac{4}{3}x + \frac{2}{3} \right]$$

$$= 3\left[\left(x^2 - \frac{4}{3}x + \frac{4}{9} \right) + \frac{2}{9} \right]$$

$$= 3\left[\left(x - \frac{2}{3} \right)^2 + \frac{2}{9} \right]$$

or $\qquad 3\left(x - \frac{2}{3} \right)^2 + \frac{2}{3}$

Since the perfect square term is always positive, the function itself (after the addition of $\frac{2}{3}$) will also remain positive. Furthermore, when the perfect square term is zero, the function will take its least value, i.e. $\frac{2}{3}$.

Functions with a negative x^2 term

When the x^2 term is negative the shape of the graph is inverted and the function has a maximum rather than a minimum value. To express such a function in terms of a perfect square and a constant it is usual to begin by removing a negative factor. We shall use the function $1 - 2x - 2x^2$ to illustrate this.

$$1 - 2x - 2x^2 = -2\left[x^2 + x - \frac{1}{2} \right]$$

$$= -2\left[\left(x^2 + x + \frac{1}{4} \right) - \frac{3}{4} \right]$$

$$= -2\left[\left(x + \frac{1}{2} \right)^2 - \frac{3}{4} \right]$$

or $\qquad \frac{3}{2} - 2\left(x + \frac{1}{2} \right)^2$

This function takes a maximum value of $\frac{3}{2}$, which occurs when the perfect square is zero (i.e. when $x = -\frac{1}{2}$). A sketch of the function is shown in Fig. 6.

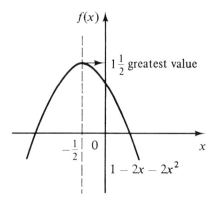

$f(x)$

$1\frac{1}{2}$ greatest value

$-\frac{1}{2}$ 0

x

$1 - 2x - 2x^2$

Fig. 6

Exercise 5(b)

1. Sketch the following functions, indicating their axes of symmetry clearly:
   (i) $x^2 - 4$ (ii) $(x + 2)^2$
   (iii) $(x - 1)^2 + 2$ (iv) $(x + 4)^2 - 3$
2. Express the following functions in the form $(x + a)^2 + b$ where a and b are constants. Hence make a simple sketch of each function, marking clearly the least value and the value of x for which it occurs.
   (i) $x^2 + 2x + 5$ (ii) $x^2 - 6x + 5$
   (iii) $x^2 + x - 1$ (iv) $x^2 - 5x + 7$
3. (i) Find the value of c for which the function $x^2 + 3x + c$ has a least value of $\frac{3}{4}$.
   (ii) State the smallest value of c for which this function is always positive.
4. Express the following functions in the form $p(x + q)^2 + r$ where p, q, r are constants. Hence state the minimum value of each function.
   (i) $2x^2 - 8x + 9$ (ii) $5x^2 + 10x + 2$
   (iii) $3x^2 + 2x + 1$ (iv) $2x^2 - 3x - 1$
   Which of these functions are always positive?
5. In each case state whether the function has a maximum or a minimum value and determine this value.
   (i) $3 + 4x - x^2$ (ii) $5 - 3x + x^2$
   (iii) $1 - 4x - 2x^2$ (iv) $x - x^2 + 4$
   (v) $2 + 6x - 5x^2$ (vi) $a + bx + x^2$ (a, b constants)
*6. Show that the quadratic function $ax^2 + bx + c$ may be expressed in the form

$$a\left[\left(x + \frac{b}{2a}\right)^2 - \left(\frac{b^2 - 4ac}{4a^2}\right)\right]$$

Hence find, in terms of a, b and c, the values of x for which the function takes the value zero.

5.3 Quadratic inequalities

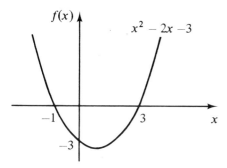

Fig. 7

Fig. 7 shows a sketch of the function $x^2 - 2x - 3$. This may be factorized as $(x - 3)(x + 1)$ so the function takes the value zero at $x = 3$ and $x = -1$. These are the intersections of the graph with the x-axis.

Where the graph lies above the x-axis the function takes positive values. Thus the **quadratic inequality** $x^2 - 2x - 3 > 0$ is true for $x > 3$ and $x < -1$; these are said to be the solutions of the inequality. The function is negative where the graph lies below the x-axis and the solutions of the inequality $x^2 - 2x - 3 < 0$ are therefore $-1 < x < 3$.

Quadratic inequalities are best solved by sketching the function concerned in this way. It is important to remember that when the x^2 term is negative the shape of the graph is inverted (as in the next example).

Example 26

Solve the inequality $10 + 3x - x^2 \leqslant 0$.

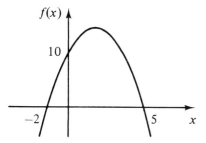

Fig. 8

The function factorizes as $(5 - x)(2 + x)$ so that it is zero for $x = 5$ and $x = -2$. Fig. 8 is a sketch of the function (the shape is inverted since the x^2

term is negative). The function is less than or equal to zero for $x \leqslant -2$ and $x \geqslant 5$. We may set the working out as follows:

$$10 + 3x - x^2 \leqslant 0$$
$$(5 - x)(2 + x) \leqslant 0$$
$$\Rightarrow \underline{x \geqslant 5 \text{ or } x \leqslant -2}$$

5.4 The discriminant

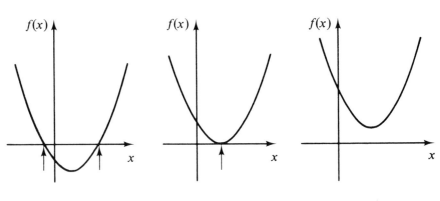

Fig. 9a   Fig. 9b   Fig. 9c

Solving the quadratic equation $ax^2 + bx + c = 0$ is equivalent to finding values of x for which the quadratic function $ax^2 + bx + c$ takes the value zero. As we have seen these are the intersections of the function with the x-axis. Bearing this in mind Fig. 9 shows that three types of quadratic equation may be expected

Equations with 2 distinct solutions – Fig. 9a
Equations with 1 solution only   – Fig. 9b
Equations with no solutions   – Fig. 9c.

We may distinguish between these three cases by using the **discriminant.** This is the quantity $b^2 - 4ac$ which arises in the formula for the roots of a quadratic equation, i.e.

$$x = \frac{-b \pm \sqrt{b^2 - 4ac}}{2a}$$

When taking the square root in this formula three possibilities arise.

(i) $b^2 - 4ac > 0$ Two square roots exist (one positive, one negative). The equation has **two distinct roots**. (Fig. 9a).

(ii) $b^2 - 4ac = 0$ The square root is zero and the two solutions coincide. The equation is said to have a **repeated root**. (Fig. 9b).

(iii) $b^2 - 4ac < 0$ The square root does not exist. The equation is insoluble. We sometimes say it has **imaginary roots** (Fig. 9c).

Note: In Fig. 9 we assume that the x^2 term is positive. The same results apply when the x^2 term is negative though the shapes of the graphs are inverted.

Example 27

Determine the *nature of the roots* for each of the following equations:
(i) $x^2 - x - 4 = 0$ (ii) $3x^2 + 2x + 1 = 0$ (iii) $4x^2 - 4x + 1 = 0$

Equation (i) $a = 1, b = -1, c = -4$

Discriminant $b^2 - 4ac = 17 \Rightarrow$ two distinct roots

Equation (ii) $a = 3, b = 2, c = 1$

Discriminant $b^2 - 4ac = -8 \Rightarrow$ imaginary roots

Equation (iii) $a = 4, b = -4, c = 1$

Discriminant $b^2 - 4ac = 0 \Rightarrow$ repeated root

Types of quadratic function

We may also use the discriminant $b^2 - 4ac$ to distinguish between the following types of quadratic function:
(i) Functions which take both positive and negative values – as in Fig. 9a. Here the graph has 2 intersections so $b^2 - 4ac > 0$.
(ii) Functions which are always positive – as in Fig. 9c. (Or, where the shape is inverted, always negative). Here $b^2 - 4ac < 0$, since there are no intersections.

Example 28

(i) Show that the function $2x^2 - 3x + 2$ is always positive
(ii) Find the values of x for which $2x^2 - 3x + 1$ is negative.

(i) We have $a = 2, b = -3, c = 2 \Rightarrow$ discriminant $b^2 - 4ac = -7$. The function is therefore always positive or always negative. But when $x = 0$ the function takes the value 2. Hence it must be always positive.

(ii) (The discriminant here is $+1$ so the function will take both positive and negative values.) Since $2x^2 - 3x + 1$ may be factorized as $(2x - 1)(x - 1)$, it is equal to zero when $x = \frac{1}{2}$ and $x = 1$. The graph will resemble that of Fig. 9a so that the function is negative for $\frac{1}{2} < x < 1$.

Note: Part (i) may also be done by completing the square, as in example 25.

Exercise 5(c)

1. Establish the nature of the roots of the following quadratic equations. (Do not solve the equations.)

(i) $x^2 + 5x + 3 = 0$ (ii) $x^2 - 5x + 7 = 0$
(iii) $3x^2 - x - 1 = 0$ (iv) $4x^2 + 12x + 9 = 0$
(v) $2x^2 = 3x - 4$ (vi) $x^2 + ax + a^2 = 0$

2. Factorize the following functions, sketch their graphs and state the values of x for which they are positive

(i) $x^2 + x - 6$ (ii) $3x^2 - 5x + 2$
(iii) $5 + 4x - x^2$ (iv) $6 - x - 2x^2$

3. Find the value of the constant c for which the roots of the equation $3x^2 + 8x + c = 0$ are equal.

4. State which of the following functions are always positive, which are always negative and which take both positive and negative values.

(i) $x^2 - 2x + 7$ (ii) $2x^2 + 5x + 3$
(iii) $5 + 4x - x^2$ (iv) $3x^2 + x - 1$
(v) $1 - 3x + 5x^2$ (vi) $4x - x^2 - 5$

5. Solve the inequalities

(i) $x^2 - 4x + 3 < 0$ (ii) $2x^2 + 3x - 5 \geqslant 0$
(iii) $x^2 + x > 12$ (iv) $8 + 2x - x^2 > 0$
(v) $6 - 5x + x^2 \geqslant 0$ (vi) $3x^2 < 11x + 4$

*6. (i) Find any intersections of $y = x^2$ with the line $y = 6x - 9$. What can you deduce?
(ii) Find the value of c for which the line $y = 3x + c$ is a tangent to the curve $y = x^2$.

7. (i) Show that the function $3x^2 - 5x + 4$ is always positive.
(ii) Find the values of x for which this function exceeds the value 16.

8. If $f(x) = x^2 - 5x - 6$ find the values of x for which $f(x) = 0$. By considerations of symmetry state the value of x for which the function takes its least value and find this value.

9. (i) Prove that $x^2 > 3x - 3$ for all values of x.
(ii) Solve the inequality $x^2 > 3x - 2$.

10. (i) Find the values of x for which the function $3x^2 + 4x - 4$ is negative.
(ii) Find the least value of the constant c for which the function $3x^2 + 4x + c$ takes no negative values.

5.5 Sum and product of the roots

The roots of the equation $2x^2 + 3x - 4 = 0$ are not immediately obvious (i.e. the equation cannot be solved quickly by factors). There is, however, a method which enables us to write down immediately the sum of these roots and also their product.

If the quadratic equation $ax^2 + bx + c = 0$ has roots α and β then it could be written in factors as $(x - \alpha)(x - \beta) = 0$. Notice that in this form the coefficient of x^2 is 1. If we divide the original equation through by a, so that the x^2 coefficient is reduced to 1, it must then be true that

$$x^2 + \frac{bx}{a} + \frac{c}{a} \equiv (x - \alpha)(x - \beta)$$

i.e. $x^2 + \frac{bx}{a} + \frac{c}{a} \equiv x^2 - (\alpha + \beta)x + \alpha\beta$

Equating the coefficients of x in these functions, and also the constant terms, we obtain

Sum of roots $\alpha + \beta$	$= \dfrac{-b}{a}$
Product of roots $\alpha\beta$	$= \dfrac{c}{a}$

For the equation $2x^2 + 3x - 4 = 0$ we have $a = 2$, $b = 3$ and $c = -4$ so that

$$\text{sum of roots} \quad = \frac{-3}{2}$$

$$\text{product of roots} \quad = \frac{-4}{2} \quad \text{or} \quad -2$$

This does not tell us the values of the roots themselves but, in fact, occasions when the sum or the product may themselves be of use are not infrequent.

Note: It is interesting that these results are true even for equations with imaginary roots. For example, the equation $\frac{1}{2}x^2 - x + 2 = 0$ may be said to have roots $\alpha = 1 + \sqrt{-3}$ and $\beta = 1 - \sqrt{-3}$, these being obtained from the usual formula. The student may verify that the sum and product of these expressions agree with the results predicted by this method, i.e.

$$\text{sum} \quad = -\frac{b}{a} = 2$$

$$\text{product} \quad = \frac{c}{a} = 4$$

Example 29

If α and β are the roots of $3x^2 - 2x - 6 = 0$ find the values of (i) $\alpha^2 + \beta^2$ (ii) $\alpha^3 + \beta^3$.

For this equation we have

$$\text{sum of roots } \alpha + \beta \quad = \frac{2}{3}$$

$$\text{product of roots } \alpha\beta \quad = -\frac{6}{3} \quad \text{or} \quad -2$$

From these results we may solve the question as follows:

(i)
$$(\alpha + \beta)^2 = \alpha^2 + 2\alpha\beta + \beta^2$$
$$\frac{4}{9} = \alpha^2 + \beta^2 - 4$$
$$\Rightarrow \alpha^2 + \beta^2 = 4\tfrac{4}{9}$$

(ii) $(\alpha + \beta)^3 = \alpha^3 + 3\alpha^2\beta + 3\alpha\beta^2 + \beta^3$
$$= \alpha^3 + \beta^3 + 3\alpha\beta(\alpha + \beta)$$
$$\frac{8}{27} = \alpha^3 + \beta^3 - 6\left(\frac{2}{3}\right)$$

$\Rightarrow \alpha^3 + \beta^3 = 4\tfrac{8}{27}$

Note: Questions 1–6 of Exercise 5(d) may now be attempted.

Example 30

If α and β are the roots of $3x^2 - 2x - 6 = 0$, find the equations whose roots are

(i) 3α and 3β (ii) $\dfrac{1}{\alpha^2}$ and $\dfrac{1}{\beta^2}$

As in the previous example we have

$$\alpha + \beta = \frac{2}{3}, \qquad \alpha\beta = -2, \qquad \alpha^2 + \beta^2 = 4\tfrac{4}{9}$$

(i) For the equation with roots 3α and 3β

sum of roots $= 3\alpha + 3\beta = 3(\alpha + \beta) = 2$
product of roots $= 9\alpha\beta = -18$

The equation is therefore

$$x^2 - 2x - 18 = 0$$

(ii) For the equation with roots $\dfrac{1}{\alpha^2}$ and $\dfrac{1}{\beta^2}\ \ldots$

sum of roots $= \dfrac{1}{\alpha^2} + \dfrac{1}{\beta^2}$

$$= \frac{\alpha^2 + \beta^2}{\alpha^2\beta^2} = \frac{4\tfrac{4}{9}}{4} = \frac{10}{9}$$

product of roots $= \dfrac{1}{\alpha^2\beta^2} = \dfrac{1}{4}$

The equation is therefore

$$x^2 - \frac{10}{9}x + \frac{1}{4} = 0$$

or $36x^2 - 40x + 9 = 0$

Exercise 5(d)

1. Write down the sum and the product of the roots for each of the following equations:

(i) $x^2 + 3x + 4 = 0$ (ii) $2x^2 + x - 5 = 0$
(iii) $3x^2 - 4x - 2 = 0$ (iv) $5x^2 - x + 1 = 0$

(v) $2x^2 = 5x - 6$ (vi) $x - x^2 = 5$

(vii) $x - \dfrac{1}{x} + 1 = 0$ (viii) $(2x + 1)^2 = x$

2. If the roots of the equation $2x^2 - 4x + 1 = 0$ are α and β find the values of

(i) $\alpha^2 + \beta^2$ (ii) $\dfrac{1}{\alpha} + \dfrac{1}{\beta}$ (iii) $\alpha^3 + \beta^3$ (iv) $\dfrac{1}{\alpha^2} + \dfrac{1}{\beta^2}$

3. Repeat question 2 for the equation $4x^2 + 6x + 1 = 0$.

4. If the roots of the equation $2x^2 - 3x - 6 = 0$ are α and β find the values of

(i) $(\alpha + 1)(\beta + 1)$ (ii) $\dfrac{\alpha}{\beta} + \dfrac{\beta}{\alpha}$ (iii) $(\alpha - \beta)^2$ (iv) $\alpha^2 - \beta^2$

5. Repeat question 4 for the equation $3x^2 + 2x - 4 = 0$

6. Find the value of the constant p such that the roots of $x^2 - 5x + p = 0$
(i) are equal   (ii) differ by 2.

*7. The line $y = 2x - 3$ intersects the curve $y^2 = 2x$ twice. Find a quadratic equation the roots of which give the x coordinates of the two points of intersection. Without solving this equation, find the midpoint of the line joining the intersections.

8. Find possible values of the constant k such that one root of the equation $2x^2 + kx + 9 = 0$ is double the other.

9. If the roots of the equation $x^2 - x - 4 = 0$ are α and β, find the equations whose roots are (i) 2α and 2β (ii) α^2 and β^2 (iii) $\dfrac{1}{\alpha}$ and $\dfrac{1}{\beta}$

10. Repeat question 9 for the equation $3x^2 + 5x + 1 = 0$.

11. If the roots of the equation $x^2 + 3x + 4 = 0$ are p and q, find the equations whose roots are (i) p^2q and pq^2 (ii) $p + 2q$ and $2p + q$ (iii) $\dfrac{p}{q}$ and $\dfrac{q}{p}$.

12. If the roots of the equation $2x^2 + 4x - 3 = 0$ are h and k, find the equations whose roots are (i) $1 + h$ and $1 + k$ (ii) $\dfrac{1}{h^2}$ and $\dfrac{1}{k^2}$ (iii) h^3 and k^3.

5.6 The cubic function ($px^3 + qx^2 + rx + s$)

Fig. 10 shows the typical shapes for the graphs of cubic functions (x^3 term positive). When the x^3 term is negative these shapes are inverted.

(less pronounced)

Fig. 10

The student should plot the functions of Exercise 5(e) question 1 as examples.

Cubic equations ($px^3 + qx^2 + rx + s = 0$)

We must find the values of x for which the cubic function is zero, i.e. intersects with the x-axis. Fig. 11 illustrates the various possibilities which may arise.

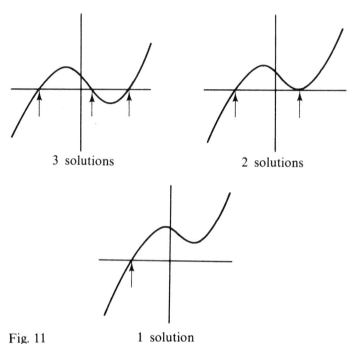

3 solutions   2 solutions

1 solution

Fig. 11

It is important to notice that all cubic equations have at least one solution.

To solve a cubic equation, given one root

Let us suppose that we have a cubic equation, e.g. $x^3 - x^2 - 10x - 8 = 0$ and that one solution is known: $x = -2$. (The reader may verify by substitution that this satisfies the equation.) How this root is discovered we leave until the next section. The question we consider at present is this: given one root, can we decide if any further roots exist and, if so, can we find them?

The solution $x = -2$ corresponds to a factor $(x + 2)$ and we begin by removing this factor. This can usually be done by inspection

$$x^3 - x^2 - 10x - 8 = (x + 2)(x^2 \qquad -4)$$

$$+ 2x^2$$

$$- 3x^2$$

To establish the terms of the remaining factor, which is quadratic, consider in turn

(i)   the x^3 term of the cubic; hence x^2 in the quadratic factor
(ii) the term -8 in the cubic; hence -4 in the quadratic factor
(iii) the term $-x^2$ in the cubic; this is the sum of two separate products, one of which is seen to be $+2x^2$. Since the other product must be $-3x^2$ the missing term is established as $-3x$. We now have

$$x^3 - x^2 - 10x - 8 = 0$$
$$\Rightarrow (x+2)(x^2 - 3x - 4) = 0$$
$$\Rightarrow x = -2 \quad \text{or} \quad x^2 - 3x - 4 = 0$$

We now see how the different possibilities of Fig. 11 arise. If the quadratic equation has two distinct roots ($b^2 - 4ac > 0$) then we have three solutions in all. If it has no roots ($b^2 - 4ac < 0$) then the cubic equation has a single solution only. If two equal roots are obtained then the graph touches the x-axis at the point concerned.

In the example considered, the equation $x^2 - 3x - 4 = 0$ is readily factorized and leads to two further solutions: $x = -1$ and $x = 4$. The three solutions ($x = -2$, $x = -1$ and $x = 4$) correspond to intersections with the x-axis. A sketch of the function $x^3 - x^2 - 10x - 8$ is shown in Fig. 12.

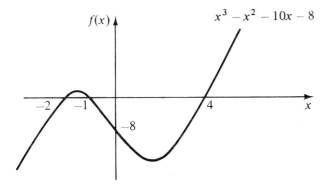

Fig. 12

As a further example consider the equation $2x^3 - x^2 + x + 1 = 0$ for which $x = -\frac{1}{2}$ is one solution. Removing a factor $(2x + 1)$ we have

$$2x^3 - x^2 + x + 1 = 0$$
$$\Rightarrow (2x + 1)(x^2 - x + 1) = 0$$
$$\Rightarrow x = -\frac{1}{2} \quad \text{or} \quad x^2 - x + 1 = 0$$

Here the quadratic is insoluble ($b^2 - 4ac = -3$) and no further roots are obtained.

Exercise 5(e)

1. Draw tables of values for the following functions taking x from -2 to $+3$ in each case. Plot the graphs and hence determine the values of x for which the functions are zero.

(i) $x^3 + x - 10$ (ii) $x^3 - 2x^2 + 4$ (iii) $x^3 - x^2 - 3x$
(iv) $5 + 4x - x^3$

2. Make simple sketches of the following functions:
(i) $(x+1)(x+2)(x+3)$ (ii) $(x+2)(x-3)^2$ (iii) $x(x^2-4)$
(iv) $(1+x)(2-x)(3+x)$ (v) $x^3 - 1$ (vi) $x^3 - x$
(vii) $x^3 - x^2$ (viii) $(1+2x)^2(1-2x)$

3. One root is given for each of the following cubic equations. Determine any further roots.
(i) $x^3 - 2x^2 - 5x + 6 = 0,\ x = -2$
(ii) $3x^3 - x^2 - x - 1 = 0,\ x = 1$
(iii) $2x^3 + 3x^2 - 1 = 0,\ x = \frac{1}{2}$
(iv) $2x^3 + x^2 - 13x + 6 = 0,\ x = 2$
(v) $x^3 + 3x^2 + 2x + 6 = 0,\ x = -3$
(vi) $4x^3 + 4x^2 - 7x - 6 = 0,\ x = -1\frac{1}{2}$

5.7 The remainder theorem

If we divide the function $3x^3 - x^2 - x + 2$ by $x + 1$ the division may be set out as follows. (Space does not permit a detailed explanation of this process.)

$$
\begin{array}{r}
3x^2 - 4x + 3 \\
\hline
x+1\ \big)\ 3x^3 - x^2 - x + 2 \\
3x^3 + 3x^2 \\
\hline
-4x^2 - x \\
-4x^2 - 4x \\
\hline
3x + 2 \\
3x + 3 \\
\hline
-1
\end{array}
$$

When the division is complete there is a **remainder** of -1. $3x^2 - 4x + 3$ is called the **quotient**. We may write

$$3x^3 - x^2 - x + 2 \equiv (x+1)(3x^2 - 4x + 3) - 1$$

The remainder theorem gives a method by which the remainder may be found without performing the actual division. If division of the function $f(x)$ by $(x - a)$ leads to a quotient $Q(x)$ and remainder R, then, in analogy to the particular case above, we have

$$f(x) \equiv (x - a) \cdot Q(x) + R$$

This identity must be true for all values of x. Putting $x = a$ we obtain

$$f(a) = 0 . Q(a) + R$$
i.e. $f(a) = R$

Thus the remainder on division by $(x - a)$ is given by the value of the function when $x = a$. In our first example, where $f(x) = 3x^3 - x^2 - x + 2$, the remainder on division by $x + 1$ is given by $f(-1)$, i.e.

$$-3 - 1 + 1 + 2 = -1$$

Example 31

Find the remainders for the following divisions:
(i) $x^3 - 2x^2 + 3x - 8 \div x - 3$
(ii) $2x^3 - x^2 - 3x - 1 \div 2x + 1$

(i) $f(x) = x^3 - 2x^2 + 3x - 8$
remainder $= f(3) = 27 - 18 + 9 - 8 = 10$

(ii) $f(x) = 2x^3 - x^2 - 3x - 1$

remainder $= f(-\frac{1}{2}) = -\dfrac{1}{4} - \dfrac{1}{4} + \dfrac{3}{2} - 1 = 0$

Note: For division by $(px - q)$, where p and q are constants, the remainder is given by $f\left(\dfrac{q}{p}\right)$ as in the second part of the above example.

Factors

If the remainder in such a division is zero then the divisor divides *exactly* and is therefore a factor of the function concerned. Thus, in the above example, $2x + 1$ is shown to be a factor of $2x^3 - x^2 - 3x - 1$.

This means that the remainder theorem can be used as a method of testing for factors, as is illustrated by the following example.

Example 32

Factorize the cubic function $2x^3 - 3x^2 - 10x + 3$.

Possible factors are $x + 1$, $x - 1$, $x + 3$, $x - 3$ and also $2x + 1$, $2x - 1$, $2x + 3$, $2x - 3$ (these contain factors of $2x^3$ and of $+3$). We proceed to test these systematically using the remainder theorem.

$$f(x) = 2x^3 - 3x^2 - 10x + 3$$

Divide by			
$x + 1$	$R = f(-1) = -2 - 3 + 10 + 3$	$= 8$
$x - 1$	$R = f(1) = 2 - 3 - 10 + 3$	$= -8$
$x + 3$	$R = f(-3) = -54 - 27 + 30 + 3$	$= -48$
$x - 3$	$R = f(3) = 54 - 27 - 30 + 3$	$= 0$

$(x - 3)$ is therefore a factor. The question is now completed by the method of Section 5.6, i.e.

$$2x^3 - 3x^2 - 10x + 3 = \underline{(x - 3)(2x^2 + 3x - 1)}$$

(Since the quadratic factor does not itself factorize, further work with the remainder theorem would have been fruitless.)

Exercise 5(f)

1. Find the remainders in the following divisions:
   (i) $3x^2 + 5x + 2$ $\div x + 2$ (ii) $x^3 + 7x^2 - 2$ $\div x + 1$
   (iii) $x^3 - 2x^2 + 3x - 6$ $\div x - 2$ (iv) $x^3 + 3x^2 - 7x - 4$ $\div x + 4$
   (v) $x^5 + x - 9$ $\div x - 1$ (vi) $4x^3 - 5x + 4$ $\div 2x - 1$
   (vii) $4x^3 + 6x^2 + 3x + 2$ $\div 2x + 3$ (viii) $x^6 - 3x^4 + 4$ $\div x^2 - 2$

2. Find the constants a, b and c if
   (i) $2x^2 + ax - 5$ $\div x - 3$ leaves remainder   4.
   (ii) $x^3 + bx^2 + 3x - 1$ $\div x + 2$ leaves remainder -3.
   (iii) $cx^3 - 5x + 2$ has factor $2x - 1$.

3. Factorize the following functions:
   (i) $x^3 - 2x^2 - 2x - 3$ (ii) $4x^3 - 8x^2 + x + 3$
   (iii) $2x^3 + x^2 - 8x - 4$ (iv) $2x^3 - x^2 + 2x - 1$
   (v) $x^3 - 11x - 20$ (vi) $6x^3 + 5x^2 - 3x - 2$

*4. For what values of the constants p and q would both $x + 1$ and $x - 2$ be factors of the expression $x^3 + px^2 + 2x + q$?

5. Solve the equations
   (i) $2x^3 - x^2 - 2x + 1 = 0$ (ii) $x^3 + x^2 - x + 2 = 0$
   (iii) $x^3 - x^2 - 3x + 2 = 0$ (iv) $6x^3 - 11x^2 - 37x + 70 = 0$

*6. (i)   Prove that $x - a$ is a factor of $x^3 - a^3$ and find the other factor.
   (ii) Prove that $x + a$ is a factor of $x^3 + a^3$ and find the other factor.
   (iii) Hence write down the factors of $x^3 - 8$ and $x^3 + 1$.

6

Maxima and Minima

6.1 Higher derivatives

Notation

In Chapter 3 we introduced the notation $\dfrac{dy}{dx}$ for the derived function and we now extend this notation. We regard $\dfrac{d}{dx}$ as an operator (or instruction) meaning **differentiate with respect to** x. Thus $\dfrac{d(y)}{dx}$ or $\dfrac{dy}{dx}$ means **differentiate** y **with respect to** x. The result of this operation, of course, is the derived function (or **derivative**) of y.

There are situations where it is useful to differentiate a second time: the result then obtained is called the **second derivative**. The notation used for this is $\dfrac{d^2y}{dx^2}$,

i.e. $\quad \dfrac{d}{dx}\left(\dfrac{dy}{dx}\right) \quad$ or $\quad \dfrac{d}{dx}\cdot\dfrac{d}{dx}(y) \quad$ or $\quad \dfrac{d^2y}{dx^2}$

This process may be continued. We next obtain the **third derivative** which is written

$$\dfrac{d}{dx}\cdot\dfrac{d}{dx}\cdot\dfrac{d}{dx}(y) \quad \text{or} \quad \dfrac{d^3y}{dx^3}$$

As a simple example consider the function $x^4 - 2x^3 + 5$

$$\text{If} \quad y \quad = x^4 - 2x^3 + 5$$

$$\text{then} \quad \dfrac{dy}{dx} \quad = 4x^3 - 6x^2 \qquad \text{(1st derivative)}$$

$$\dfrac{d^2y}{dx^2} = 12x^2 - 12x \qquad \text{(2nd derivative)}$$

$$\dfrac{d^3y}{dx^3} = 24x - 12 \qquad \text{(3rd derivative)}$$

Note: Using function notation $x \to f(x)$ the derived function or first derivative is denoted $f'(x)$, the second derivative $f''(x)$ and the third derivative $f'''(x)$.

Sign of the first derivative or gradient

If the gradient $\dfrac{dy}{dx}$ is positive then the function is **increasing**, i.e. the function takes progressively larger values as x increases (see Fig. 1). When $\dfrac{dy}{dx}$ is negative the function is **decreasing** (see Fig. 2). Many functions, of course, will increase for certain values of x and decrease for others. The whole point, however, is that this can be readily ascertained by considering the sign of $\dfrac{dy}{dx}$. For example, with the function $x^4 - 2x^3 + 5$ considered above we have

$$\frac{dy}{dx} = 4x^3 - 6x^2 = 2x^2(2x - 3)$$

Since x^2 is always positive the gradient is positive if $2x - 3 > 0$ and negative if $2x - 3 < 0$. Thus the function is increasing for all values of $x > 1\frac{1}{2}$ but is decreasing for $x < 1\frac{1}{2}$.

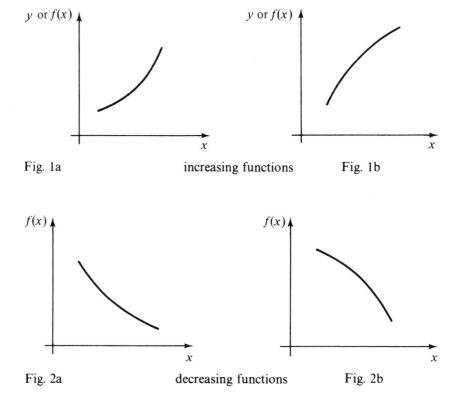

Fig. 1a   increasing functions   Fig. 1b

Fig. 2a   decreasing functions   Fig. 2b

Sign of the second derivative

This can also provide useful information about the behaviour of a function or its graph. The important point to grasp is that the second derivative gives us the same information about the gradient as the gradient gives us about the function itself. Just as a positive gradient tells us that the **function** is increasing, so a positive second derivative tells us that the **gradient** is increasing. Hence the shape of the graph must be as in Fig. 1a (where the gradient is clearly getting steeper) or as in Fig. 2a (where the gradient becomes 'less negative' and hence increases). Similarly if the second derivative is negative then the gradient of the function is decreasing and the graph corresponds to either Fig. 1b or Fig. 2b.

   This may seem complicated at first but what it amounts to is that the second derivative determines the **direction of curvature** of the graph. This can be quite simply remembered as in Fig. 3.

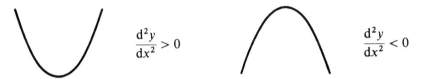

$$\frac{d^2y}{dx^2} > 0 \qquad\qquad \frac{d^2y}{dx^2} < 0$$

Fig. 3a Gradient increasing Fig. 3b Gradient decreasing

Example 33

Prove that the function $x - \dfrac{1}{x}$ ($x \in \mathbb{R}$, $x \neq 0$) is always increasing. Establish also the direction of curvature on the section $x > 0$.

(Notice that the question excludes $x = 0$ from the domain of the function since $1/x$ cannot be defined at $x = 0$.)

Let $y = x - \dfrac{1}{x}$

then $\dfrac{dy}{dx} = 1 + \dfrac{1}{x^2}$ and $\dfrac{d^2y}{dx^2} = \dfrac{-2}{x^3}$

Since x^2 is always positive it follows that the gradient $\dfrac{dy}{dx}$ is positive for all values of x ($x \neq 0$). The function is therefore always increasing.

   For $x > 0$ we see that the second derivative is always negative so the curvature is as for Fig. 3b. But since the function is always increasing we can be more precise; the shape on this section of the curve will resemble Fig. 1b. (A sketch of this curve will be found in Section 6.3, Fig. 10a.)

Exercise 6(a)

1. Find $\dfrac{dy}{dx}$ and $\dfrac{d^2y}{dx^2}$ for each of the following:

   (i) $y = 2x^3 - 5x^2 + x$ (ii) $y = (2x - 1)(x + 4)$

   (iii) $y = 5x - \dfrac{1}{x}$ (iv) $y = \dfrac{x + 2}{x^2}$

2. Simplify

(i) $\dfrac{d}{dx}(x^5 - 1)$

(ii) $\dfrac{d^2}{dx^2}(3x^2 - x + 1)$

(iii) $\dfrac{d}{dh}(3 + h - \tfrac{1}{4}h^2)$

(iv) $\dfrac{d^2}{dt^2}(t^4 - 3t^2 + 1)$

3. If $f(x) = x^2 - x^3$, find $f'(x), f''(x), f'(3)$ and $f''(0)$. Find also the values of x for which

(i) $f'(x) = 0$ (ii) $f''(x) < 0$

4. Determine whether the following functions are increasing or decreasing at the points indicated:

(i) $x^2 - 5x + 3$ at $x = 2$ (ii) $\left(x + \dfrac{1}{x}\right)^2$ at $x = -\tfrac{1}{2}$

5. Determine whether the gradients of the following functions are increasing or decreasing at the points indicated:
(i) $1 + 5x^2 - x^3$ at $x = 1\tfrac{1}{2}$ (ii) $r^3 - 2r^4$ at $r = \tfrac{1}{2}$

6. Make simple sketches of the functions

(i) x^3, $(x \in \mathbb{R})$ (ii) $\dfrac{1}{x}$, $(x \in \mathbb{R}, x \neq 0)$

Verify, by using the first derivatives, that x^3 is always increasing and $1/x$ always decreasing. Use the second derivatives to check the curvature of your sketches for $x > 0$.

7. Prove the truth of the following statements:
   (i)   The function $x^5 + x^3 + x$ is always increasing.
   (ii) The function $3x^2 - 12x + 5$ increases for all values of $x > 2$.

   (iii) The function $x^2 - \dfrac{1}{x^2}$ decreases for $x < 0$.

8. By considering the second derivative verify that the quadratic function $ax^2 + bx + c$ has the shape of Fig. 3a when $a > 0$ (i.e. the x^2 term is positive) and the shape of Fig. 3b when $a < 0$.

*9. (i)   Prove that the function $x^3 - 3x^2 + 4x$ is always increasing.
   (ii) Show that the direction of curvature changes at $x = 1$.
   (iii) Sketch the function.

10. Prove that the cubic function $x^3 - 3x^2 + 1$ decreases for $0 < x < 2$ but increases for other values of x.

6.2 Turning points

Quadratic functions

As we have seen, quadratic functions with positive x^2 terms have the shape of Fig. 4a. Such a function decreases until the lowest point on the graph is reached (point A) and then increases again. At point A the function takes its least possible value and this is therefore called a **minimum point**.

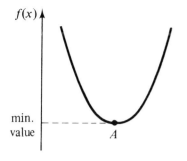

Fig. 4a

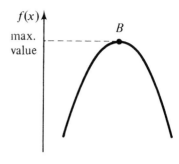

Fig. 4b

For functions with negative x^2 terms the shape of the graph is inverted (Fig. 4b). These functions increase to a maximum value at the **maximum point**, *B*, and then decrease again.

Cubic functions

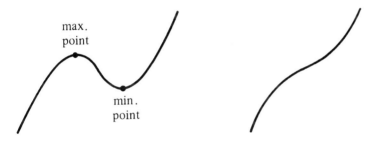

Fig. 5a   Fig. 5b

Fig. 5a shows the typical shape of a cubic function with a positive x^3 term. Such a function has both a maximum point and a minimum point. (Some functions, however, exhibit the less pronounced shape of Fig. 5b and these have neither a maximum nor a minimum point.) When the x^3 term is negative these shapes are again inverted.

Note: It is important to realise that the maximum point of Fig. 5a is not a maximum for the curve as a whole (since the function clearly takes larger values still on the far right-hand section of this graph). It is still called a maximum point, however, because *in this vicinity* the curve takes the characteristic maximum point shape of Fig. 4b. The same is true of the minimum point in Fig. 5a.

Locating turning points

Maximum and minimum points are often given the general name **turning points** (or sometimes **stationary values**). These points are of great importance.

Fortunately there is a fairly straight forward way of finding them; if the tangent to the curve is drawn in at either a maximum point or a minimum point it would be horizontal. So we deduce that *at all turning points the gradient* $\dfrac{dy}{dx}$ *is zero.*

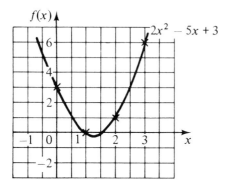

Fig. 6

As a first example consider the function $f(x) = 2x^2 - 5x + 3$. We shall first work out a few values of this function.

$$
\begin{aligned}
\text{When } x = 0 \quad & f(0) = 0 - 0 + 3 = 3 \\
x = 1 \quad & f(1) = 2 - 5 + 3 = 0 \\
x = 2 \quad & f(2) = 8 - 10 + 3 = 1 \\
x = 3 \quad & f(3) = 18 - 15 + 3 = 6
\end{aligned}
$$

On plotting these values (Fig. 6) we might be tempted to suppose that the minimum point is at $x = 1$ but in fact it lies somewhere between $x = 1$ and $x = 2$ and the least value of the function is a little below zero. The minimum point may be located exactly as follows:

let $\qquad\qquad y = 2x^2 - 5x + 3$

then $\qquad$ gradient $\dfrac{dy}{dx} = 4x - 5$

gradient $= 0$ $\quad$ when $\quad 4x - 5 = 0 \qquad \Rightarrow x = 1\tfrac{1}{4}$

The minimum point occurs where the gradient is zero and this is at $x = 1\tfrac{1}{4}$. The least value of the function is therefore

$$
f\left(\frac{5}{4}\right) = \frac{50}{16} - \frac{25}{4} + 3 = \underline{-\frac{1}{8}}
$$

In the next example we consider a cubic function.

Example   34

Find the turning points on $y = x^3 - 3x^2 + 1$ and hence make a simple sketch of the function.

To find the turning points we find where the gradient is zero

$$y = x^3 - 3x^2 + 1 \tag{1}$$

gradient $\dfrac{dy}{dx} = 3x^2 - 6x$

gradient $= 0$ when $3x^2 - 6x = 0$

$$3x(x - 2) = 0$$

$\Rightarrow$ turning points are $\left. \begin{array}{l} x = 0 \\ y = 1 \end{array} \right\}$ and $\left. \begin{array}{l} x = 2 \\ y = -3 \end{array} \right\}$

The y coordinates are found by substituting the values of x into (1). On plotting these points (Fig. 7) it is clear that $(0, 1)$ is a maximum point and $(2, -3)$ a minimum point. (We expect a graph resembling Fig. 5a.)

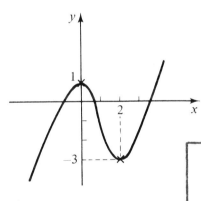

Fig. 7

NEW COLLEGE

HELSTON ROAD   SWINDON   WILTS.

MATHEMATICS AND BUSINESS

STUDIES FACULTY

Exercise 6(b)

1. State whether each of the following functions has a maximum or a minimum value. Find this value and state also the value of x for which it occurs.
   (i) $2x^2 - 12x + 7$ (ii) $10 + 8x - x^2$ (iii) $3 + x - x^2$

2. Find the turning points on the following curves, stating whether each is a maximum or a minimum point. Make a simple sketch of each function.
   (i) $3 + 6x^2 - x^3$ (ii) $\frac{1}{3}x^3 - x^2 - 3x$ (iii) $x^3 - 3x + 1$
   (iv) $x - x^2 - x^3$

*3. Prove that the following functions have no maximum or minimum points:
   (i) $x^3 + x^2 + x$ (ii) $x^3 + 5x$ (iii) $2x^3 - 4x^2 + 3x + 1$

4. A farmer has 24 metres of fencing with which he is to make a rectangular enclosure against a wall (Fig. 8a), the wall forming one side of the enclosure. If he uses x metres of fencing on each of the two sides indicated in Fig. 8a, obtain, in terms of x, an expression for the area enclosed. Hence find the maximum possible area which he may enclose.

5. A rectangle is to have perimeter 50 cm. Find the lengths of the sides for which the area is a maximum.

wall

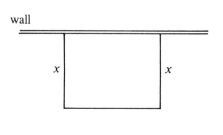

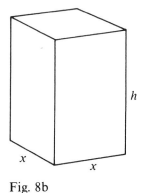

Fig. 8a   Fig. 8b

6. Fig. 8b shows a rectangular block with a square base. If the sum of the measurements x and h is 60 cm, obtain an expression for the volume of the block in terms of x only. Hence find the measurements which give the greatest possible volume.

6.3 To distinguish between maxima and minima

Turning points occur where the gradient is zero, but this method does not enable us to establish whether a particular turning point is a maximum or a minimum point. With the quadratic and cubic functions considered in the previous section there was little possibility of confusion since the shapes of these functions are well known. But in dealing with more involved functions, the graphs of which may be unfamiliar to us, we need a method for determining which turning points are maxima and which are minima.

If the student has grasped the ideas of Section 6.1 he will find that Figs. 3a and 3b provide a ready answer to this problem. Fig. 3a shows that at a minimum point the second derivative is positive (because the gradient is increasing) whereas at a maximum point (Fig. 3b) the second derivative is negative. For a fuller explanation of this the reader should refer again to Section 6.1.

To illustrate the application of this method consider the cubic function $x^3 - 3x$ for which we have

$$\text{gradient } \frac{dy}{dx} = 3x^2 - 3 = 3(x^2 - 1)$$

$$\text{second derivative } \frac{d^2y}{dx^2} = 6x$$

The gradient is zero at $x = 1$ and $x = -1$ so there are two turning points. At $x = 1$ the second derivative is 6 (i.e. positive) so this will be a minimum point. At $x = -1$ the second derivative is -6 (i.e. negative) and this is therefore a maximum point.

Example 35

Identify any turning points on the curve $y = 16x + \dfrac{1}{x^2}$ ($x \in \mathbb{R}, x \neq 0$) stating whether they are maxima or minima.

$$y = 16x + \frac{1}{x^2} \tag{1}$$

$$\Rightarrow \frac{dy}{dx} = 16 - \frac{2}{x^3}, \qquad \frac{d^2y}{dx^2} = \frac{6}{x^4}$$

Turning points occur when the gradient $\dfrac{dy}{dx}$ is zero

i.e. when $\qquad 16 - \dfrac{2}{x^3} = 0 \quad$ or $\quad 16 = \dfrac{2}{x^3}$

$$x^3 = \frac{1}{8} \quad \Rightarrow \quad x = \frac{1}{2} \text{ only}$$

So there is a single turning point at $x = \frac{1}{2}$ and this is a minimum point since at $x = \frac{1}{2}$ the value of $\dfrac{d^2y}{dx^2}$ is clearly positive. Obtaining the y coordinate from the equation of the curve (1) we have

minimum point at $(\frac{1}{2}, 12)$

Note: The general shape of this function resembles that of Fig. 10b below. Notice that the function is increasing for all negative values of x since the gradient $16 - \dfrac{2}{x^3}$ must always be positive for $x < 0$.

6.4 Curve sketching (functions involving $1/x$ and $1/x^2$)

Some guidance is now given on sketching functions of the type considered in the above example. It is very helpful in examples of this type if one has some idea what sort of graph to expect.

Fig. 9a Involving $\dfrac{1}{x}$ Fig. 9b Involving $\dfrac{1}{x^2}$ Fig. 9c Involving $-\dfrac{1}{x}$

(i) Any function containing a term in $1/x$ or $1/x^2$ will become infinite as x approaches zero. As this happens the sign of $1/x^2$ is always positive but that of $1/x$ is positive for positive x and negative for negative x. Thus, close to $x = 0$, functions containing these terms will behave as indicated in Figs. 9a and 9b. Signs are reversed, of course, if these terms are negative and Fig. 9c shows the behaviour of a function with a negative $1/x$ term.

(ii) For large values of x a term in $1/x$ or $1/x^2$ will be negligible. We consider three examples

$$y = x - \frac{1}{x} \qquad \text{behaves as } y = x \qquad \text{for large values of } x$$

$$y = 2x + \frac{1}{x^2} \qquad \text{behaves as } y = 2x \qquad \text{for large values of } x$$

$$y = x^2 + \frac{1}{x} \qquad \text{behaves as } y = x^2 \qquad \text{for large values of } x.$$

Remembering this, and also the behaviour close to $x = 0$, we may already draw quite good sketches of these functions (see Figs. 10 a, b, c). Extra detail may, of course, be added to these sketches by locating turning points and intersections with the x-axis.

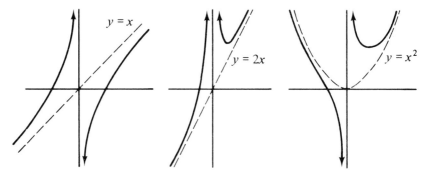

Fig. 10a $y = x - \dfrac{1}{x}$ Fig. 10b $y = 2x + \dfrac{1}{x^2}$ Fig. 10c $y = x^2 + \dfrac{1}{x}$

Notes: (i) The dotted lines in Fig. 10 are the lines to which the graphs tend for large values of x. These are often called **asymptotes**. It is helpful to draw these on first. (ii) The arrows in Fig. 10 are only to indicate how the behaviour near $x = 0$ is in accordance with Fig. 9.

Exercise 6(c)

1. Find the stationary values of the following functions and use the second derivative to check whether they are maximum or minimum points:

(i) $(3 + 2x)(2 - x)$ (ii) $x^3 - 2x^2 + x$

Sketch each of the functions, marking also any intersections with the x-axis

2. Show that the function $x^4 - 8x^2$ has three turning points. Determine the nature of these points and sketch the function.

3. Find the turning points of the following functions and sketch their graphs for $x \in \mathbb{R}$ $(x \neq 0)$:

(i) $x + \dfrac{9}{x}$ (ii) $x^2 + \dfrac{1}{x^2}$

(iii) $x - \dfrac{4}{x^2}$ (iv) $4x^2 - \dfrac{1}{x}$

4. Prove that the function $x^5 - 5x^3 + 10x$ has four stationary values and determine their nature. Sketch the function.

5. Prove that the following functions are always increasing and make rough sketches of their graphs, marking any intersections with the x-axis:

(i) $x^3 - \dfrac{16}{x}$ (ii) $y = \dfrac{(x+1)(x-3)}{x}$

6. Prove that the function $\dfrac{1}{x} - \dfrac{1}{x^2}$

(i) has a single intersection with the x-axis. Find this point.
(ii) is always positive for $x > 1$ and always negative for $x < 1$.
(iii) has a single turning pont. Find this point.
(iv) is decreasing for $x < 0$.
Sketch the function, showing clearly the nature of the turning point and the behaviour for large x and close to $x = 0$.

6.5 Problems

Imagine that we wish to manufacture open boxes (i.e. without lids) with square bases and volume 100 cm^3. The amount of material used in making such a box will vary according to the dimensions we choose to employ. For example, the low squat box of Fig. 11a uses $25 + 4(20) = 105 \text{ cm}^2$ of material whereas the tall narrow box uses $4 + 4(50) = 204 \text{ cm}^2$ and would therefore be far less economical. If we are to make a large number of these boxes we would clearly like to find the dimensions which use as little material as possible.

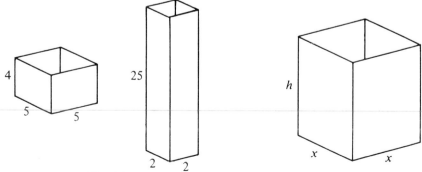

Fig. 11a   Fig. 11b

Example   36

Find, for the above-mentioned box, the dimensions for which the total surface area is a minimum.

Suppose the dimensions are as in Fig. 11b. The area of material needed is then $x^2 + 4xh$ and we must find the minimum value of this function. In problems on maxima and minima, however, we can only consider functions *of a single variable*. One of the two variables x and h must therefore be eliminated. This is achieved by using the condition that the volume must be 100 cm^3,

$$\text{i.e. volume}\quad x^2 h = 100 \quad \Rightarrow h = \frac{100}{x^2} \tag{1}$$

$$\text{thus surface area} = x^2 + 4xh = x^2 + \frac{400}{x} \qquad\text{from (1)}$$

For the minimum value the gradient of this function will be zero, i.e.

$$2x - \frac{400}{x^2} = 0$$
$$\Rightarrow 2x^3 = 400$$
$$x = \sqrt[3]{200} \;\approx 5.85 \text{ cm}$$

h is found by substituting into (1). This may be effected quite neatly as follows:

$$h = \frac{100}{x^2} = \frac{100x}{x^3} = \frac{100x}{200} = \frac{1}{2}x$$

This shows that the height should be exactly one half the base measurement (≈ 2.93 cm). The required dimensions are therefore

base 5.85 cm.   height 2.93 cm.

Note: To check that this is a minimum area of surface rather than a maximum we may check the second derivative $2 + (800/x^3)$ which is clearly positive for the value of x obtained.

Questions 1–5 of Exercise 6(d) may now be attempted.

Example   37

A closed cylindrical tin is to be made with a total surface area of 300 cm^2. Show that to achieve the maximum possible volume the height of the cylinder should be exactly twice the base radius and find this maximum volume to the nearest cm^3.

We must find the maximum value of the expression $\pi r^2 h$ where r is the radius and h the height. Again, one of these two variables must be eliminated. To do this we use the condition that the total surface area must be 300 cm², i.e.

$$2\pi r^2 + 2\pi rh = 300$$

$$\Rightarrow r + h = \frac{150}{\pi r} \qquad \text{(dividing by } 2\pi r\text{)}$$

$$h = \frac{150}{\pi r} - r \qquad\qquad\qquad\qquad\qquad (1)$$

Thus volume $V = \pi r^2 h = \pi r^2 \left(\dfrac{150}{\pi r} - r \right)$

$$\Rightarrow V = 150r - \pi r^3 \qquad\qquad\qquad\qquad (2)$$

gradient $\dfrac{\mathrm{d}V}{\mathrm{d}r} = 150 - 3\pi r^2$

For maximum volume $\dfrac{\mathrm{d}V}{\mathrm{d}r} = 0 \qquad \Rightarrow \pi r^2 = 50 \qquad (3)$

We do not, as yet, obtain an approximate value for the required radius since we are asked to prove that the height should be *exactly* twice the radius. Returning to equation (1) a slight modification gives

$$h = \frac{150r}{\pi r^2} - r = \frac{150r}{50} - r = 2r \qquad\qquad \text{using (3)}$$

So the result is proved. The maximum volume is found from (2). Once again we can simplify the working by using the result (3)

$$\text{maximum volume} = r(150 - \pi r^2) = 100r \qquad \text{since } \pi r^2 = 50$$

$$= 100 \sqrt{\frac{50}{\pi}} \approx \underline{399 \text{ cm}^3}$$

Note: The second derivative here is $-6\pi r$ which is necessarily negative for a positive value of the radius. So the answer will be a maximum value.

Exercise 6(d)

1. The farmer of Exercise 6(b) question 4 wishes to use his 24 metres of fencing to make two identical pens as in Fig. 12a. (There is no wall this time.) Find an expression for the total area enclosed in terms of x. Hence find the maximum value possible for this area.

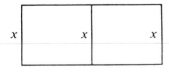

Fig. 12a

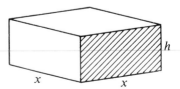

Fig. 12b

2. A box on a square base is to be open at one side (Fig. 12b). If the volume is to be 400 cm^2 find, correct to two decimal places, the values of x and h for which the area of material used will be a minimum.

3. Half a pound of butter occupies approximately 200 cm^3. A certain brand is packed in rectangular blocks for which the base measurements are in the ratio 2:1 as these proportions are felt to be pleasing to the customer. The butter deteriorates less rapidly if the surface area of the block is kept to a minimum and this also leads to a saving on wrapping paper. What should be the dimensions of each block?

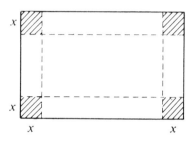   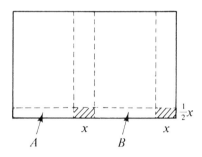

Fig. 13a   Fig. 13b

4. A manufacturer of cattle troughs has several months supply of 8 ft × 3 ft metal sheets laid in. From these he removes a square from each corner and folds up the four flaps remaining to make a rectangular trough (Fig. 13a). Obtain an expression for the volume of the trough in terms of x and hence find the dimensions of the trough for which this volume is a maximum.

5. The same manufacturer also uses the 8 ft × 3 ft metal sheets to make large rectangular litter bins for parks and picnic spots. Here he removes two rectangles whose dimensions are in the ratio 2:1 (Fig. 13b) and folds the remainder as indicated. The edges of flaps A and B are welded together along the centre of the base. Show that the volume of the bin is $\frac{1}{2}x^3 - 5x^2 + 12x$ and hence find the value of x for which the capacity of the bin is greatest.

6. An open cylindrical tub is to be made with a total surface area of 6 m^2. Find to the nearest cm the base radius and height for which the volume of the tub will be a maximum.

7. Another brand of butter is packed in cylindrical blocks again of volume 200 cm^3. Find correct to two decimal places the base radius and height for which the surface area of the block will be kept to a minimum.

8. The hypotenuse of a right-angled triangle is 10 cm. If one of the shorter sides is x cm show that $A^2 = 25x^2 - \frac{1}{4}x^4$ where A cm^2 is the area of the triangle. By differentiating A^2 find the maximum possible area of the triangle.

9. The surrounds of a window are in the form of three sides of a rectangle and a semi-circle (Fig. 14a). If the perimeter of the window is 5 metres, show that maximum light will be admitted if $r = h = 5/(\pi + 4)$ (metres).

10. Fig. 14b shows a section through the axis of a right circular cone inscribed within a sphere. If the radius of the sphere is 6 cm prove that the volume of

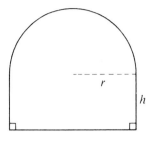

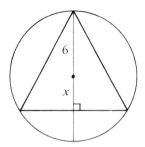

Fig. 14a   Fig. 14b

the cone is $\frac{1}{3}\pi(36 - x^2)(6 + x)\,\text{cm}^3$ where x cm is the distance of the base of the cone below the centre of the sphere. Hence find the maximum possible volume of the cone.

11. A gas container is in the form of an open cylinder surmounted by a hemispherical shell. The cylinder is to have capacity 5 litres ($5000\,\text{cm}^3$). If the radius and height of the cylinder are r cm and h cm respectively, prove that the total surface area of the container is $(10000/r) + (5\pi r^2/3)\,\text{cm}^2$. Hence find the values of r and h for which the minimum surface area is achieved.

12. An isosceles triangle is to have fixed perimeter p. Show that $b = \dfrac{p}{2} - \dfrac{2h^2}{p}$ where b and h are the base and altitude of the triangle respectively. Hence obtain an expression for the area, A, of the triangle in terms of p and h only. Show that $\dfrac{\mathrm{d}A}{\mathrm{d}h} = 0$ when $h^2 = p^2/12$ and hence prove that the area of the triangle is a maximum when it is equilateral.

6.6 Points of inflexion

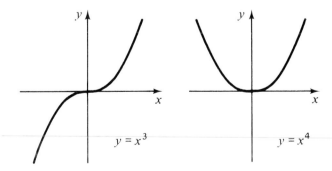

Fig. 15a   Fig. 15b

In Section 6.3 we saw that a stationary value is a maximum if the second derivative is negative and a minimum if it is positive. What happens if the second derivative is zero? Here a complication arises. For if the second derivative is zero the point may be a **point of inflexion**. The simplest example of a point of inflexion is the point $x = 0$ on $y = x^3$ (Fig. 15a) where both the gradient, $3x^2$, and the second derivative, $6x$, are zero. At this point the curve flattens out for an instant (gradient $= 0$ at $x = 0$) before continuing to increase. (The gradient $3x^2$ is always positive except at $x = 0$.)

It would be convenient if a zero second derivative always meant a point of inflexion but unfortunately this is not the case. Consider, for example, the point $x = 0$ on $y = x^4$ where again the gradient, $4x^3$, and the second derivative, $12x^2$, are both zero. This point, however, is clearly a minimum point since the function x^4 is always positive except at $x = 0$.

We therefore have to be very careful when we find stationary values for which the second derivative is zero. These points may be maxima, minima or points of inflexion. To distinguish between these three possibilities we normally use the gradient to determine the values of x for which the function is increasing and those for which it is decreasing. A simple sketch may then be made. This procedure is illustrated by the next example.

Example 38

Investigate the stationary values of the function $3x^4 - 2x^3$ and sketch its graph.

We begin by identifying the stationary values in the usual way

let $\quad y = 3x^4 - 2x^3$

then $\quad \dfrac{dy}{dx} = 12x^3 - 6x^2 = 6x^2(2x - 1)$

$\Rightarrow$ stationary values at $\quad \left. \begin{array}{l} x = 0 \\ y = 0 \end{array} \right\}$ and $\left. \begin{array}{l} x = \frac{1}{2} \\ y = \frac{3}{16} - \frac{1}{4} = -\frac{1}{16} \end{array} \right\}$

$\dfrac{d^2y}{dx^2} = 36x^2 - 12x$

at $x = 0 \qquad \dfrac{d^2y}{dx^2} = 0$

at $x = \frac{1}{2} \qquad \dfrac{d^2y}{dx^2} = 9 - 6 = 3$ (positive) $\qquad$ minimum point

To investigate the point $x = 0$ at which the second derivative is zero we now take a closer look at the gradient $6x^2(2x - 1)$. The sign of the gradient depends on the factor $(2x - 1)$ since x^2 is always positive. Thus the function increases for $x > \frac{1}{2}$ (gradient positive) and decreases for $x < \frac{1}{2}$ (gradient negative). Bearing this in mind there is only one way in which we can sketch the graph. (Fig. 16). The point $x = 0$ is a point of inflexion.

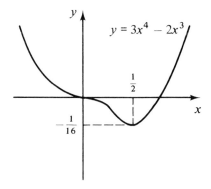

Fig. 16

Summary

Second derivative	+	Minimum point
	−	Maximum point
	0	Max, Min or Inflexion

Exercise 6(e)

Determine the nature of any stationary values for the following functions and sketch their graphs:

1. $y = x^5$
2. $y = x^4 - 4x$
3. $y = x^4 - 4x^3$
4. $y = x^3 - 6x^2 + 12x$
5. $y = 3x^4 + 8x^3 + 6x^2$
6. $y = 6x^5 - 15x^4 + 10x^3$
7. $y = x^5 + 20x^2$
8. $y = 3x^5 - 5x^3$

7

Solution of Triangles

7.1 The sine rule

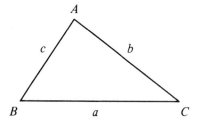

Fig. 1

The sine rule states that

$$\frac{a}{\sin A} = \frac{b}{\sin B} = \frac{c}{\sin C}$$

where A, B and C are the three angles of the triangle and a, b and c the lengths of the sides opposite these angles. (Fig. 1).

Proof

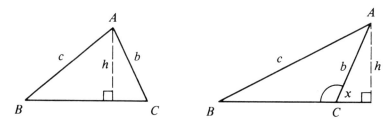

Fig. 2a   Fig. 2b

There are two cases to consider: acute angled triangles (Fig. 2a) and obtuse angled triangles (Fig. 2b). Draw the altitude h onto both figures as marked. Then from the right angled triangles so obtained we have

$$h = c \sin B \quad \text{and} \quad h = b \sin C$$

(In Fig. 2b it is necessary to realise that the sine of the obtuse or second quadrant angle C is the same as $\sin x$.)

Equating these two results

$$c \sin B = b \sin C$$

$$\Rightarrow \frac{c}{\sin C} = \frac{b}{\sin B}$$

By drawing the altitude from a second vertex it is easy to establish that both these terms are equal to $a/\sin A$.

The area of a triangle

It is convenient at this point to derive a formula for the area of a triangle which is frequently of use. In both Figs. 2a and 2b the base of the triangle is side a and the height is $h = b \sin C$. So we may write

$$\text{area} = \tfrac{1}{2} \text{base} \times \text{height} = \tfrac{1}{2} ab \sin C$$

The important thing to notice about this result is that it involves two sides (a and b in the formula) and the sine of the **included angle** i.e. the angle contained between these two sides.

Example   39

In triangle ABC, $AB = 9$ cm, $A = 29°$ and $C = 108°$. Find the length of AC and the area of the triangle.

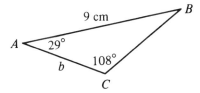

Fig. 3

We require side b (Fig. 3). The size of the opposite angle B is needed and this is found to be 43°. From the sine rule we have

$$\frac{b}{\sin B} = \frac{c}{\sin C}$$

i.e. $\dfrac{b}{\sin 43°} = \dfrac{9}{\sin 108°}$ or $\dfrac{9}{\sin 72°}$

$$b = \frac{9 \sin 43°}{\sin 72°} \approx 6.45 \text{ cm}$$

The area of the triangle is found using the two sides 9 cm and 6.45 cm together with the sine of the included angle 29°.

$$\text{area} = \tfrac{1}{2} \times 9 \times 6.45 \times \sin 29° \approx 14.1 \text{ cm}^2$$

Exercise 7(a)

1. $A = 63°$, $B = 49°$ and $a = 14$ cm. Find b.
2. $B = 27°$, $C = 105°$ and $a = 5.6$ m. Find c.
3. In triangle ABC, $A = 43°$, $B = 21°$ and $AB = 6.8$ m. Find the length of AC and the area of the triangle.
4. In triangle RST, $RS = 16$ cm, $S = 58°$ and $T = 40°$. Find the length of ST and the area of the triangle.
5. Two observation posts A and B are 3.1 km apart on a coastline running east-west. At midday a ship is observed to be on a bearing of $051°$ from A and $029°$ from B. Find the distance of the ship from B to the nearest tenth of a kilometre.
6. The angle of elevation of the top of a tower is measured from two points A and B, both due south of the tower. From A it is $42°$ and from B, which is 30 metres further from the tower, it is $24°$. Find the height of the tower to the nearest metre.
7. The cross section of a right triangular prism is a triangle ABC in which $A = 25°$, $B = 70°$ and $AB = 7$ cm. The length of the prism is 12 cm. Find its volume.
8. The bearing of a lighthouse from a port is $057°$. A ship leaves the port at 11.30 a.m. and sails at 15 km hr^{-1} on bearing $043°$. At 11.54 a.m. the ship is due west of the lighthouse. Find
   (i) the distance of the lighthouse from the port.
   (ii) the closest distance between the ship and the lighthouse, assuming that the ship remains on the same course.

7.2 The cosine rule

The cosine rule is also used when two sides of a triangle and the included angle are known. It enables the third side of the triangle to be calculated and there are three different versions of the formula, depending on which of the sides, a, b or c is to be found

$$a^2 = b^2 + c^2 - 2bc \cos A$$
$$b^2 = a^2 + c^2 - 2ac \cos B$$
$$c^2 = a^2 + b^2 - 2ab \cos C$$

These formulae are of course identical in form. As with the sine rule they are valid for any triangle.

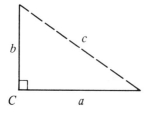

Fig. 4a

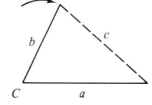

Fig. 4b

Note: The cosine rule may conveniently be thought of as an improved version of Pythagoras' Theorem. Imagine that we keep the lengths of sides a and b fixed. If the triangle is right-angled (Fig. 4a) then length c may be found by Pythagoras' Theorem, i.e. $c^2 = a^2 + b^2$. If side b is rotated (keeping its length constant) in such a way that angle C is decreased (Fig. 4b), then c^2 must now be less than $a^2 + b^2$. The cosine rule tells us how much less and, as we would expect, the amount that must be subtracted from the previous result (i.e. $2ab \cos C$) depends on the size of angle C.

If b is rotated in the opposite direction then c^2 will exceed $a^2 + b^2$. This is also consistent with the cosine rule, for when angle C is obtuse (i.e. second quadrant) the term $-2ab \cos C$ becomes positive. (The cosine is negative.)

Proof

In Figs. 5a and 5b the altitudes h have again been drawn. Let x denote the distance from C to the foot of the altitude in both diagrams. Then by Pythagoras' Theorem we have

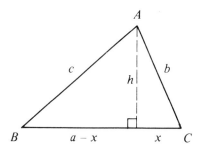

Fig. 5a

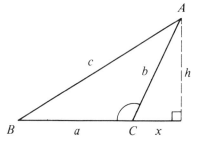

Fig. 5b

$$c^2 = h^2 + (a-x)^2$$
$$= (h^2 + x^2) + a^2 - 2ax$$
$$= b^2 + a^2 - 2ax$$

$$c^2 = h^2 + (a+x)^2$$
$$= (h^2 + x^2) + a^2 + 2ax$$
$$= b^2 + a^2 + 2ax$$

(In both diagrams $h^2 + x^2 = b^2$, again by Pythagoras.) The proof is completed by noticing that in Fig. 5a $x = b \cos C$ and in Fig. 5b $x = -b \cos C$, since $\cos C$ is negative. Thus in both cases we obtain the result

$$c^2 = a^2 + b^2 - 2ab \cos C$$

Example   40

Find the lengths of the missing sides in Figs. 6a and 6b.

Notice that in both diagrams the data given consists of two sides and the included angle.

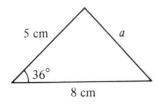

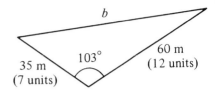

Fig. 6a   Fig. 6b

In Fig. 6a

$$a^2 = 5^2 + 8^2 - 2 \cdot 5 \cdot 8 \cos 36°$$
$$= 25 + 64 - 80 \cos 36°$$
$$= 89 - 64.72$$
$$a^2 = 24.28 \qquad \Rightarrow a \approx 4.93 \text{ cm}$$

In Fig. 6b the working may be simplified by choosing a new unit of distance. Let 1 unit = 5 metres then

$$b^2 = 7^2 + 12^2 - 2.7.12 \cos 103°$$
$$= 49 + 144 + 168 \cos 77°$$
$$= 193 + 37.8$$
$$b^2 = 230.8 \qquad \Rightarrow b \approx 15.2 \text{ units}$$
$$\text{i.e.} \qquad 76.0 \text{ metres}$$

In the second example cos 103° is negative so the sign is changed to + on the last term. The *value* of the cosine is obtained from cos 77°.

Exercise 7(b)

1. $a = 7$ cm, $b = 6$ cm and $C = 68°$. Find c.
2. $b = 36$ m, $c = 48$ m and $A = 107°$. Find a.
3. In triangle ABC, $AB = 15$ m, $BC = 10$ m and $B = 47°$. Find the length AC.
4. In triangle PQR, $PQ = 2.8$ m, $PR = 3.5$ m and $P = 97°$. Find QR.
5. Triangle ABC is acute-angled and $AB = 20$ cm, $BC = 13$ cm and the area of the triangle is 50 cm². Find angle B and the length AC.
6. The hands of a clock are of length 12 cm and $7\frac{1}{2}$ cm. Find the distance between their tips at
   (i) 2 o'clock   (ii) 3 o'clock   (iii) 4 o'clock.
7. A certain golf hole is 240 metres from the tee. A golfer drives his ball 220 metres but his shot is 21° off the correct line. How far is the ball from the hole?
8. A parallelogram has sides 11 cm and 8 cm and one of the angles is 63°. Find the lengths of both diagonals and the area of the parallelogram.
9. A radar scanner at the entrance to a harbour shows that a certain ship is 7.1 km away on bearing 105°. Fifteen minutes later the ship is 5.8 km away on bearing 136°. How fast is the ship travelling? (Assume that it travels at constant speed and remains on the same course.)

7.3 Finding angles

Both the sine and the cosine rules may be used to calculate the size of angles in triangles.

Alternative form for the cosine rule

When using the cosine rule to find an angle it helps if the formula is first rearranged so that the cosine of the required angle is made the subject. If, for example, we wish to find angle A, we take the formula involving $\cos A$ and rearrange it as follows:

$$a^2 = b^2 + c^2 - 2bc \cos A$$

$$2bc \cos A = b^2 + c^2 - a^2$$

$$\boxed{\cos A = \frac{b^2 + c^2 - a^2}{2bc}}$$

This formula may be used when all three sides of a triangle are known. Consider, for example, the triangle shown in Fig. 7. Here we obtain

$$\cos A = \frac{7^2 + 5^2 - 4^2}{2 \cdot 7 \cdot 5} = \frac{49 + 25 - 16}{70}$$

$$\cos A = \frac{58}{70} \approx 0.8286$$

$$\underline{A \approx 34.0°}$$

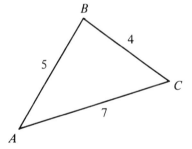

Fig. 7

Two exactly similar formula exist for $\cos B$ and $\cos C$. If we require angle B in Fig. 7 then

$$\cos B = \frac{5^2 + 4^2 - 7^2}{2 \cdot 5 \cdot 4} = \frac{25 + 16 - 49}{40}$$

$$\cos B = \frac{-8}{40} = -0.2$$

The negative cosine obtained here can only mean that the angle B is obtuse.

$$B \approx 180° - 78.5° \quad \text{or} \quad \underline{101.5°}$$

Use of the sine rule

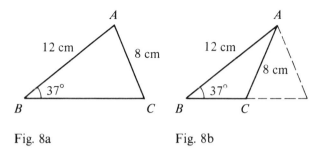

Fig. 8a   Fig. 8b

When two sides and a non-included angle are known, the sine rule may be used to determine one of the other angles. When finding angles each term of the sine rule is inverted, i.e.

$$\frac{\sin A}{a} = \frac{\sin B}{b} = \frac{\sin C}{c}$$

Thus in Fig. 8a we may find the angle C

$$\frac{\sin C}{12} = \frac{\sin 37°}{8}$$

$$\sin C = \frac{12 \sin 37°}{8} = 0.9027$$

$$C \approx 64.5°$$

There is one important point to be wary of when using the sine rule in this way: there may often be *two triangles* consistent with the data given. This in fact is the case with the example we have considered and Fig. 8b shows the second triangle in which angle C is obtuse. We may obtain this solution by taking the second quadrant solution at the last step in the above working, i.e.

$$\sin C = 0.9027$$

$$\Rightarrow C \approx 64.5° \text{ (1st quadrant) or } 115.5° \text{ (2nd quadrant)}$$

The two possible values for angle A may now be found by summing the angles to $180°$ in each triangle.

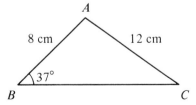

Fig. 9

Note: Where the longer of the two sides is opposite the given angle this difficulty does not arise. In Fig. 9, for example, where the measurements have been reversed, we cannot 'swing the 12 cm side round' to obtain an obtuse-angled triangle. It is interesting to observe what happens in the calculation

$$\sin C = \frac{8 \sin 37°}{12} = 0.4012$$

$$\Rightarrow C \approx 23.7° \text{ (1st quadrant) or } 156.3° \text{ (2nd quadrant)}$$

The second solution is impossible since we exceed 180° in the triangle with angles *B* and *C* alone.

Exercise 7(c)

1. $a = 7$ cm, $b = 5$ cm, $c = 9$ cm. Find A and C.
2. $a = 10$ m, $b = 11$ m, $c = 16$ m. Find B and C.
3. In triangle ABC, $AB = 13$ cm, $AC = 20$ cm and $B = 42°$. Find C and the length BC.
4. In triangle ABC, $AB = 9$ m, $BC = 16$ m and $C = 30°$. Find the possible values of A and the difference between the corresponding values of AC.
5. A weight is supported by two strings, of lengths 70 cm and 80 cm, attached to points 1 metre apart on a horizontal beam. Find the angle each string makes with the beam.
6. A mast is supported by various wire stays. The wire to the west of the pole is 25 metres long and makes an angle of 67° with the ground. The wire to the east of the pole is 35 metres long. Find the angle this wire makes with the ground. Find also the distance between the lower ends of these two wires.
7. An aircraft leaves an airfield and travels for 150 km on a bearing of 032°. It then changes onto a course of 060° and travels a further 120 km. How far from the airfield is the aircraft now and on what bearing?
8. In trapezium $ABCD$, $AB = 8$ cm, $BC = 15$ cm, $CD = 7$ cm and $AC = 12$ cm. The parallel sides are AD and BC. Show that there are two trapeziums with these measurements and find the possible values of angle D.

7.4 Three-dimensional problems

Angle between a line and a plane

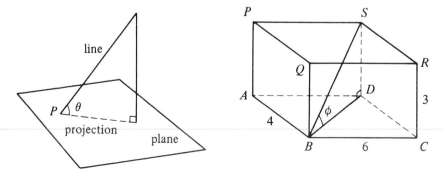

Fig. 10a   Fig. 10b

Imagine that a certain line meets a plane at point *P* (Fig. 10a). Where do we measure the angle between the line and the plane? In everyday terms we may say that this angle is measured 'directly beneath' the line, i.e. between the line and its **projection**, which is the shadow the line would cast if the sun shone directly down onto the plane. This is the angle θ in Fig. 10a.

As a simple example consider a rectangular box with dimensions $4 \times 6 \times 3$ units as in Fig. 10b. If asked to find the angle between the diagonal *BS* and the base plane *ABCD* we first find the projection which is *BD* (the shadow of *BS* on the plane *ABCD*). The angle required is therefore that marked ϕ. This may be found from the right-angled triangle *BDS* since $DS = 3$ units and $BD = \sqrt{36 + 16} = \sqrt{52}$ units (by Pythagoras' Theorem), i.e.

$$\phi = \arctan\left(\frac{3}{\sqrt{52}}\right) \approx 22.6°$$

Note: To find the projection of *BS* on a plane such as the back plane of the box *ADSP*, imagine that we are looking directly down onto this plane, i.e. in the direction parallel to the edges *BA*, *QP* etc. The projection is then seen to be *AS*, directly beneath the line *BS*.

Lines of greatest slope

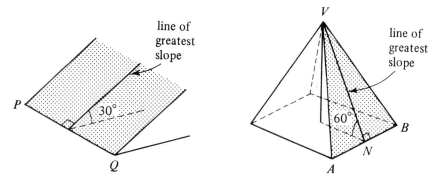

Fig. 11a   Fig. 11b

What exactly is meant by saying that a certain plane (or perhaps a certain hillside) slopes at 30° to the horizontal? In a situation like this we always take a line which climbs *directly* up the slope, (i.e. at right-angles to the horizontal line at the foot of the slope) and measure the angle between such a line and the horizontal – see Fig. 11a. To be more precise we should say the angle between such a line and its **horizontal projection** (i.e. the projection of the line on a horizontal surface below).

Lines which climb directly up a slope are called **lines of greatest slope** since they give the steepest line of ascent. As walkers will know, lines which slant up an incline rise less steeply. This is because a greater distance has to be covered to gain the same increase in height. See also Example 41.

Whenever we talk of the angle a plane makes with the horizontal we should measure the angle in this way. Thus if one of the faces of a pyramid is said to be inclined at $60°$ to the horizontal then the $60°$ angle is measured beneath a line of greatest slope, i.e. a line at right-angles to the bottom edge of the face concerned (see Fig. 11b). It is important to realise that the angles which the slant edges of the pyramid make with the horizontal are less. Fig. 11b shows that the slant edges VA and VB correspond in fact to lines slanting up the shaded face VAB rather than ascending it directly. They are therefore less steep than the line of greatest slope VN.

Angle between two planes

The angle between two planes is measured in a manner very similar to that described for lines of greatest slope. In fact Fig. 11a could equally well represent two planes meeting at an angle of $30°$. The angle is measured between lines which are perpendicular to the line in which the planes meet (PQ in Fig. 11a). This is the angle we would see between the planes if we looked at them 'end-on', i.e. along the line of intersection QP.

Example 41

A hillside rises at $25°$ to the horizontal. On this hillside a path is at $40°$ to the lines of greatest slope. At what angle to the horizontal does the path ascend?

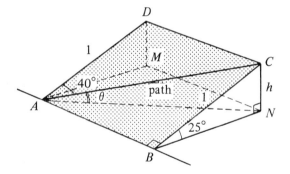

Fig. 12

Consider a rectangular section of the hillside $ABCD$ in which AB and DC are horizontal, AD and BC are lines of greatest slope and the diagonal AC represents a section of the path (Fig. 12). If AM and BN are the horizontal projections of the lines of greatest slope then the horizontal projection of the path is AN and the angle we require is θ. Let the distances AD and BC be 1 unit. Then in travelling along the path from A to C

Vertical height gained $h = 1 . \sin 25°$ (from triangle BNC)

Distance travelled $AC \quad = \dfrac{1}{\cos 40°}$ (from triangle ACD)

hence $\quad \sin\theta = \dfrac{h}{AC} = \sin 25 \times \cos 40° \approx 0.3238$

$\Rightarrow \theta \approx 18.9°$

So the path rises at approximately $19°$ to the horizontal.

Example   42

A triangular pyramid $VABC$ has its base ABC in the form of an equilateral triangle of side 6 units. The slant edges VA, VB and VC are each 8 units in length. Calculate
(i) the angle between a slant edge and the horizontal
(ii) the angle between a triangular face and the horizontal.

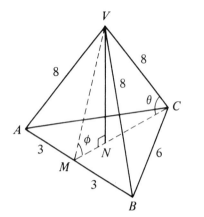

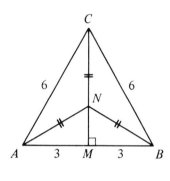

Fig. 13a   Fig. 13b

The point N in the base which is directly below the vertex V is equidistant from A, B and C. This is because the three slant edges are equal, so that when viewed from above the pyramid resembles Fig. 13b. Since the triangular base ABC is equilateral, N will therefore be at the intersection of the medians which is the point dividing any one median in the ratio $2:1$, (i.e. $CN:NM = 2:1$). By Pythagoras'

$$CM^2 = 6^2 - 3^2 = 27$$
$$CM = \sqrt{27} = 3\sqrt{3}$$
$$\text{hence } CN = 2\sqrt{3} \quad \text{and} \quad NM = \sqrt{3} \text{ units}$$

(i) The projection of the slant edge VC is NC so that the required angle is θ

$$\cos\theta = \frac{CN}{VC} = \frac{2\sqrt{3}}{8} = \frac{\sqrt{3}}{4}$$
$$\Rightarrow \theta \approx 64.3°$$

(ii) The line VM is a line of greatest slope for the face VAB. (It is perpendicular to AB since triangle VAB is isosceles.) The required angle is therefore ϕ

$$\cos\phi = \frac{NM}{VM} = \frac{\sqrt{3}}{\sqrt{55}}$$

where VM is found by Pythagoras' from triangle VAM.

Hence $\phi \approx 76.5°$

So the slant edges are at about $64.3°$ and the faces $76.5°$ to the horizontal.

Exercise 7(d)

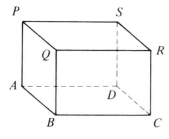

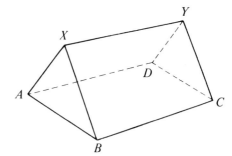

Fig. 14a   Fig. 14b

The first two questions refer to Fig. 14a which represents a rectangular block
1. If $AB = 8$ cm, $BC = 15$ cm and $CR = 6$ cm, find the angles between
    (i)   the diagonal BS and the plane $ABCD$.
    (ii) the diagonal BS and the plane $SRCD$.
    (iii) the planes $SABR$ and $ABCD$.
2. If $AB = 8$ cm, $BC = 12$ cm and $CR = 9$ cm find the angles between
    (i)   the diagonal AR and the plane $ABCD$.
    (ii) the diagonal AR and the plane $BCRQ$.
    (iii) the planes $ADSP$ and $BCSP$.
3. Fig. 14b represents a right triangular prism in which $AB = 12$ cm, $XA = XB = 10$ cm and $BC = 18$ cm. The base plane $ABCD$ is horizontal. Calculate
    (i)   the height of X and Y above the base.
    (ii) the angle between the plane YAB and the horizontal.
    (iii) the angle between the line YB and the horizontal.
4. A vertical flagpole stands in the corner C of a rectangular parade ground $ABCD$ in which $AB = 120$ metres and $BC = 35$ metres. The angle of elevation of the top of the flagpole from D is $8°$. Calculate the height of the flagpole and the angles of elevation from A and B.
5. A pyramid stands on a rectangular base $ABCD$ in which $AB = 50$ cm and $BC = 30$ cm. The four slant edges are equal. If the face VBC is inclined at $60°$ to the base, find the height of the pyramid and the inclination of the face VAB to the base.
6. A horizontal road runs along the foot of a hillside inclined at $22°$ to the horizontal. From a point on the road a path ascends a line of greatest slope to reach a house on the hillside. The distance along the path from the road to the house is 75 metres. The house may also be reached by a straight lane which starts from a point 180 metres further down the road. Find
    (i)   the height of the house above the road.
    (ii) the length of the lane.
    (iii) the angle to the horizontal at which the lane ascends.
7. An equilateral triangle ABC is at rest on a horizontal surface. The triangle is rotated about the edge BC until it is at $30°$ with the horizontal. Find the angle between the edge AB and the horizontal.

8. The angle of elevation of the top of a church tower is $22°$ from a point A, 200 metres due south of the tower. What will be the angle of elevation from the point B, 80 metres north-east of A?

9. When ascended directly a mountainside rises at an angle of $35°$ to the horizontal, but by taking a path which zig-zags up the slope the angle of ascent may be reduced to $20°$. What angle does the path make with a line of greatest slope?

10. A pyramid $VABCD$ stands on a square base $ABCD$ of side 16 metres. The slant edges VA and VB are both 20 metres long and are both inclined at $60°$ to the base. Find
    (i)   the height of the pyramid.
    (ii) the lengths of the slant edges VC and VD.
    (iii) the inclinations of the faces VAB and VCD to the horizontal.

11. An aircraft is flying at a constant height of 500 metres. From a certain observation point it is first seen on bearing N.$21°$ W at an elevation of $14°$. A short time later it is observed on bearing N.$33°$ E at an elevation of $9°$. How far has the aircraft travelled during this time? (Answer to the nearest 10 metres.)

12. A vertical flagpole PQ is supported by three 10 metre guy ropes attached to the point P on the pole and to points A, B and C on the ground where $AB = 6$ metres and $AC = BC = 8$ metres. Find the distance of the foot of the pole, Q, from C and hence find the height of the pole. What angle do the guy ropes make with the ground?

8

Series

8.1 Introduction

A **series** is a sequence of numbers which is obtained in accordance with some definite law or rule. Two examples are

(i) 1, 8, 27, 64, 125 ...

(ii) $\dfrac{1}{2}, \dfrac{2}{3}, \dfrac{3}{4}, \dfrac{4}{5}, \dfrac{5}{6} \ldots$

The series (i) consists of the cubes of the natural numbers. The numerators of the fractions in series (ii) follow the sequence of natural numbers and each denominator exceeds the corresponding numerator by one. The law by which a series may be obtained may often be expressed by means of a mathematical formula (see Section 8.7) but this need not always be the case.

Two important types of series which we shall be concerned with in this chapter are the **arithmetic** and the **geometric** series.

The arithmetic progression (A.P.)

Here each term is formed from the preceding term by the addition (or subtraction) of a constant number. This constant number is called the **common difference**. Examples are

1, 4, 7, 10, 13 ... common difference $+3$
18, 11, 4, -3, -10 ... common difference -7

Notice that the common difference is considered to be negative for decreasing A.P.s.

The geometric progression (G.P.)

In this type of series each term is formed by multiplying the preceding term by a constant number. This number is called the **common ratio**. Examples are

2, 6, 18, 54 ... common ratio 3
24, -12, 6, -3 ... common ratio $-\frac{1}{2}$

When the common ratio is negative the series is said to *alternate* (i.e. the signs of the terms are alternatively positive and negative).

Exercise 8(a)

Write down the next two terms for each of the following series. State which of the series are arithmetic and which are geometric and give the value of the common difference or the common ratio in these cases.

1. 2, 8, 14, 20, 26 . . .
2. 1, 4, 9, 16, 25 . . .
3. 1, 2, 4, 8, 16 . . .
4. 1, $\frac{1}{2}$, $\frac{1}{3}$, $\frac{1}{4}$, $\frac{1}{5}$ . . .
5. 1, $-\frac{1}{2}$, $\frac{1}{4}$, $-\frac{1}{8}$, $\frac{1}{16}$ . . .
6. 1, 2, 3, 5, 8, 13 . . .
7. 20, 17, 14, 11, 8 . . .
8. 16, -24, 36, -54 . . .
9. x, $2x$, $3x$, $4x$ . . .
10. $\frac{1}{3}$, $-\frac{2}{5}$, $\frac{3}{7}$, $-\frac{4}{9}$ . . .
11. 1, x, x^2, x^3 . . .
12. 0.1, 0.02, 0.003, 0.0004 . . .
13. $40\frac{1}{2}$, $13\frac{1}{2}$, $4\frac{1}{2}$, $1\frac{1}{2}$, $\frac{1}{2}$ . . .
14. 1, $2x$, $3x^2$, $4x^3$, . . .
15. 1, 3, 6, 10, 15 . . .
16. $\frac{1}{12}$, $\frac{1}{8}$, $\frac{1}{6}$, $\frac{5}{24}$, $\frac{1}{4}$ . . .
17. 60, 30, 20, 15, 12, 10 . . .
18. 2, -3, -6, 18, -108 . . .

Note: Answers to Exercise 8(a) are not supplied.

8.2 Intuitive methods for the arithmetic progression

Many questions on A.P.s are easily solved by common-sense methods, as the next two examples show.

Example   43

(i) How many terms are there in the arithmetic progression

1, 4, 7, 10 . . . 91, 94   ?

(ii) Find also the 20th term in this series.

(i) Between the first three terms of this series there are two 'gaps' (or common differences) of 3 and between the first four terms there are three such gaps, i.e. *the number of terms exceeds the number of gaps by 1.* Now from the first term 1 to the last term 94 there is a total difference of 93. This corresponds to 31 gaps of 3. Therefore the number of terms is 32.

(ii) Again it helps to look at the first few terms of the series. Starting always from the 1st term we may obtain

the 2nd term by adding 1 common difference : $1 + 1 \cdot (3) = 4$
the 3rd term by adding 2 common differences: $1 + 2 \cdot (3) = 7$
the 4th term by adding 3 common differences: $1 + 3 \cdot (3) = 10$

The number of differences to add is always one less than the number of the term required.

Thus   20th term $= 1 + 19 \cdot (3) = \underline{58}$

Example 44

Find the sums of the following arithmetic series:
(i) $3 + 5 + 7 + 9 + \ldots + 57$
(ii) $48 + 45 + 42 + 39 + \ldots$ to 35 terms

The best method of summing an arithmetic progression is to use the idea of *pairing off* front and back. Fig. 1 shows how this is done for the series (i). Notice that each pair sums to 60.

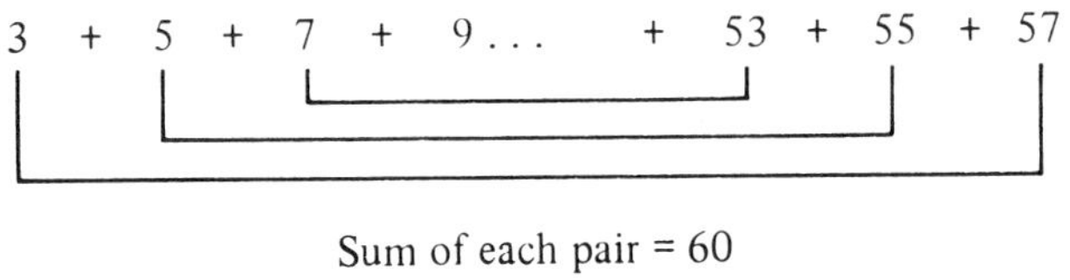

$$3 \quad + \quad 5 \quad + \quad 7 \quad + \quad 9 \ldots \quad + \quad 53 \quad + \quad 55 \quad + \quad 57$$

Sum of each pair = 60

Fig. 1

(i) We need only determine the number of terms in the series. From 3 to 57 is a difference of 54, i.e. 27 gaps of 2.

Thus   number of terms $= 28$
number of pairs $= 14$
sum of series $= 14 \times 60 = \underline{840}$

(ii) Using the method of example 43 part (ii)

35th term $= 48 - 34$ (differences of 3)
$= 48 - 102 = -54$
1st term + last term $= 48 + (-54) = -6$

Each pair of terms will add to -6 and with 35 terms there are $17\frac{1}{2}$ such pairs.

Sum of series $= 17\frac{1}{2} \times (-6) = \underline{-105}$

Note: The reader may be worried about the 'half-pair' in this last example. With an odd number of terms there will always be one term in the centre of the series which is not paired off. This term will in fact be the average of the first and last terms so its contribution to the sum is equivalent to half a pair, e.g.

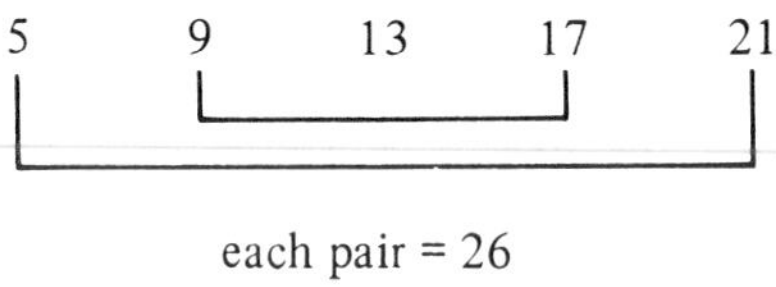

$$5 \qquad 9 \qquad 13 \qquad 17 \qquad 21$$

each pair = 26

Fig. 2

Exercise 8(b)

1. How many terms are there in the series
   (i)　5, 10, 15 ... 75?
   (ii)　1, 8, 15 ... 85?
   (iii) 50, 46, 42 ... 14?
   (iv) 38, 32, 26 ... -52?
2. Find the common difference and hence fill in the missing terms for each of the following arithmetic series:
   (i)　5, —, 21
   (ii)　12, —, —, 36
   (iii) 16, —, —, —, 4
   (iv)　6, —, —, —, —, 17
3. Find
   (i)　the 10th term in the series 1, 5, 9, 13 ...
   (ii)　the 15th term in the series 2, 9, 16, 23 ...
   (iii) the 25th term in the series 6, $7\frac{1}{2}$, 9, $10\frac{1}{2}$ ...
   (iv) the 30th term in the series 21, 18, 15, 12 ...
4. Sum the following series:
   (i)　$3 + 7 + 11 + 15 \ldots + 87$
   (ii)　$68 + 66 + 64 + 62 \ldots + 20$
   (iii)　$3 + 4\frac{1}{2} + 6 + 7\frac{1}{2} \ldots + 69$
5. Find the sum of
   (i)　the first 16 terms of the series 1, 4, 7, 10 ...
   (ii)　the first 15 terms of the series 50, 44, 38, 32 ...
   (iii) the first 40 odd numbers.
6. Find the sum of all the multiples of 3 which are less than 100. Hence find the sum of all numbers less than 100 which are not multiples of 3.
7. The first and last terms of an arithmetic progression are -12 and 22 respectively. The sum of all the terms is 260. Find (i) the number of terms (ii) the common difference (iii) the 20th term.
8. The sum of the first 28 terms of a certain A.P. is 350. The last term is 17. Find (i) the first term (ii) the common difference (iii) the sum of the first 10 terms.

8.3 Formulae for the A.P.

If the first term of the series is a and the common difference is d then the terms of the series are as follows

1st	2nd	3rd	4th	nth
a	$a + d$	$a + 2d$	$a + 3d$	$a + (n-1)d$

As we saw in the previous section the number of differences d which must be added to the first term a is one less than the number of the term.

A formula for the sum of the first n terms may now be obtained. When the terms are paired off front and back each pair will sum to the same value as that obtained from the first and last terms, i.e.

each pair $\quad = a + \left[a + (n-1)d \right] = 2a + (n-1)d$

number of pairs $= \frac{1}{2}n$

$\Rightarrow$ Sum of n terms $= \frac{1}{2}n\{2a + (n-1)d\}$

nth term of A.P.	$a + (n-1)d$
sum of n terms	$\dfrac{n}{2}\left\{2a + (n-1)d\right\}$

Example 45

The 15th term of an A.P. is 25 and the sum of the first 10 terms is 60. Find the first term, the common difference, and the sum of the first 16 terms.

Using the formula $a + (n-1)d$ for the 15th term we have

$$a + 14d = 25 \tag{1}$$

Using also the formula for the sum of n terms and substituting $n = 10$ we have

$$5\{2a + 9d\} = 60$$
$$\Rightarrow \quad 2a + 9d = 12 \tag{2}$$

Equations (1) and (2) are now solved simultaneously to obtain $d = 2$ $a = -3$

i.e. first term $= -3$ common difference $= 2$

The sum of 16 terms may be found from the formula by substituting $n = 16$, $a = -3$ and $d = 2$

Sum of 16 terms $= 8\{ -6 + 15(2)\} = 8 \times 24 = \underline{192}$

Example 46

How many terms of the series $8 + 15 + 22 + 29 + \ldots$ must be taken if the sum is to exceed 600?

For this series we have $a = 8$ and $d = 7$. Suppose that a sum of 600 is given by n terms. Then

$$\frac{n}{2}\left\{2a + (n-1)d\right\} = 600$$

$$\frac{n}{2}\left\{16 + 7(n-1)\right\} = 600$$

$$n(9 + 7n) = 1200$$

$$\Rightarrow \quad 7n^2 + 9n - 1200 = 0$$

Solving this equation by the formula we obtain

$$n = \frac{-9 \pm \sqrt{81 + 33\,600}}{14} \approx \frac{-9 \pm 183.5}{14}$$

$n \approx 12.46$ (discounting the negative solution).

The implication of this result is that a sum of 600 lies somewhere between the sum of 12 terms and the sum of 13 terms. Since our answer must be an integer we will require 13 terms if the sum is to exceed 600.

Exercise 8(c)

1. Use the formula for the sum of n terms to find
   (i)   the sum of the first 30 terms of the series $2 + 9 + 16 + 23 + \ldots$
   (ii) the sum of the first 45 terms of the series $10 + 12\frac{1}{2} + 15 + 17\frac{1}{2} + \ldots$
   (iii) the sum of the first 52 terms of the series $1 + 2\frac{1}{3} + 3\frac{2}{3} + 5 + \ldots$
   (iv) the sum of the first 25 terms of the series $19 + 16 + 13 + 10 + \ldots$
2. In a certain A.P. the 10th term is 8 and 18th term is 20. Find (i) the 1st term (ii) the common difference and (iii) the sum of the first 18 terms.
3. A length of railway track is to be relaid and supplies of materials are to be deposited at 24 points along the track at $\frac{1}{4}$ km intervals. Supplies are taken by a train from a depot which is 15 km from the first of these points and the supplies to be taken are sufficient to require separate journeys for each point. Find the total distance travelled by the supply train.
4. The sum of 16 terms of an A.P. is 192 and the tenth term is 13. Find the difference between the first and the 16th terms.
5. A length of wire 32 metres long is cut into 16 pieces, each 0.2 metre longer than the preceding piece. Calculate the length of (i) the first piece (ii) the twelfth piece (iii) the longest piece.
6. How many terms of the series $5 + 8 + 11 + 14 + \ldots$ must be taken for the sum to exceed 150?
7. The sum of the first 20 terms of an A.P. is 60 and the sum of the next 10 terms is also 60. Find the first term, the common difference and the sum of the first 10 terms.
8. An accelerating body covers distances of 20, 21, 22, 23 ... metres in successive seconds. After how many seconds (approximately) has the body travelled 1 km?

8.4 The geometric progression

Each term in a geometric series is obtained by multiplying the preceding term by a constant number (the **common ratio**). Some examples were given in Section 8.1.

If the first term is a and the common ratio is r then the terms of the series are as follows:

1st	2nd	3rd	4th		n^{th}
a	ar	ar^2	ar^3		ar^{n-1}

The power of r involved is always one less than the number of the term.

For many questions this is all that need be known about the geometric progression.

Example   47

The 2nd and 5th terms of a G.P. are 4 and $62\frac{1}{2}$ respectively. Find the common ratio and the sum of the first 6 terms.

It is convenient to represent the terms of the series as follows (a dash representing an unknown term)

$$—, \ 4, \ —, \ —, \ 62\tfrac{1}{2}, \ —$$

If the common ratio is r then the terms which follow 4 are $4r$, $4r^2$, $4r^3$ etc. It follows that

$$4r^3 = 62\tfrac{1}{2} = \frac{125}{2}$$

$$r^3 = \frac{125}{8} \qquad \Rightarrow r = \frac{5}{2} \quad \text{or} \quad 2\tfrac{1}{2}$$

It is now a simple matter to find the missing terms

3rd term $(4r)$	$= \ 4 \times 2\tfrac{1}{2}$	$= 10$
4th term $(4r^2)$	$= 10 \times 2\tfrac{1}{2}$	$= 25$
6th term	$= 62\tfrac{1}{2} \times 2\tfrac{1}{2}$	$= 156\tfrac{1}{4}$
1st term	$= \ 4 \div 2\tfrac{1}{2}$ or	$4 \times \tfrac{2}{5} = 1.6$

The series is now summed by ordinary addition. (The formula of the next section is not needed.)

$$\text{Sum} = 1.6 + 4 + 10 + 25 + 62.5 + 156.25 = 259.35$$

Example 48

The 1st, 4th and 9th terms of an arithmetic series form consecutive terms in a geometric progression. If the first term is 12 find the common difference of the arithmetic series.

The 1st, 4th and 9th terms of an A.P. with first term 12 may be written 12, $12 + 3d$ and $12 + 8d$ (with the usual notation). If these terms form a geometric progression then 12 multiplied by the common ratio r must give $(12 + 3d)$ and $(12 + 3d)$ multiplied by r must in turn give $(12 + 8d)$, i.e.

$$12r = 12 + 3d \tag{1}$$
$$(12 + 3d)r = 12 + 8d \tag{2}$$

Subtraction removes the terms $12r$ and 12. Hence

$$3dr = 5d$$

$$\Rightarrow \qquad r = \frac{5}{3} \qquad \text{(providing } d \neq 0)$$

Substituting this value into (1) then gives

$$20 = 12 + 3d$$
$$\Rightarrow \text{common difference } d = 2\tfrac{2}{3}$$

The geometric mean

The **geometric mean** of two numbers a and b is the number x between a and b such that a, x, b form a geometric progression.

It is easily shown that the geometric mean is given by $\sqrt{ab}$ for if the common ratio of the series is r we must have

$$ar = x \quad \text{and} \quad xr = b$$
$$\Rightarrow \frac{x}{a} = \frac{b}{x} \quad (= r)$$
$$\Rightarrow x^2 = ab \quad \text{or} \quad x = \sqrt{ab}$$

So the geometric mean of 4 and $6\frac{1}{4}$ is $\sqrt{4 \times 6\frac{1}{4}} = \sqrt{25} = 5$ (-5 would not normally be given as a geometric mean here).

In the same way the **arithmetic mean** of a and b is the number y such that a, y, b are in arithmetic progression. This is the number midway between a and b (or the 'average' of a and b). The arithmetic mean of 4 and $6\frac{1}{4}$ is $5\frac{1}{8}$.

Exercise 8(d)

1. (i) Find the 6th term of the series 8, 12, 18 . . .
   (ii) Find the 5th term of the series $\frac{3}{8}$, $-\frac{1}{2}$, $\frac{2}{3}$ . . .
2. Find the missing terms in the following G.P.s:
   (i)   5, —, 80, —, —
   (ii) 54, —, —, 16, —
   (iii) 24, —, —, $\frac{1}{9}$, —
   (iv) —, 32, —, —, (-500)
3. Find the arithmetic and geometric means for each of the following pairs of numbers:
   (i) 4 and 16   (ii) 18 and 50   (iii) $\frac{1}{4}$ and $\frac{1}{9}$ (iv) $1\frac{1}{4}$ and $3\frac{1}{5}$
4. The 3rd and 6th terms of a G.P. are $1\frac{1}{2}$ and -12 respectively. Find the sum of the first 7 terms of the series.
5. k, $k + 5$ and $k + 15$ are the first three terms of a G.P. Find the value of k and the sum of the first 6 terms.
6. Prove that the sum of the 4th, 5th and 6th terms of a G.P. with common ratio r is r^3 times the sum of the first 3 terms. In a certain G.P. the sum of the first 3 terms is -9 and the sum of the first 6 terms is 63. Find the 1st term and the common ratio.
7. The 1st term of a G.P. is 4 and the sum of the first 3 terms is 39. Find the two possible values of the common ratio and state the 2nd and 3rd terms in each case.
8. The 1st and 2nd terms of a G.P. are p and q respectively. Find expressions for the 3rd, 4th and nth terms.
9. The 1st, 5th and 8th terms of an arithmetic series form consecutive terms of a G.P. If the 1st term is 16 find the common difference of the arithmetic series.
10. The 3rd term of a G.P. exceeds the 2nd term by 4 and the 4th term exceeds the 3rd term by 3. Find the sum of the first 4 terms.

8.5 The sum of a G.P.

The sum of the first n terms of a G.P. may be written

$$S = a + ar + ar^2 + ar^3 \ldots + ar^{n-1} \tag{1}$$

If each term is multiplied by r then in effect it is moved along one place in the sequence, i.e. a becomes ar, ar becomes ar^2 and so on. Also the sum of the terms will be multiplied by r, so we have

$$rS = ar + ar^2 + ar^3 \ldots + ar^{n-1} + ar^n \qquad (2)$$

On subtraction all the terms except a in line (1) and ar^n in line (2) are removed in pairs. There are two cases to consider

(i) Common ratio $r > 1$
$$rS - S = ar^n - a$$
$$(r-1)S = a(r^n - 1)$$
$$S = \frac{a(r^n - 1)}{r - 1}$$

(ii) Common ratio $r < 1$
$$S - rS = a - ar^n$$
$$(1-r)S = a(1 - r^n)$$
$$S = \frac{a(1 - r^n)}{1 - r}$$

Example 49

Find the sum of the first 15 terms of the series
$$4 + 6 + 9 + 13\tfrac{1}{2} + \ldots$$

This is a geometric series with first term $a = 4$ and common ratio $r = 1\tfrac{1}{2}$. Since $r > 1$ it is more convenient to use the first of the two formulae above

$$S = \frac{4\left\{\left(\frac{3}{2}\right)^{15} - 1\right\}}{\frac{1}{2}} = 8\left\{\left(\frac{3}{2}\right)^{15} - 1\right\}$$

As can be seen the formula does not remove all the difficulty from the question: the $(\frac{3}{2})^{15}$ presents quite a problem and in many situations the answer may be left in this form. Alternatively using a calculator with a y^x button we may proceed as follows:

$$(1.5)^{15} \approx 437.9 \qquad \text{(from calculator)}$$
$$\Rightarrow S \approx 8 \times 436.9 \qquad \text{or} \quad \underline{3495.2}$$

Exercise 8(e)

Use a calculator with a y^x function to obtain the sums of the following series. Keep your answers for reference in Section 8.6.

1. The series $3 + 6 + 12 + 24 + \ldots$
   for (i) 10 terms   (ii) 15 terms   (iii) 20 terms
2. The series $25 + 30 + 36 + 43.2 + \ldots$
   for (i) 10 terms   (ii) 20 terms   (iii) 30 terms
3. The series $16 + 12 + 9 + 6.75 + \ldots$
   for (i) 10 terms   (ii) 20 terms   (iii) 30 terms   (iv) 50 terms
4. The series $100 + 80 + 64 + 51.2 + \ldots$
   for (i) 10 terms   (ii) 20 terms   (iii) 30 terms   (iv) 50 terms
5. A wise man tempts a king to wager 1 penny on the 1st square of a chessboard, 2 pence on the 2nd square, 4 pence on the 3rd square, 8 pence on

the 4th square and so on until all 64 squares are accounted for. How many pounds would be at stake?
6. Find the sums of
    (i) the first 11 terms of the series $2 - 6 + 18 - 54 + \ldots$
    (ii) the first 20 terms of the series $25 - 15 + 9 - 5.4 + \ldots$
7. It is said that it is impossible to fold any sheet of paper, however large, more than 9 times. If 10 sheets of paper have a thickness of 1 mm estimate the thickness of 1 sheet if it could be folded in half (i) 10 times (ii) 20 times.

8.6 Convergence of an infinite G.P.

When the magnitude of the common ratio r is greater than 1 the terms of a geometric progression get progressively larger in magnitude and the sum of the series increases without limit. This is illustrated by the answers to questions 1 and 2 of Exercise 8(e). Such series are said to **diverge**. If the common ratio is negative the sum fluctuates from positive to negative values but still diverges, e.g. for the series $2 - 4 + 8 - 16 + 32 - 64 + \ldots$

the sum of 3 terms $S_3 = 6$
and $S_4 = -10$, $S_5 = 22$, $S_6 = -42$ etc.

Questions 3 and 4 of Exercise 8(e) show that if $|r| < 1$ (i.e. $-1 < r < 1$) then the sum of the series approaches a definite limit which cannot be exceeded no matter how many terms are considered. This is because the terms get progressively smaller and eventually become so small that they make no significant difference to the sum of the series. Thus the series of question 3 appears to approach a limiting sum of 64 and that of question 4 a limiting sum of 500. These series are said to **converge** and the limiting value which their sums approach is sometimes called the **sum to infinity**.

A simple illustration of a sum to infinity is provided by the following G.P.:

$$\frac{1}{10} + \frac{1}{100} + \frac{1}{1\,000} + \frac{1}{10\,000} + \ldots \qquad \left(r = \frac{1}{10}\right)$$

In decimals this series may be written

$$0.1 + 0.01 + 0.001 + 0.0001 + \ldots$$

so we have, for example, $S_3 = 0.111$, $S_4 = 0.1111$, $S_5 = 0.11111$ etc. Clearly the sum of all terms may be written $0.\dot{1}$ (recurring) and this is equivalent to the fraction $\frac{1}{9}$, i.e. sum to infinity $S_\infty = \frac{1}{9}$.

Formula for the sum to infinity

If $|r| < 1$ then r, r^2, r^3, $r^4 \ldots$ get progressively smaller in magnitude, i.e. $r^n \to 0$ as the power n is increased. From Section 8.5 we have

$$\text{sum of } n \text{ terms} = \frac{a(1 - r^n)}{1 - r}$$

So as $n \to \infty$, $r^n \to 0$ and we obtain

$$\text{sum to infinity} = \frac{a}{1 - r}$$

Using this formula we may now verify the results stated above for the limiting sums of the series in questions 3 and 4 of Exercise 8(e).

(i) For the series $16 + 12 + 9 + 6.75 + \ldots$

$$a = 16, \ r = \tfrac{3}{4}, \ S_\infty = \frac{a}{1-r} = \frac{16}{\tfrac{1}{4}} = 64$$

(ii) For the series $100 + 80 + 64 + 51.2 + \ldots$

$$a = 100, \ r = 0.8, \ S_\infty = \frac{a}{1-r} = \frac{100}{0.2} = 500$$

The same result may also be used for alternating series. For example the series $16 - 12 + 9 - 6.75 + \ldots +$ has $a = 16, r = -\tfrac{3}{4}$ and the sum to infinity is

$$S_\infty = \frac{16}{1-(-\tfrac{3}{4})} = \frac{16}{\tfrac{7}{4}} = \frac{64}{7} \text{ or } 9\tfrac{1}{7}$$

Summary

The geometric series $a, ar, ar^2, ar^3 \ldots$ has sum to n *terms*

$$\frac{a(r^n - 1)}{r - 1} \quad \text{or} \quad \frac{a(1 - r^n)}{1 - r}$$

The series is convergent if $|r| < 1$ and the sum to infinity is $\dfrac{a}{1-r}$

Note: The terms convergent and divergent may of course be used for any series, not just for geometric series.

Exercise 8(f)

1. State which of the following geometric series converge and which diverge:
   (i) $24 + 4 + \tfrac{2}{3} + \tfrac{1}{9} + \ldots$
   (ii) $8 + 12 + 18 + 27 + \ldots$
   (iii) $\tfrac{1}{8} + \tfrac{1}{12} + \tfrac{1}{18} + \tfrac{1}{27} + \ldots$
   (iv) $1 + \sin\theta + \sin^2\theta + \sin^3\theta + \ldots$ (where $0 < \theta < 90°$)
   (v) $1 + \sec\theta + \sec^2\theta + \sec^3\theta + \ldots$ (where $0 < \theta < 90°$)
2. Find the sums to infinity of the following series:
   (i) $25 + 10 + 4 + 1.6 + \ldots$
   (ii) $10 + 9 + 8.1 + 7.29 + \ldots$
   (iii) $3 - 1 + \tfrac{1}{3} - \tfrac{1}{9} + \ldots$
   (iv) $99 + 9.9 + 0.99 + 0.099 + \ldots$
   (v) $64 - 48 + 36 - 27 + \ldots$
   (vi) $\tfrac{3}{8} + \tfrac{1}{4} + \tfrac{1}{6} + \tfrac{1}{9} + \ldots$
3. If the sum to infinity of a G.P. is five times the first term find the common ratio.
4. Find, as simply as possible, expressions for the sums of the following series:
   (i) $1 + \cos^2\theta + \cos^4\theta + \cos^6\theta + \ldots$
   (ii) $1 - \tan^2\theta + \tan^4\theta - \tan^6\theta + \ldots$

The first of these results is valid for all angles θ such that $0 < \theta < 180°$. For which angles in this range is the second result valid?

5. A G.P. with second term 6 converges to a sum of 27. Find the two possible values of the common ratio and state the first term of the series in each case.

6. The sum of the first two terms of a G.P. is 7 and the sum to infinity is 16. Find the two possible values of the common ratio and determine the first two terms of the series in each case.

7. Prove that the sum of the odd-numbered terms in a convergent G.P. is given by $a/(1-r^2)$ and write down an expression for the sum of the even-numbered terms. In a certain G.P. the sum of the even-numbered terms is 12 and the first term is 18. Find the sum to infinity of the complete series.

8. Prove that if $-45° < \theta < 45°$ then
$$\sec 2\theta = 1 + 2\sin^2\theta + 4\sin^4\theta + 8\sin^6\theta + 16\sin^8\theta + \ldots$$

9. A ball dropped initially from a height of 2 metres always bounces to $\frac{3}{8}$ of the height of the previous bounce. Find the total distance covered by the ball before it comes to rest.

8.7 Sigma notation

This notation provides a useful shorthand for writing out work on series. The sum

$$1^2 + 2^2 + 3^2 + 4^2 + \ldots$$

is written $\sum r^2$ which means *the sum of all terms like r^2*. Here r^2 is sometimes called the **general term** for the series

i.e. substituting $r = 1$ into r^2 gives the 1st term 1^2
            $r = 2$ r^2 2nd term 2^2
            $r = 3$ r^2 3rd term 3^2
            $r = 10$ r^2 10th term 10^2 etc.

Usually only certain terms of the series are required and limits are attached to the Σ sign to indicate the values of r for the first and last terms to be considered. For example

$$\sum_{1}^{5} r^2 = 1^2 + 2^2 + 3^2 + 4^2 + 5^2$$

$$\sum_{10}^{20} r^2 = 10^2 + 11^2 + 12^2 + \ldots + 19^2 + 20^2$$

$$\sum_{2}^{6} \frac{12}{r} = \frac{12}{2} + \frac{12}{3} + \frac{12}{4} + \frac{12}{5} + \frac{12}{6} \text{ or } 6 + 4 + 3 + 2\cdot4 + 2$$

$$\sum_{5}^{8} r(r+1) = 5\cdot6 + 6\cdot7 + 7\cdot8 + 8\cdot9 \text{ or } 30 + 42 + 56 + 72$$

Example   50

Evaluate   (i) $\displaystyle\sum_{10}^{40} (5r - 3)$ (ii) $\displaystyle\sum_{1}^{\infty} 64\left(-\tfrac{3}{4}\right)^r$

(i) $\displaystyle\sum_{10}^{40} (5r - 3) = \quad 47 + \quad 52 + \quad 57 + \ldots + \quad 197$

$\qquad\qquad\qquad r = 10 \;\; r = 11 \;\; r = 12 \qquad\quad r = 40$

This is an A.P. Since there are 31 numbers from $r = 10$ to $r = 40$ inclusive (not 30) the sum is given by

$$\frac{31}{2} \times (47 + 197) \qquad\qquad \text{(No. of pairs} \times \text{sum of each pair)}$$

i.e. $\quad \dfrac{31}{2} \times 244 = 3782$

(ii) $\displaystyle\sum_{1}^{\infty} 64(-\tfrac{3}{4})^r = 64(-\tfrac{3}{4}) + 64(-\tfrac{3}{4})^2 + 64(-\tfrac{3}{4})^3 + \ldots$ to infinity

$$= -48 + 36 - 27 + \ldots$$

This is a G.P. with $r = -\tfrac{3}{4}$ and first term -48 (not 64). The sum to infinity is

$$\frac{a}{1-r} = \frac{-48}{1+\tfrac{3}{4}} = \frac{-192}{7} = -27\tfrac{3}{7}$$

Example 51

Write the following summations in the Σ notation:

(i) $\tfrac{1}{4} + \tfrac{2}{9} + \tfrac{3}{16} + \tfrac{4}{25} + \tfrac{5}{36}$

(ii) $1 + 5 + 9 + 13 + \ldots + 45$

(i) $\dfrac{1}{4} + \dfrac{2}{9} + \dfrac{3}{16} + \dfrac{4}{25} + \dfrac{5}{36} = \dfrac{1}{2^2} + \dfrac{2}{3^2} + \dfrac{3}{4^2} + \dfrac{4}{5^2} + \dfrac{5}{6^2} = \displaystyle\sum_{1}^{5} \dfrac{r}{(r+1)^2}$

(ii) This is an A.P. with $a = 1$ and $d = 4$. One method of obtaining the general term is to use the result for the nth term, i.e. $a + (n-1)d$.

Thus rth term $= a + (r-1)d$
$$= 1 + 4(r-1) = 4r - 3$$

(It is sensible to check that the first few terms required are obtained for $r = 1$, $r = 2$ etc.) Finally we notice that the last term, 45, is given by $r = 12$.

$$1 + 5 + 9 + 13 + \ldots + 45 = \sum_{1}^{12} (4r - 3)$$

Exercise 8(g)

1. Write out in full (but do not sum)

(i) $\displaystyle\sum_{1}^{6} \frac{1}{r}$

(ii) $\displaystyle\sum_{3}^{8} (3r + 2)$

(iii) $\displaystyle\sum_{1}^{5} 2^r$

(iv) $\displaystyle\sum_{5}^{10} r(r+2)$

(v) $\displaystyle\sum_{0}^{6} 108(\tfrac{2}{3})^r$

(vi) $\displaystyle\sum_{2}^{6} \frac{(-1)^r}{r^2}$

2. Evaluate

(i) $\displaystyle\sum_{1}^{10} (2r + 1)$ (ii) $\displaystyle\sum_{10}^{30} (100 - 3r)$ (iii) $\displaystyle\sum_{0}^{6} 2^r$

(iv) $\displaystyle\sum_{1}^{\infty} 12(\tfrac{1}{4})^r$ (v) $\displaystyle\sum_{1}^{n} 3^r$ (vi) $\displaystyle\sum_{1}^{n} ar$ (*a* constant)

3. Write in the Σ notation
   (i) $1 + 8 + 27 + 64 + \ldots + 216$
   (ii) $2 + 4 + 6 + 8 + \ldots + 20$
   (iii) $1 + \dfrac{1}{4} + \dfrac{1}{9} + \dfrac{1}{16} + \ldots + \dfrac{1}{100}$
   (iv) $\dfrac{1}{2} + \dfrac{2}{3} + \dfrac{3}{4} + \ldots + \dfrac{9}{10}$
   (v) $1 + 4 + 7 + 10 + \ldots + 40$
   (vi) $54 + 36 + 24 + 16 + \ldots$ to infinity

4. Find an expression for the general term (*r*th term where $r = 1$ gives the first term) for each of the following series:
   (i) $20, 17, 14, 11, 8 \ldots$
   (ii) $1, 2x, 3x^2, 4x^3, 5x^4 \ldots$
   (iii) $60, 30, 20, 15, 12 \ldots$
   (iv) $1, 2, 4, 8, 16 \ldots$
   (v) $0.1, 0.02, 0.003, 0.0004 \ldots$
   (vi) $8, -12, 18, -27 \ldots$

5. (i)   Show $\displaystyle\sum_{1}^{n} (2 + 3r) = \sum_{1}^{3n}\left(1 + \dfrac{r}{3}\right)$

   (ii)   Find *a* if $\displaystyle\sum_{1}^{10} (a + 2r) = 250$ (*a* is constant)

   (iii) Find *n* if $\displaystyle\sum_{1}^{n} (4r - 1) = 300$

8.8 Three useful series results

$$\sum_{1}^{n} r = \frac{n}{2}(n+1) \qquad \text{sum of first powers} \qquad (1)$$

$$\sum_{1}^{n} r^2 = \frac{n}{6}(n+1)(2n+1) \qquad \text{sum of squares} \qquad (2)$$

$$\sum_{1}^{n} r^3 = \frac{n^2}{4}(n+1)^2 \qquad \text{sum of cubes} \qquad (3)$$

The first of these results may easily be proved since the series of natural numbers is an arithmetic progression, i.e.

$$\sum_{1}^{n} r = 1 + 2 + 3 + 4 \ldots + n$$

Using the pairing off method of Example 44 we have

sum of each pair $= (n + 1)$
number of pairs $= \frac{1}{2}n$

$$\Rightarrow \sum_1^n r = \frac{1}{2}n(n + 1)$$

The results for the series of squares and cubes are best proved by the method of **induction**. This is illustrated in Example 52. Notice that the result for Σr^3 is the square of the result for Σr. This rather interesting fact is a useful way of remembering the formula for Σr^3.

Example 53 demonstrates the application of the above results to certain other series.

Example 52

Prove by induction that $\displaystyle\sum_1^n r^2 = \frac{n}{6}(n + 1)(2n + 1)$

The result we are required to prove states that

$$1^2 + 2^2 + 3^2 + \ldots + n^2 = \frac{n}{6}(n + 1)(2n + 1)$$

We begin by *assuming* that this result is true for the particular case $n = k$, i.e. when the number of terms considered is k. By adding on one further term we then show that the result must also be true when $n = (k + 1)$, i.e.

assume $1^2 + 2^2 + 3^2 + \ldots + k^2 = \dfrac{k}{6}(k + 1)(2k + 1)$

then $\quad 1^2 + 2^2 + 3^2 + \ldots + k^2 + (k + 1)^2 = \dfrac{k}{6}(k + 1)(2k + 1) + (k + 1)^2$

$\qquad = \dfrac{(k + 1)}{6}\{k(2k + 1) + 6(k + 1)\}$

$\qquad = \dfrac{(k + 1)}{6}\{2k^2 + 7k + 6\}$

$\qquad = \dfrac{(k + 1)}{6}(k + 2)(2k + 3)$

$\qquad = \dfrac{n}{6}(n + 1)(2n + 1) \qquad$ where $\quad n = (k + 1)$

So we have established that

result true for $n = k \Rightarrow$ result true for $n = k + 1$

To complete the proof we need only demonstrate that the result holds for $n = 1$, for then

result true for $n = 1 \Rightarrow$ result true for $n = 2$
result true for $n = 2 \Rightarrow$ result true for $n = 3$
result true for $n = 3 \Rightarrow$ result true for $n = 4$

and so on. (The proof is said to follow **by induction**.)

When $n = 1$, $\dfrac{n}{6}(n+1)(2n+1) = \dfrac{1}{6} \times 2 \times 3 = 1$ which is correct for the sum of the series 1^2 (taking the first term only). The proof is therefore complete.

Example   53

Express the following series in Σ notation and hence find their sums.
(i) $3^2 + 6^2 + 9^2 + 12^2 + \ldots$ to 20 terms
(ii) $1\cdot2 + 3\cdot4 + 5\cdot6 + 7\cdot8 + \ldots$ to n terms

(i)   Here the general term is easily observed to be $(3r)^2$ or $9r^2$. Therefore we have

$$\text{sum} = \sum_{1}^{20} 9r^2 \qquad\qquad = 9 \cdot \sum_{1}^{20} r^2$$

$$\text{but } \sum_{1}^{20} r^2 = \frac{20}{6} \times 21 \times 41 \qquad = 2\,870 \qquad \text{using result (2)}$$

$$\text{so } \quad \text{sum} = 9 \times 2\,870 \qquad\qquad = \underline{25\,830}$$

(ii) The second number of each pair is $2r$ and the first number is always one less than the second, i.e.

$$\text{sum} = \sum_{1}^{n} (2r-1)\cdot 2r = \sum_{1}^{n} (4r^2 - 2r)$$

$$= 4 \cdot \sum_{1}^{n} r^2 - 2 \cdot \sum_{1}^{n} r$$

$$= \frac{2n}{3}(n+1)(2n+1) - n(n+1) \quad \text{using (1) and (2)}$$

$$= \frac{n(n+1)}{3} \cdot \left\{ (4n+2) - 3 \right\}$$

$$= \frac{n}{3}(n+1)(4n-1)$$

It is sensible to check that this formula is correct for a simple case, e.g. $n = 2$.
When $n = 2$, $\text{sum} = 1\cdot2 + 3\cdot4 = 14$

$$\frac{n}{3}(n+1)(4n-1) = \frac{2}{3} \times 3 \times 7 = 14$$

Exercise 8(h)

1. Find the sums of (i) the squares (ii) the cubes of the first 12 natural numbers.
2. Find the sum of the squares of all numbers from 30 to 50 inclusive.
3. Find the sum of the cubes of all numbers from 10 to 20 inclusive.
4. Write the following series in Σ notation and hence obtain formulae for their sums:

(i) $2 + 4 + 6 + 8 + \ldots$ to n terms
(ii) $2^3 + 4^3 + 6^3 + 8^3 + \ldots$ to n terms

(iii) $1 \ +3 \ +5 \ +7 \ + \ldots$ to n terms

(iv) $1 \cdot 4 + 2 \cdot 7 + 3 \cdot 10 + 4 \cdot 13 + \ldots$ to n terms

5. Write the following series in Σ notation and hence find their sums:

   (i) $1 \cdot 2 \ +2 \cdot 3 \ +3 \cdot 4 \ +4 \cdot 5 \ + \ldots$ to 15 terms

   (ii) $1^2 \ +3^2 \ +5^2 \ +7^2 \ + \ldots$ to 16 terms

   (iii) $1 \cdot 3 \ +3 \cdot 5 \ +5 \cdot 7 \ +7 \cdot 9 \ + \ldots$ to 25 terms

   (iv) $1 \cdot 2^2 + 2 \cdot 3^2 + 3 \cdot 4^2 + 4 \cdot 5^2 + \ldots$ to 10 terms

6. Prove by induction

   (i) $\displaystyle\sum_{1}^{n} r = \frac{n}{2}(n+1)$

   (ii) $\displaystyle\sum_{1}^{n} r^3 = \frac{n^2}{4}(n+1)^2$

   (iii) $1 \cdot 4 + 2 \cdot 5 + 3 \cdot 6 + \ldots$ to n terms $= \dfrac{n}{3}(n+1)(n+5)$

   (iv) $\dfrac{1}{1 \cdot 2} + \dfrac{1}{2 \cdot 3} + \dfrac{1}{3 \cdot 4} + \ldots$ to n terms $= \dfrac{n}{n+1}$

9

Integration

9.1 Introduction

Starting from the equation of a curve the process of **differentiation** enables us to obtain an expression for its gradient. The inverse process, where we start with the gradient of a curve and from this obtain its equation, is called **integration**.

The simplest example of this is the following: given that the gradient of a curve is $2x$, what is its equation? Clearly $y = x^2$ is a solution but it is not the only solution, for the curves $y = x^2 + 1$, $y = x^2 + 2$, $y = x^2 + 3$ etc. also have gradient $2x$. These in fact form a 'family' of curves which have the same gradient for any given value of x (Fig. 1).

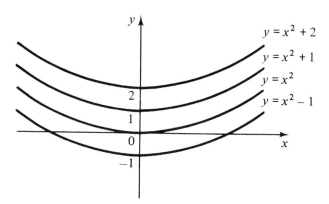

Fig. 1

We may therefore say that the solution is $y = x^2 + c$ (where c is any constant number), i.e.

$$\frac{dy}{dx} = 2x \quad \Rightarrow y = x^2 + c \qquad (c \text{ constant})$$

c is called the **constant of integration**. In general it may take any value. If, however, we are given the coordinates of one point on the curve, e.g. (3, 5), then the value of the constant c is fixed uniquely since only one of the family of curves in Fig. 1 passes through (3, 5). Substituting $x = 3$ and $y = 5$ into $y = x^2 + c$ we have

$$5 = 9 + c \quad \Rightarrow c = -4$$

So the curve with gradient $2x$ which passes through $(3, 5)$ is $y = x^2 - 4$.

Example 54

A curve passing through the point $(2, 3)$ has gradient $x^2 + \dfrac{1}{x^2}$. Find its equation.

We first perform the integration. In order to do this we ask ourselves 'what function differentiated gives $x^2 + \dfrac{1}{x^2}$?' We know that x^3 differentiated gives $3x^2$ and that $\dfrac{1}{x}$ differentiated gives $-\dfrac{1}{x^2}$. We therefore deduce that

$$y = \frac{1}{3}x^3 - \frac{1}{x} + c \qquad (c \text{ constant})$$

Since we are given a point on the curve the constant c may be found. Substituting $x = 2$ and $y = 3$ we obtain

$$3 = 2\tfrac{2}{3} - \tfrac{1}{2} + c$$
$$3 = 2\tfrac{1}{6} + c \qquad \Rightarrow c = \tfrac{5}{6}$$

So the equation of the curve is

$$y = \frac{1}{3}x^3 - \frac{1}{x} + \frac{5}{6}$$

Exercise 9(a)

1. Write down the general solution for y in each of the following cases:

(i) $\dfrac{dy}{dx} = 6x$ (ii) $\dfrac{dy}{dx} = 6x^2$

(iii) $\dfrac{dy}{dx} = 4x - 5$ (iv) $\dfrac{dy}{dx} = 4x^3 - 8x$

(v) $\dfrac{dy}{dx} = 1 + x + x^2$ (vi) $\dfrac{dy}{dx} = 2x^3 - \dfrac{1}{x^2} + 3$

2. The gradient of a curve is given by $3x - 3x^2$. If the curve passes through the point $(2, -5)$ find its equation.
3. Find the equation of the curve with gradient $2x^2 + x - 1$ which passes through the origin.
4. If $\dfrac{dy}{dx} = x^3 - 2x$ and $y = 10$ when $x = 3$, find y.
5. If $\dfrac{dy}{dx} = \left(x - \dfrac{1}{x}\right)^2$ and $y = 4$ when $x = -1$, find y.

6. The second derivative of a certain curve is $2x$. If the curve passes through the point $(3, -4)$, and has gradient 4 at this point find its equation.
7. Integrate the following expressions:
   (i) x^2 (ii) x^3 (iii) x^4 (iv) x^8
   Suggest a general result for the integral of x^n.
8. Integrate the following expressions:

   (i) $-\dfrac{1}{x^2}$ (ii) $\dfrac{1}{x^2}$ (iii) $-\dfrac{2}{x^3}$ (iv) $\dfrac{1}{x^3}$

   Is the general result suggested by question 7 consistent with the answers to parts (ii) and (iv)?

9.2 Notation

The notation $\displaystyle\int\left(4x + \dfrac{1}{x^2}\right)dx$ means **integrate** $4x + \dfrac{1}{x^2}$ **with respect to** x, (i.e. find the function whose gradient is $4x + \dfrac{1}{x^2}$).

Thus $\displaystyle\int\left(4x + \dfrac{1}{x^2}\right)dx = 2x^2 - \dfrac{1}{x} + c$ (c constant)

Note: The dx indicates that we are working in terms of x as opposed to some other variable. This may seem unnecessary in the above example but in other cases it can be less clear. For example $\int(ax + 2)dx$ and $\int(ax + 2)da$ would be quite different. In the first of these we integrate in terms of x (regarding a as constant) and in the second we integrate in terms of a (regarding x as constant), i.e.

$$\int(ax + 2)dx = \tfrac{1}{2}ax^2 + 2x + c$$

$$\int(ax + 2)da = \tfrac{1}{2}xa^2 + 2a + c$$

Table of integrals

The following table shows the integrals of the most commonly encountered powers of x. All are in accordance with the rule

$$\int x^n \, dx = \dfrac{1}{n+1} \cdot x^{n+1} + c$$

which is suggested by the results of Exercise 9(a), question 7.

Consider for example $\dfrac{1}{x^3}$ or x^{-3}. Here $n = -3$ (so that $n + 1 = -2$) and the integral obtained by this rule is $-\dfrac{1}{2}x^{-2}$ or $-\dfrac{1}{2x^2}$.

Function	Integral
x^3	$\frac{1}{4}x^4$
x^2	$\frac{1}{3}x^3$
x	$\frac{1}{2}x^2$
constant e.g. 3	$3x$
$\dfrac{1}{x}$	omitted at present
$\dfrac{1}{x^2}$	$-\dfrac{1}{x}$
$\dfrac{1}{x^3}$	$-\dfrac{1}{2x^2}$

Note: We are unable at present to find a solution for the integral of $\dfrac{1}{x}$. This problem is resolved in Chapter 18.

Example 55

Find (i) $\displaystyle\int (x+2)(2x-1)\,dx$ (ii) $\displaystyle\int \left(2x+\frac{1}{x}\right)^2 dx$

Before attempting the integration we must multiply out so as to obtain expressions which are the sums or differences of separate terms. We then integrate term by term

(i) $\displaystyle\int (x+2)(2x-1)\,dx = \int (2x^2 + 3x - 2)\,dx$

$$= \frac{2x^3}{3} + \frac{3x^2}{2} - 2x + c$$

(ii) $\displaystyle\int \left(2x+\frac{1}{x}\right)^2 dx = \int \left(4x^2 + 4 + \frac{1}{x^2}\right) dx$

$$= \frac{4x^3}{3} + 4x - \frac{1}{x} + c$$

Exercise 9(b)

1. Find the following integrals:

(i) $\displaystyle\int (1 - 2x + 3x^2)\,dx$ (ii) $\displaystyle\int (2x^3 + 6x^2 + x)\,dx$ (iii) $\displaystyle\int (x^6 + 2x^5)\,dx$

(iv) $\displaystyle\int\left(5x-\frac{4}{x^2}\right)dx$ (v) $\displaystyle\int(x^4-2x^2+3)dx$ (vi) $\displaystyle\int\left(\frac{1}{x^3}+\frac{2}{x^2}\right)dx$

2. Find the following integrals:

(i) $\displaystyle\int(1-x)^2\,dx$ (ii) $\displaystyle\int(x^2-2)(x+3)dx$ (iii) $\displaystyle\int_x^1\left(x^2-\frac{3}{x}\right)dx$

(iv) $\displaystyle\int\frac{2x^4-5x^2+1}{x^2}dx$ (v) $\displaystyle\int x(x+2)^2\,dx$ (vi) $\displaystyle\int\left(2x+\frac{1}{x^2}\right)\left(3-\frac{2}{x}\right)dx$

3. Find the following integrals:

(i) $\displaystyle\int(3t^2+6t)dt$ (ii) $\displaystyle\int\left(1+\frac{4}{s^2}\right)ds$ (iii) $\displaystyle\int(a+x+1)dx$

(iv) $\displaystyle\int(a+x+1)da$ (v) $\displaystyle\int(ax^2+bx+c)\,dx$ (vi) $\displaystyle\int(x^2+2xy+y^2)\,dy$

4. Use the rule $\displaystyle\int x^n\,dx=\frac{1}{n+1}x^{n+1}$ to integrate the following functions:

(i) x^{12} (ii) $\dfrac{1}{x^4}$ (iii) $\dfrac{1}{x^6}$

(iv) $x^{\frac{3}{2}}$ (v) $\sqrt{x}$ (vi) $\dfrac{1}{\sqrt{x}}$

9.3 The area beneath a curve

At the start of this chapter integration was applied solely to the gradients of curves (so as to determine their equations). We should now point out that *any* function may be integrated, i.e. it is not essential that the function concerned represents the gradient of some curve we are considering. Thus the function x^2+3 may be differentiated, giving its gradient $2x$, or it may be integrated giving $\frac{1}{3}x^3+3x+c$. We shall now see that the result we obtain by integrating is connected with the area beneath the curve x^2+3.

Area beneath a curve

We wish to find a function A giving the area beneath the curve $y=x^2+3$ from 0 to x on the x-axis (Fig. 2). Clearly the area A will depend on the value of x taken, i.e. A will be some function of x. In fact we shall see that the gradient of this function A is the same as the equation of the curve, i.e.

$$\frac{dA}{dx}=x^2+3$$

so, integrating $A=\displaystyle\int(x^2+3)dx=\frac{1}{3}x^3+3x+c$

The area function is therefore found by integrating the equation of the curve x^2+3.

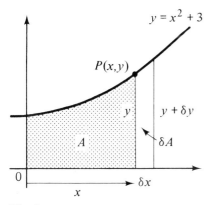

Fig. 2

Proof

First we must ask ourselves the question: what exactly is meant by $\dfrac{\mathrm{d}A}{\mathrm{d}x}$? In Section 3.4 we saw that to obtain $\dfrac{\mathrm{d}y}{\mathrm{d}x}$ we find the increase in y (i.e. δy) caused by a small increase in x (δx) and then obtain the limit of the ratio $\dfrac{\delta y}{\delta x}$ as $\delta x \to 0$. So, in the same way, we must begin by finding the increase in area δA which corresponds to a small increase δx in the x coordinate (Fig. 2).

Now if δx is small, the area δA is a narrow strip with a sloping top. It will be slightly larger than a rectangular strip of width δx and height y and slightly less than a rectangular strip of width δx and height $(y + \delta y)$ (see Fig. 2), i.e.

$$y \cdot \delta x < \delta A < (y + \delta y) \cdot \delta x$$
$$\Rightarrow y < \frac{\delta A}{\delta x} < y + \delta y$$

Now as $\delta x \to 0$, $(y + \delta y) \to y$ (Fig. 2). But the value of $\dfrac{\delta A}{\delta x}$ lies *between* y and $(y + \delta y)$,

so $\quad \dfrac{\delta A}{\delta x} \to y \qquad$ also

i.e. $\quad \dfrac{\mathrm{d}A}{\mathrm{d}x} = y$

$\Rightarrow \quad A = \displaystyle\int y \, \mathrm{d}x \quad$ or $\quad \displaystyle\int x^2 + 3 \, \mathrm{d}x$

since the y coordinate of the point P on the curve must be given by the equation of the curve $y = x^2 + 3$.

Note: The proof given here is only valid for an *increasing* function. An exactly similar proof, however, applies for decreasing functions so that in all cases we have the result

$$\text{Area} = \int y\, dx$$

Simple applications

We now see how the areas beneath curves may be calculated using the above result. Consider the curve $y = x^2 + 2x + 4$ and suppose that we are required to find the areas beneath this curve (i) from $x = 1$ to $x = 3$ (ii) from $x = -2$ to $x = 2$ (A_1 and A_2 in Figs. 3a and 3b).

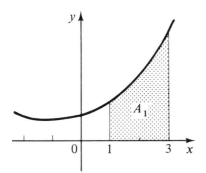

Fig. 3a   Fig. 3b

For the curve $y = x^2 + 2x + 4$ the 'area function' is given by

$$\int y\, dx = \int x^2 + 2x + 4\, dx$$

$$= \tfrac{1}{3}x^3 + x^2 + 4x + c$$

Remember that this function gives us the area from 0 to x on the x-axis (the constant c will therefore be zero since the area is zero when $x = 0$). Thus

(i) Substituting $x = 3$ area from 0 to $3 = 9 + 9 + 12 = 30$ sq. units
$\qquad\qquad\quad x = 1$ area from 0 to $1 = \tfrac{1}{3} + 1 + 4 = 5\tfrac{1}{3}$ sq. units
So, subtracting,   area $A_1 = 30 - 5\tfrac{1}{3} = 24\tfrac{2}{3}$ sq. units

(ii) Substituting $x = 2$ area from 0 to $2 = 2\tfrac{2}{3} + 4 + 8 = 14\tfrac{2}{3}$ sq. units
$\qquad\qquad\quad x = -2$ area from 0 to $-2 = -2\tfrac{2}{3} + 4 - 8 = -6\tfrac{2}{3}$ sq. units

In Fig. 3b we would expect to obtain the area A_2 by adding the areas from 0 to 2 and from 0 to -2. But since the area from 0 to -2 has come out negative the answer can be obtained by *subtracting* the two results, as in case (i)

i.e.   area $A_2 = 14\tfrac{2}{3} - (-6\tfrac{2}{3}) = 14\tfrac{2}{3} + 6\tfrac{2}{3} = 21\tfrac{1}{3}$ sq. units.

In fact the area between two **limits** on the x-axis may always be obtained by substituting the *higher* limit first and then subtracting the result obtained by substituting the lower limit.

Exercise 9(c)

1. Find the area between $y = x^2$ and the x-axis from
   (i) $x = 0$ to $x = 2$ (ii) $x = 0$ to $x = 3$ (iii) $x = 2$ to $x = 3$
2. Find the area between $y = x^2 + 1$ and the x-axis from
   (i) $x = 0$ to $x = 6$ (ii) $x = 0$ to $x = -3$ (iii) $x = -3$ to $x = 6$
3. Find the following areas:
   (i)   beneath $y = x^3$ from $x = 2$ to $x = 4$
   (ii) beneath $y = 3x^2 + x + 1$ from $x = 3$ to $x = 4$
   (iii) beneath $y = x^2 + 2x + 1$ from $x = -1$ to $x = 3$
   (iv) beneath $y = 10 - 2x^2$ from $x = -2$ to $x = 1$
4. Sketch the curve $y = 2x - x^2$ marking any intersections with the x-axis. Find the area bounded by the curve and the x-axis.
5. Sketch the line $y = 7 - \frac{1}{2}x$. Find the area between this line and the x-axis from $x = 0$ to $x = 6$
   (i) directly from your sketch   (ii) by integration.
6. Sketch the curve $y = x(x - 3)^2$. Find the closed area between the curve and the x-axis.

9.4 Definite integrals

In the previous section we saw that the area beneath a curve from $x = a$ to $x = b$ is found by substituting the 'limits' $x = a$ and $x = b$ into the area function and then subtracting the two values obtained

i.e. if $A(x) = \int y \, dx$ = area from 0 to x

then   area from $x = a$ to $x = b$ is $A(b) - A(a)$

A more economical way of summing up this procedure is

area from $x = a$ to $x = b$ is $\displaystyle\int_a^b y \, dx$

where the limits are attached to the ends of the integration sign (the higher limit should be on top) and where it is understood that the value of the integral at the upper limit $x = b$ is to be found first and then the value at the lower limit $x = a$ subtracted from it.

Such an integral, with attached limits, is called a **definite integral** since we always arrive at a definite numerical answer when working it through. Consider the following example:

$$\int_{-1}^{5} (x^2 + 3x) \, dx = \left[\frac{1}{3}x^3 + \frac{3}{2}x^2 \right]_{-1}^{5} \tag{1}$$

$$= \left(\frac{1}{3}x^3 + \frac{3}{2}x^2 \right) \quad - \quad \left(\frac{1}{3}x^3 + \frac{3}{2}x^2 \right) \tag{2}$$
$$\text{when } x = 5 \qquad\qquad \text{when } x = -1$$

$$= \left(\frac{125}{3} + \frac{75}{2}\right) - \left(-\frac{1}{3} + \frac{3}{2}\right)$$

$$= \frac{126}{3} + \frac{72}{2}$$

$$= 42 + 36 = \underline{78}$$

This answer would in fact give the area beneath $y = x^2 + 3x$ from $x = -1$ to $x = 5$. Notice how the limits are carried over to the right-hand side after the initial integration is performed on line (1). In practice line (2) may be omitted.

Example 56

Find the area bounded by the curve $y = 3 + 2x - x^2$ and the x-axis.

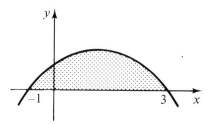

Fig. 4

We first find the intersections with the x-axis

$$y = 0 \text{ when } 3 + 2x - x^2 = 0$$
$$(3 - x)(1 + x) = 0$$

so the intersections are at $x = 3$ and $x = -1$ (Fig. 4). The required area is found by integrating between these limits, i.e.

$$\text{area} = \int_{-1}^{3} y \, dx = \int_{-1}^{3} 3 + 2x - x^2 \, dx$$

$$= \left[3x + x^2 - \frac{1}{3}x^3 \right]_{-1}^{3}$$

$$= (9 + 9 - 9) - (-3 + 1 + \tfrac{1}{3})$$

$$= 9 + 1\tfrac{2}{3} = \underline{10\tfrac{2}{3}} \text{ sq. units}$$

Exercise 9(d)

1. Evaluate the following definite integrals:

(i) $\displaystyle\int_{1}^{3} x^3 \, dx$

(ii) $\displaystyle\int_{2}^{6} \frac{12}{x^2} \, dx$

(iii) $\displaystyle\int_{-2}^{1} (3x^2 + 2) \, dx$

(iv) $\displaystyle\int_{-1}^{3} (x - 3)(x - 5) \, dx$

2. Find the areas beneath the following curves:

(i) $y = \frac{1}{2}x^4$ from $x = -2$ to $x = 3$

(ii) $y = x + \dfrac{1}{x^2}$ from $x = 4$ to $x = 6$

(iii) $y = (x+1)^2$ from $x = -1$ to $x = 2$

(iv) $y = \sqrt{x}$ from $x = 4$ to $x = 9$

3. Find the closed areas bounded by the following curves and the x-axis:
   (i) $y = 12 - 3x^2$ (ii) $y = 6 + x - x^2$

4. The gradient of a curve passing through the point $(4, 6)$ is given by $3 - 2x$. Find the equation of the curve and the area bounded by the curve and the x-axis.

5. Sketch the curve $y = (x - 1)(x^2 - 4)$ and find the area of the segment of the curve which is cut off by the x-axis and which lies above the x-axis.

9.5 Further areas

Areas beneath the x-axis

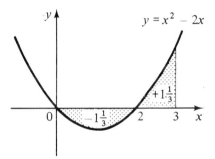

Fig. 5

The curve $y = x^2 - 2x$ or $y = x(x - 2)$ crosses the x-axis at $x = 0$ and $x = 2$ (Fig. 5). Now consider the following integral:

$$\int_0^2 (x^2 - 2x)\,dx = \left[\frac{1}{3}x^3 - x^2\right]_0^2$$

$$= \left(\frac{8}{3} - 4\right) - (0 - 0) = -1\frac{1}{3}$$

This is the area of the segment below the x-axis in Fig. 5. Areas beneath the x-axis, such as this, are always negative. This can lead to some confusing results. For example, the area between $y = x^2 - 2x$ and the x-axis from $x = 0$ to $x = 3$ should presumably be given by the integral

$$\int_0^3 (x^2 - 2x)\,dx = \left[\frac{1}{3}x^3 - x^2\right]_0^3 = (9 - 9) - (0 - 0) = 0$$

This nonsensical result is explained by a glance at Fig. 5. What we have found is the sum of two areas: one above the x-axis ($+1\frac{1}{3}$ sq. units) and one below ($-1\frac{1}{3}$ sq. units). The true area is $2\frac{2}{3}$ sq. units.

Area between two curves

Example   57

Find the area of the segment cut off from the curve $y = 5x - x^2$ by the line $y = x + 3$.

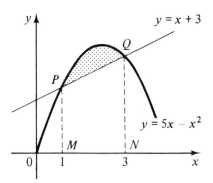

Fig. 6

The curves intersect when

$$5x - x^2 = x + 3$$
$$\Rightarrow 0 = x^2 - 4x + 3$$
$$0 = (x - 1)(x - 3)$$

Thus the points of intersection, P and Q, are at $x = 1$ and $x = 3$ (Fig. 6). There are now two methods:

Method (i)
Area = (area beneath $5x - x^2$) – trapezium $PQNM$

$$\text{area beneath } 5x - x^2 = \int_1^3 (5x - x^2)\,dx = \left[\frac{5}{2}x^2 - \frac{x^3}{3}\right]_1^3$$
$$= \left(\frac{45}{2} - 9\right) - \left(\frac{5}{2} - \frac{1}{3}\right)$$
$$= \frac{40}{2} - 9 + \frac{1}{3} = 11\frac{1}{3} \text{ sq. units}$$

$$\text{trapezium } PQNM = \frac{1}{2}(PM + QN)\cdot MN$$
$$= \frac{1}{2}(4 + 6)\cdot 2 \qquad = 10 \text{ sq. units}$$
$$\Rightarrow \text{required area} = 11\frac{1}{3} - 10 \qquad = 1\frac{1}{3} \text{ sq. units}$$

Method (ii)

Area = (area beneath $5x - x^2$) − (area beneath $x + 3$)

$$= \int_1^3 (5x - x^2)\,dx - \int_1^3 (x + 3)\,dx$$

$$= \int_1^3 (4x - x^2 - 3)\,dx \qquad (1)$$

$$= \left[2x^2 - \frac{x^3}{3} - 3x \right]_1^3$$

$$= (18 - 9 - 9) - (2 - \tfrac{1}{3} - 3) = 1\tfrac{1}{3} \text{ sq. units}$$

Note: In the second method it is possible to subtract the functions *before* performing the integrations – line (1) above.

Area between a curve and the y-axis

Example 58

Find the area bounded by the curve $y = x^2$, the y-axis and the lines $y = 1$ and $y = 4$ (Fig. 7).

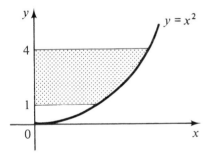

Fig. 7

The result for the area from a curve to the y-axis may be obtained by reversing the roles of x and y, i.e.

$$\text{area to } x\text{-axis} = \int y\,dx \qquad \text{area to } y\text{-axis} = \int x\,dy$$

This integration must be performed in terms of y so it is necessary to substitute an expression for x in terms of y into the integral. In this example $x = \sqrt{y}$ or $y^{\frac{1}{2}}$. Furthermore the limits must be limiting values of y. Thus

$$\text{area required} = \int_1^4 y^{\frac{1}{2}}\,dy = \left[\tfrac{2}{3}y^{\frac{3}{2}} \right]_1^4$$

$$= \tfrac{2}{3}(8) - \tfrac{2}{3}(1) = \tfrac{14}{3} \text{ sq. units}$$

Exercise 9(e)

1. Find the area bounded by the curve $y = 6x - x^2$ and the line $y = 8$.
2. Find the area between the curve $y = 3x^2 - 4x + 1$ and the x-axis.
3. Find the area of the segment cut off from the curve $y = 7 - x^2$ by the line $y = x + 5$.
4. Show that $\displaystyle\int_0^6 (x^2 - 8x + 12)\,dx = 0$. Explain how this result arises with the aid of a sketch of the curve $y = x^2 - 8x + 12$. Find the true area between this curve and the x-axis from $x = 0$ to $x = 6$.
5. Find the areas bounded by

    (i) $y = x^3$, the y-axis and the lines $y = 1$, $y = 8$

    (ii) $y = \dfrac{4}{x^2}$, the y-axis and the lines $y = 16$, $y = 25$.

6. Sketch the curve $y = x(x + 1)(x - 2)$. Find the ratio of the two segments cut off from the curve by the x-axis.
7. Find the intersections of the curves $y = x^2 + 3$ and $y = 7x - x^2$. Make a rough sketch showing both curves and find the area between the two curves.
8. (i) Sketch the curve $y = x^3 - x^2$ and find the closed area between this curve and the x-axis.

    (ii) Find the value of a for which $\displaystyle\int_0^a (x^3 - x^2)\,dx = 0$ and interpret this on your sketch.
9. Find the area bounded by the curve $y = \sqrt{x} + 1$ and the lines $x = 0$, $y = 1$, $y = 3$.

9.6 The mean value of a function

Suppose that we are asked to find the mean value of the function $x^2 - 3x + 5$ over the range $2 \leqslant x \leqslant 5$.

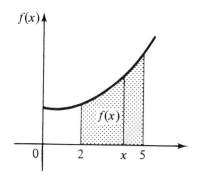

Fig. 8a

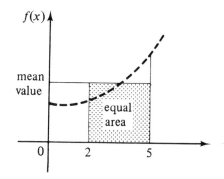

Fig. 8b

Consider the area bounded by the curve $x^2 - 3x + 5$, the x-axis and the lines $x = 2$, $x = 5$ (Fig. 8a). The value of the function $f(x)$ at any point within the range $2 \leqslant x \leqslant 5$ measures the height of this area at that point. Finding the average of *all* values taken by the function in this range is therefore equivalent to finding the average height of the area considered. This is calculated as follows:

$$\text{area from } x = 2 \text{ to } x = 5 = \int_2^5 (x^2 - 3x + 5)\,dx$$

$$= \left[\frac{1}{3}x^3 - \frac{3x^2}{2} + 5x \right]_2^5$$

$$= \left(\frac{125}{3} - \frac{75}{2} + 25 \right) - \left(\frac{8}{3} - 6 + 10 \right)$$

$$= \frac{117}{3} - 37\tfrac{1}{2} + 25 - 4$$

$$= 22\tfrac{1}{2} \text{ sq. units}$$

Divide this by the width of the area (i.e. $5 - 2 = 3$ units)

$$\Rightarrow \text{mean value (average height)} = 7\tfrac{1}{2}$$

The area beneath the mean value (Fig. 8b) will be the same as that beneath the function itself.

Note: This graphical interpretation is the most convenient way of remembering what is meant by the mean value of a function. We can, however, easily obtain a formula

$$\frac{\text{mean value of } f(x)}{\text{for } a \leqslant x \leqslant b} = \frac{\text{area beneath curve}}{\text{width of this area}} = \frac{\int_a^b f(x)\,dx}{b - a}$$

Exercise 9(f)

1. Sketch the following functions and state, without calculation, their mean values over the ranges given:

   (i) $y = 5 - x$ for $0 \leqslant x \leqslant 4$

   (ii) $y = 2x + 1$ for $2 \leqslant x \leqslant 7$

2. Find the mean values of (i) x (ii) x^2 over the range $0 \leqslant x \leqslant 2$. Hence write down, without further calculation, the mean values over the range $0 \leqslant x \leqslant 2$ of

   (iii) $x + x^2$ (iv) $3x^2 - 2x$.

3. Find the mean values of the following functions over the ranges indicated

   (i) $\dfrac{1}{x^2}$ for $1 \leqslant x \leqslant 4$

   (ii) $6x - x^2$ for $0 \leqslant x \leqslant 6$

   (iii) $x^2(x - 6)$ for $2 \leqslant x \leqslant 6$

   (iv) $x^2 + x + 2$ for $-2 \leqslant x \leqslant 3$

4. If $y = 3x + 1$ find the mean value of (i) y (ii) y^2 over the range $1 \leqslant x \leqslant 3$.

9.7 Solids of revolution

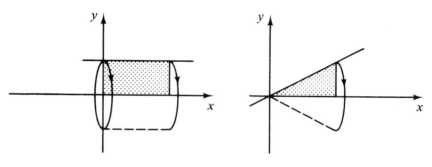

Fig. 9a

Fig. 9b

A **solid of revolution** is formed by rotating an area about one of the axes. Thus a cylinder may be obtained by rotating a rectangular area about the x-axis, as in Fig. 9a, or a cone by rotating a triangular area (Fig. 9b). More complicated solids are formed when the area beneath a curved line is rotated in this way.

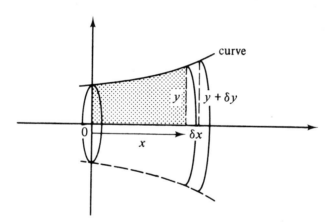

Fig. 10

We shall now see how the volumes of all such solids may be found by integration. Consider a solid of revolution formed by rotation about the x-axis and define a 'volume function' V giving the volume of the solid from 0 to x. Then a small increase δx causes an increase in the volume δV which is roughly in the form of a disc of thickness δx. In fact, from Fig. 10

disc of radius $y < \delta V <$ disc of radius $(y + \delta y)$

i.e. $\pi y^2 \cdot \delta x < \delta V < \pi (y + \delta y)^2 \cdot \delta x$

$$\Rightarrow \quad \pi y^2 < \frac{\delta V}{\delta x} < \pi (y + \delta y)^2$$

We now take the limit as $\delta x \to 0$. Since $(y + \delta y) \to y$ we obtain

$$\frac{dV}{dx} = \pi y^2$$

Integrating

$$V = \pi \int y^2 \, dx$$

The gradient of the volume function V is given by πy^2 so V is found by integrating πy^2. (π is a constant and may be left multiplying the integral.) It is necessary to substitute for y, using the equation of the curve concerned, so that the integration is performed in terms of x. As with areas, the integration is usually evaluated between limits.

Example 59

The area beneath $y = x^2 + 1$ from $x = 1$ to $x = 3$ is rotated about the x-axis. Find the volume of the solid of revolution so formed.

No diagram is needed. We integrate between the limits $x = 1$ and $x = 3$.

$$\text{volume} = \pi \int_1^3 y^2 \, dx = \pi \int_1^3 (x^2 + 1)^2 \, dx$$

$$= \pi \int_1^3 (x^4 + 2x^2 + 1) \, dx$$

$$= \pi \left[\frac{x^5}{5} + \frac{2x^3}{3} + x \right]_1^3$$

$$= \pi \left(\frac{243}{5} + \frac{54}{3} + 3 \right) - \pi \left(\frac{1}{5} + \frac{2}{3} + 1 \right)$$

$$= \pi \left(\frac{242}{5} + \frac{52}{3} + 2 \right)$$

$$= \pi \left(48\frac{2}{5} + 17\frac{1}{3} + 2 \right) = 67\frac{11}{15} \pi \, \text{cu. units}$$

The expression for y (in this case $x^2 + 1$) must be squared out before the integration is performed. π is usually left as a factor in the answer.

Exercise 9(g)

1. Make a sketch of the line $y = \frac{1}{3}x$ and shade the area below the line for $0 \leqslant x \leqslant 6$. Describe the solid formed by rotating this area about the x-axis and find its volume (i) by integration (ii) by conventional methods.
2. Find the volumes of the solids of revolution formed by rotating the areas beneath the following curves about the x-axis

    (i) $y = x^2$ from $x = 0$ to $x = 2$

    (ii) $y = \dfrac{4}{x}$ from $x = 2$ to $x = 8$

    (iii) $y = x + 2$ from $x = 1$ to $x = 3$

(iv) $y^2 = x^2 + 9$ from $x = 1$ to $x = 4$

(v) $y = 1 + \sqrt{x}$ from $x = 0$ to $x = 4$

(vi) $y = x^2 + \dfrac{1}{x}$ from $x = 2$ to $x = 3$

*3. Find the volumes of the solids formed when the following areas are rotated about the y-axis:
(i) the area bounded by $y = x^2 - 1$, the y-axis, $y = 3$ and $y = 5$
(ii) the area bounded by $y = x^4$, the y-axis, $y = 1$ and $y = 4$

4. The section of the curve $y^2 = 2x$ from $x = 0$ to $x = 8$ is rotated about (i) the x-axis (ii) the y-axis. Find the ratio of the volumes of the two solids formed.

5. The area cut off from the curve $y = x(2 - x)$ by the x-axis is rotated about the x-axis. Find the volume of the solid so formed.

*6. Show that if (x, y) is any point on a circle of radius r with centre at the origin then $y^2 + x^2 = r^2$. By considering this circle to be rotated about the x-axis, prove that the volume of a sphere is $\frac{4}{3}\pi r^3$.

7. Describe the solid formed by rotating the area bounded by $y = 9 - x^2$ and the line $y = 8$ about the x-axis. Find its volume.

8. A concave lens is in the form of the solid obtained by rotating the area bounded by $y = 1 + \frac{1}{16}x^2$, the positive axes and $x = 4$ about the y-**axis**. Find the volume of the lens.

9. The area bounded by the curve $y = 4 - x^2$ and the positive axes is rotated (i) about the x-axis (ii) about the y-axis. Find the ratio of the volumes of the two solids formed.

10

The Compound Angle Formulae

10.1 The sum of two angles

It is a frequent mistake to assume, for example, that $\sin 30° + \sin 45° = \sin 75°$, i.e. that $\sin A + \sin B = \sin(A+B)$. A moment's thought should show that this cannot be true. In the example quoted $\sin 30° = \frac{1}{2}$ or 0.5 and $\sin 45° = 1/\sqrt{2} \approx 0.7$ so that $\sin 30° + \sin 45°$ exceeds 1 and cannot possibly equal $\sin 75°$. However the sine of the **compound angle** $(A+B)$ must presumably be related in some way to the sines and cosines of the angles A and B. In this section we show how formulae for $\sin(A+B)$ and $\cos(A+B)$ can indeed be obtained.

Before starting on this it is advisable to revise briefly our definition of $\sin \theta$ and $\cos \theta$ as the y and x coordinates when the rotating arm is of unit length (Fig. 1a). Enlargement of this triangle indicates that when the hypotenuse of a right-angled triangle is r then the lengths of the other two sides are given by $r \sin \theta$ and $r \cos \theta$ (Fig. 1b). This idea is vital to the working that follows.

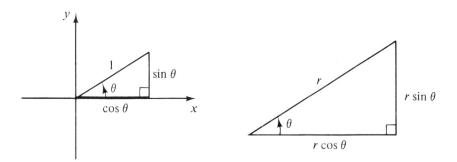

Fig. 1a   Fig. 1b

Formulae for $\sin(A+B)$ and $\cos(A+B)$

Imagine that the rotating arm OP, of unit length, is turned first through angle B and then through angle A so that the total angle of turn is $(A+B)$. The values of $\sin(A+B)$ and $\cos(A+B)$ are then given by the measurements indicated in Fig. 2. (The basis for this diagram may be remembered as a rectangle tilted about one corner. The perpendiculars PS, QR and QT have then been added.) The following features of this diagram are of importance:

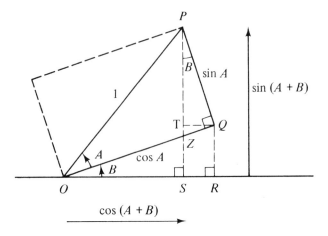

Fig. 2

(i) In triangle OPQ the lengths of the sides PQ and OQ are given by $\sin A$ and $\cos A$ respectively.
(ii) Angle QPT = angle B. (This is because the triangles PQZ and OZS have two pairs of equal angles: the right angles at Q and S and the vertically opposite angles at Z.)

The formulae are now established as follows:

$$\begin{aligned} \sin(A+B) &= PT + QR \\ &= \sin A \cos B + \cos A \sin B \end{aligned} \tag{1}$$

$$\begin{aligned} \cos(A+B) &= OR - SR \\ &= OR - QT \\ &= \cos A \cos B - \sin A \sin B \end{aligned} \tag{2}$$

Note: To understand why $PT = \sin A \cos B$, the student should apply the result of Fig. 1b to triangle PTQ, in which the hypotenuse is of length $\sin A$.

Example   60

Find the value of $\sin 75°$ exactly (i.e. without using tables).

We return, in effect, to the starting point of this section. $75°$ may be regarded as the sum of $30°$ and $45°$, the ratios of which are known exactly (see Exercise 4(a) questions 4 and 5).

$$\sin(A+B) = \sin A \cos B + \cos A \sin B$$

$$\Rightarrow \sin(30° + 45°) = \sin 30° \cos 45° + \cos 30° \sin 45°$$

$$= \frac{1}{2} \cdot \frac{1}{\sqrt{2}} + \frac{\sqrt{3}}{2} \cdot \frac{1}{\sqrt{2}}$$

i.e. $$\sin 75° = \frac{1 + \sqrt{3}}{2\sqrt{2}}$$

(This is approximately 2.732/2.828 or 0.966.)

Example 61

x and y are acute angles such that $\sin x = \frac{2}{3}$ and $\sin y = \frac{2}{7}$. Find the exact values of $\sin (x + y)$ and $\cos (x + y)$.

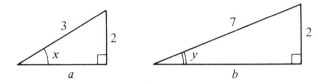

Fig. 3

We do *not* begin by finding the angle whose sine is 0.6667 from tables (i.e. 41° 49′) since this is an approximation and all hope of an *exact* answer is lost. Instead we sketch the triangles of Fig. 3 and find the lengths of a and b by Pythagoras' Theorem.

i.e. $\quad a^2 = 9 - 4 = 5 \quad \Rightarrow a = \sqrt{5}$

$\qquad b^2 = 49 - 4 = 45 \quad \Rightarrow b = \sqrt{45} = 3\sqrt{5}$

Then, using the formulae (1) and (2) above, we have

$$\sin (x + y) = \sin x \cos y + \cos x \sin y$$

$$= \frac{2}{3} \cdot \frac{3\sqrt{5}}{7} + \frac{\sqrt{5}}{3} \cdot \frac{2}{7} = \frac{8\sqrt{5}}{21}$$

$$\cos (x + y) = \cos x \cos y - \sin x \sin y$$

$$= \frac{\sqrt{5}}{3} \cdot \frac{3\sqrt{5}}{7} - \frac{2}{3} \cdot \frac{2}{7} = \frac{11}{21}$$

Exercise 10(a)

1. Find the exact values of (i) $\cos 75°$ (ii) $\sin 105°$.
2. A and B are acute angles such that $\sin A = \frac{3}{5}$ and $\sin B = \frac{8}{17}$. Find the exact values of $\sin (A + B)$ and $\cos (A + B)$. Deduce the value of $\tan (A + B)$.
3. P and Q are acute angles such that $\sin P = \frac{1}{2}$ and $\cos Q = \frac{1}{7}$. Find the exact values of $\sin (A + B)$ and $\cos (A + B)$. Explain why the second result is negative.
4. Find, without using tables, the values of
   (i) $\sin 70° \cos 20° + \cos 70° \sin 20°$
   (ii) $\cos 30° \cos 15° - \sin 30° \sin 15°$
   (iii) $\cos^2 15° - \sin^2 15°$
   (iv) $\sin 85° \sin 35° - \cos 85° \cos 35°$
5. Simplify (i) $\sin (x + 90°)$ (ii) $\cos (180° + x)$.
6. Let α be the smallest angle in the well-known 3-4-5 triangle. Write down $\sin \alpha$ and $\cos \alpha$. Obtain the sine, cosine and tangent of the angle twice as large as α. Hint: $\sin 2\alpha = \sin (\alpha + \alpha)$.

7. x and y are acute angles such that $\sin x = \frac{3}{5}$ and $\cos y = \frac{12}{13}$
   Find   (i) $\sin(x+y)$ and $\cos(x+y)$
          (ii) $\sin(2x+y)$ and $\cos(2x+y)$

8. (i) Prove that $\sin(x+45°) = \dfrac{1}{\sqrt{2}}(\sin x + \cos x)$ and obtain a similar
       expression for $\cos(x+45°)$.
   (ii) If $\sin(x+45°) = 2\cos(x+45°)$ prove that $x = \arctan\left(\frac{1}{3}\right)$

10.2 The difference of two angles

Negative angles

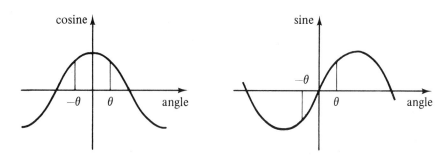

Fig. 4a   Fig. 4b

Before continuing it is necessary to note two important results concerning negative angles. Figs. 4a and 4b show sections of the familiar cosine and sine graphs. The cosine graph is **symmetrical** about the vertical axis so that the cosines of an angle θ and the corresponding negative angle $-\theta$ are equal, i.e.

$$\cos(-\theta) = \cos\theta$$

The sine function, however, is **asymmetric**: the values for negative angles are exactly opposite to those for the corresponding positive angles (Fig. 4b)

$$\sin(-\theta) = -\sin\theta$$

Formulae for sin (A − B) and cos (A − B)

The angle $(A-B)$ may be regarded as the **sum** of the angles A and $-B$. So using the results (1) and (2) of the previous section we have

$$\sin(A-B) = \sin[A+(-B)] = \sin A\cos(-B) + \cos A\sin(-B)$$
$$= \sin A\cos B - \cos A\sin B$$
$$\cos(A-B) = \cos[A+(-B)] = \cos A\cos(-B) - \sin A\sin(-B)$$
$$= \cos A\cos B + \sin A\sin B$$

Notice that the only difference between these results and those of the previous section is a change in the sign between the two terms.

Summary

The following results should be memorised:

$$\sin(A+B) = \sin A \cos B + \cos A \sin B$$
$$\sin(A-B) = \sin A \cos B - \cos A \sin B$$
$$\cos(A+B) = \cos A \cos B - \sin A \sin B$$
$$\cos(A-B) = \cos A \cos B + \sin A \sin B$$

Exercise 10(b)

1. Find the exact values of (i) $\sin 15°$ (ii) $\cos 15°$.
2. A and B are acute angles such that $\sin A = \frac{2}{3}$ and $\sin B = \frac{1}{9}$. Find the exact values of $\sin(A-B)$, $\cos(A-B)$ and $\tan(A-B)$.
3. P and Q are acute angles such that $\cos P = \frac{3}{5}$ and $\cos Q = \frac{8}{17}$. Find $\sin(P-Q)$ and explain why the result is negative. Find also $\sec(P-Q)$ and $\cot(P-Q)$.
4. R and S are acute angles such that $\cos R = \frac{7}{9}$ and $\sin S = \frac{1}{3}$. Find the exact value of $\sin(R-S)$. What can be deduced?
5. Simplify (i) $\sin(90° - x)$ (ii) $\cos(180° - x)$
6. Prove that (i) $\cos(60° + x) = \sin(30° - x)$
   (ii) $\sin(x + 45°) = \sin(135° - x)$
7. If $\sin(A+B) = 2\sin(A-B)$ prove that $\tan A = 3\tan B$.
8. Verify the identity $\cos^2\theta + \sin^2\theta = 1$ by using the formula for $\cos(A-B)$.
9. Prove that (i) $\sin(A+B) + \sin(A-B) = 2\sin A \cos B$
   (ii) $\cos(A+B) + \cos(A-B) = 2\cos A \cos B$

   Hence show that $\dfrac{\sin(A+B) + \sin(A-B)}{\cos(A+B) + \cos(A-B)} = \tan A$

10. We know that $\sin(A+B) \neq \sin A + \sin B$ and $\sin(A-B) \neq \sin A - \sin B$. Show, however, that $\sin(A+B)\sin(A-B) = \sin^2 A \cos^2 B - \cos^2 A \sin^2 B$ and hence prove the following rather remarkable result:

    $$\sin(A+B)\sin(A-B) = (\sin A + \sin B)(\sin A - \sin B)$$

11. Solve the equation $\cos(x + 30°) = \sin(x - 30°)$ for $0 \leqslant x \leqslant 360°$.
12. Prove that $\dfrac{\sin(A+B)}{\sin(A-B)} = \dfrac{\tan A + \tan B}{\tan A - \tan B}$

10.3 Tangent results

Formulae for $\tan(A+B)$ and $\tan(A-B)$ may be obtained by dividing the formulae we have already obtained for the sines and the cosines of these angles.

$$\tan(A+B) = \frac{\sin(A+B)}{\cos(A+B)} = \frac{\sin A \cos B + \cos A \sin B}{\cos A \cos B - \sin A \sin B}$$

$$= \frac{\tan A + \tan B}{1 - \tan A \tan B}$$

$$\tan(A-B) = \frac{\sin(A-B)}{\cos(A-B)} = \frac{\sin A \cos B - \cos A \sin B}{\cos A \cos B + \sin A \sin B}$$

$$= \frac{\tan A - \tan B}{1 + \tan A \tan B}$$

Note: In both cases the second line follows by dividing both numerator and denominator by $\cos A \cos B$.

$$\tan(A+B) = \frac{\tan A + \tan B}{1 - \tan A \tan B} \qquad \tan(A-B) = \frac{\tan A - \tan B}{1 + \tan A \tan B}$$

Example   62

If $\tan A = \frac{2}{3}$ and $\tan B = \frac{5}{4}$, find $\cot(A+B)$.

We begin by finding $\tan(A+B)$

$$\tan(A+B) = \frac{\tan A + \tan B}{1 - \tan A \tan B} = \frac{\frac{2}{3} + \frac{5}{4}}{1 - \frac{2}{3} \cdot \frac{5}{4}}$$

This is best simplified by multiplying each term by 12, i.e.

$$\tan(A+B) = \frac{8+15}{12-10} = \frac{23}{2}$$

$$\Rightarrow \cot(A+B) = \frac{2}{23}$$

Example   63

Prove that the angle between the lines $2y = 3x - 5$ and $3y - x + 4$ is $\arctan(\frac{7}{9})$.

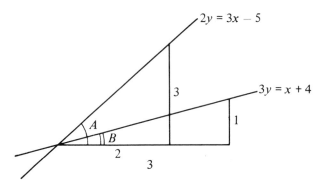

Fig. 5

We require the angle $(A-B)$ where A and B are the angles that the lines make with the horizontal (Fig. 5). The tangents of A and B are given by the gradients of the lines, i.e.

$$\tan A = \tfrac{3}{2} \qquad \text{(gradient of } 2y = 3x - 5\text{)}$$
$$\tan B = \tfrac{1}{3} \qquad \text{(gradient of } 3y = x + 4\text{)}$$

$$\text{hence} \quad \tan(A - B) = \frac{\tan A - \tan B}{1 + \tan A \tan B} = \frac{\tfrac{3}{2} - \tfrac{1}{3}}{1 + \tfrac{3}{2} \cdot \tfrac{1}{3}} = \frac{9 - 2}{6 + 3} = \frac{7}{9}$$

So the angle required is the angle whose tangent is $\tfrac{7}{9}$, i.e. $\arctan(\tfrac{7}{9})$.

Exercise 10(c)

1. If $\tan A = \tfrac{3}{4}$ and $\tan B = \tfrac{1}{5}$ find $\tan(A + B)$, $\cot(A - B)$.
2. If X and Y are acute angles such that $\tan X = 3$ and $\tan Y = \tfrac{1}{2}$, prove that $X - Y = 45°$.
3. Show that $\tan 15° = \dfrac{\sqrt{3} - 1}{\sqrt{3} + 1}$. Find also $\tan 105°$.
4. If $\tan A = \tfrac{2}{3}$ find the tangent of the angle $2A$. Hint: use $\tan(A + A)$. Find also the tangent of $3A$.
5. Given that $\tan(A + 45°) = \tfrac{3}{2}$ find $\tan A$.
6. If $\tan(A - 60°) = \tfrac{1}{2}$ show that $\tan A = \dfrac{1 + 2\sqrt{3}}{2 - \sqrt{3}}$
7. Find, without using tables, the values of
   (i) $\dfrac{\tan 40° + \tan 20°}{1 - \tan 40° \cdot \tan 20°}$ (ii) $\dfrac{1 - \tan 15°}{1 + \tan 15°}$
8. Find the tangents of the angles between the following pairs of lines
   (i) $y = x + 7$ and $y = 2x$
   (ii) $y = 4x - 1$ and $2y - x = 1$
   (iii) $3y + x = 2$ and $3y - 2x = 5$
9. Prove that $\cot(A + B) = \dfrac{\cot A \cot B - 1}{\cot A + \cot B}$
10. If $\tan(45° + x) = 2\tan(45° - x)$ prove that $\tan x = 3 \pm 2\sqrt{2}$.

10.4 Double and half-angle formulae

Double angles

Imagine that the sine, cosine and tangent of a particular angle θ are known and that we wish to find the values of these functions for the angle twice as large as θ, i.e. we require $\sin 2\theta$, $\cos 2\theta$ and $\tan 2\theta$. Formulae may be obtained as follows

$$\text{We have} \quad \sin(A + B) = \sin A \cos B + \cos A \sin B$$
$$\cos(A + B) = \cos A \cos B - \sin A \sin B$$

$$\tan(A+B) = \frac{\tan A + \tan B}{1 - \tan A \tan B}$$

Substituting $A = B = \theta$ into these results so that $(A + B) = 2\theta$ gives

$$\sin 2\theta = \sin \theta \cos \theta + \cos \theta \sin \theta = 2 \sin \theta \cos \theta$$
$$\cos 2\theta = \cos \theta \cos \theta - \sin \theta \sin \theta = \cos^2 \theta - \sin^2 \theta$$
$$\tan 2\theta = \frac{\tan \theta + \tan \theta}{1 - \tan \theta \tan \theta} \qquad = \frac{2 \tan \theta}{1 - \tan^2 \theta}$$

There are two further forms of the $\cos 2\theta$ formula since, as a consequence of the identity $\sin^2 \theta + \cos^2 \theta = 1$, we may write

$$\cos^2 \theta - \sin^2 \theta = \cos^2 \theta - (1 - \cos^2 \theta) = 2 \cos^2 \theta - 1$$
or $\quad \cos^2 \theta - \sin^2 \theta = (1 - \sin^2 \theta) - \sin^2 \theta = 1 - 2 \sin^2 \theta$

The results may be summarised as follows

$$
\begin{array}{ll}
\sin 2\theta = 2 \sin \theta \cos \theta & (1) \\
\left.
\begin{array}{l}
\cos 2\theta = \cos^2 \theta - \sin^2 \theta \\
\qquad = 2 \cos^2 \theta - 1 \\
\qquad = 1 - 2 \sin^2 \theta
\end{array}
\right\} & (2) \\
\tan 2\theta = \dfrac{2 \tan \theta}{1 - \tan^2 \theta} & (3)
\end{array}
$$

Example   64

If A is an acute angle such that $\tan A = \frac{3}{2}$ find (i) $\sin 2A$ (ii) $\cos 2A$ (iii) $\sin 3A$.

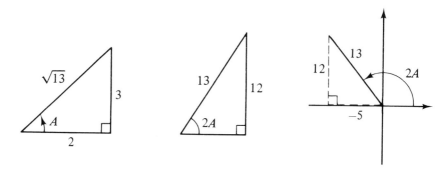

Fig. 6a   Fig. 6b   Fig. 6c

(i) Draw a right-angled triangle such that $\tan A = \frac{3}{2}$ (Fig. 6a). The hypotenuse of this triangle is $\sqrt{13}$. Hence

$$\sin 2A = 2 \sin A \cos A = 2 \cdot \frac{3}{\sqrt{13}} \cdot \frac{2}{\sqrt{13}} = \frac{12}{13}$$

(ii) There is a trap here which we must be careful to avoid. Since $\sin 2A = \frac{12}{13}$ it is tempting to draw the triangle of Fig. 6b from which, by Pythagoras', it would seem that $\cos 2A = \frac{5}{13}$. This is wrong because the angle A clearly exceeds $45°$ so that the angle twice as large, i.e. $2A$, will be obtuse and its cosine negative. To avoid this pitfall it is best to *start afresh* using the $\cos 2A$ formula

$$\cos 2A = \cos^2 A - \sin^2 A = \frac{4}{13} - \frac{9}{13} = \frac{-5}{13}$$

The correct diagram for this situation is Fig. 6c.

(iii) The angle $3A$ may be regarded as the sum of the angles A and $2A$. Thus

$$\sin 3A = \sin (A + 2A) = \sin A \cos 2A + \cos A \sin 2A$$
$$= \frac{3}{\sqrt{13}} \cdot \frac{-5}{13} + \frac{2}{\sqrt{13}} \cdot \frac{12}{13}$$
$$= \frac{9}{13\sqrt{13}} \quad \text{or} \quad \frac{9\sqrt{13}}{169}$$

Half angles

The important feature of the formulae (1), (2) and (3) above is that one angle should be double the other. Thus instead of using 2θ and θ we may equally well write the formulae in terms of θ and $\frac{1}{2}\theta$. This gives

$$\sin \theta = 2 \sin \tfrac{1}{2}\theta \cdot \cos \tfrac{1}{2}\theta \qquad (4)$$

$$\left. \begin{aligned} \cos \theta &= \cos^2 \tfrac{1}{2}\theta - \sin^2 \tfrac{1}{2}\theta \\ &= 2 \cos^2 \tfrac{1}{2}\theta - 1 \\ &= 1 - 2 \sin^2 \tfrac{1}{2}\theta \end{aligned} \right\} \qquad (5)$$

$$\tan \theta = \frac{2 \tan \tfrac{1}{2}\theta}{1 - \tan^2 \tfrac{1}{2}\theta} \qquad (6)$$

The most useful of these for finding the ratios of half-angles are the alternative forms of formula (5), i.e.

$$\cos \theta = 2 \cos^2 \tfrac{1}{2}\theta - 1 \quad \text{and} \quad \cos \theta = 1 - 2 \sin^2 \tfrac{1}{2}\theta$$

Given the value of $\cos \theta$, we may obtain from these formulae the values of $\cos \tfrac{1}{2}\theta$ and $\sin \tfrac{1}{2}\theta$.

Example 65

If B is an acute angle such that $\sin B = \frac{8}{17}$, find (i) $\cos \frac{1}{2}B$ (ii) $\tan \frac{1}{2}B$.

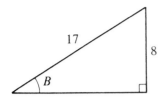

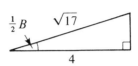

Fig. 7a   Fig. 7b

(i) Formula (4) is of little help since it gives $\frac{8}{17} = 2 \sin \frac{1}{2} B \cos \frac{1}{2} B$ which contains two unknown quantities. We therefore use Pythagoras' Theorem (Fig. 7a) to obtain $\cos B = \frac{15}{17}$ and use the appropriate version of formula (5), i.e.

$$\cos B = 2 \cos^2 \tfrac{1}{2} B - 1$$

$$\Rightarrow \quad \frac{15}{17} = 2 \cos^2 \tfrac{1}{2} B - 1$$

$$2 \cos^2 \tfrac{1}{2} B = \frac{32}{17} \quad \Rightarrow \cos \tfrac{1}{2} B = \frac{4}{\sqrt{17}}$$

(ii) We may now draw another right-angled triangle (Fig. 7b) to represent the angle $\frac{1}{2} B$. (This is necessarily acute.) The missing side in Fig. 7b is found to have length 1 so that

$$\tan \tfrac{1}{2} B = \frac{1}{4}$$

_____

Exercise 10(d)

1. Simplify, without using tables,

    (i) $2 \sin 10° \cos 10°$ (ii) $1 - 2 \sin^2 40°$ (iii) $\sin x \cos x$
    (iv) $2 \cos^2 3\theta - 1$

2. Find the value of $\tan 2\theta$ when $\tan \theta = \frac{4}{5}$. Hence find $\tan 3\theta$.

3. Find the value of $\cos 2x$ when

    (i) $\sin x = \frac{3}{7}$ (ii) $\cos x = \frac{2}{5}$.

4. A is an acute angle such that $\tan A = \frac{5}{3}$. Find

    $\sin 2A$, $\cos 2A$ and $\tan 2A$.

5. B is an acute angle such that $\sin B = \frac{3}{5}$. Find

    (i) $\sin 2B$ and $\cos 2B$ (ii) $\sin 3B$ and $\cos 3B$.

6. If $\sin \theta = \frac{4}{5}$ find $\cos \frac{1}{2}\theta$ and $\tan \frac{1}{2}\theta$.

7. ϕ is an acute angle such that $\tan \phi = \dfrac{5}{12}$.

   Find $\sin \frac{1}{2}\phi$ and $\tan \frac{1}{2}\phi$. Find also $\tan \frac{3}{2}\phi$

8. Prove that (i) $\dfrac{\sin 2A}{1 + \cos 2A} = \tan A$ (ii) $\dfrac{\sin 2A}{1 - \cos 2A} = \cot A$.

9. Prove that (i) $\cot A + \tan A = 2 \operatorname{cosec} 2A$
   (ii) $\cot A - \tan A = 2 \cot 2A$.

10. A right-angled triangle containing an angle θ has hypotenuse of fixed length r. Show that the area of the triangle is $\frac{1}{4}r^2 \sin 2\theta$ and deduce that this is a maximum when the triangle is isosceles.

11. An isosceles triangle is inscribed in a circle of radius r. Prove that the area of the triangle is given by $\frac{1}{2}r^2 (\sin 2\theta + 2 \sin \theta)$ where θ is the angle between the equal sides.

12. Use the half-angle formulae to prove that $\tan \frac{1}{2}\theta = \dfrac{1 - \cos \theta}{\sin \theta}$.

10.5 Further identities and equations

Example 66

Prove the identities

(i) $\sec 2\alpha = \dfrac{1 + \tan^2 \alpha}{1 - \tan^2 \alpha}$ (ii) $\cos 3\theta = 4 \cos^3 \theta - 3 \cos \theta$

(i) l.h.s. $\qquad \sec 2\alpha = \dfrac{1}{\cos 2\alpha} = \dfrac{1}{\cos^2 \alpha - \sin^2 \alpha}$

$\qquad\qquad\qquad = \dfrac{\sec^2 \alpha}{1 - \tan^2 \alpha}$

$\qquad\qquad\qquad = \dfrac{1 + \tan^2 \alpha}{1 - \tan^2 \alpha} \qquad$ r.h.s.

The second line follows by dividing both numerator and denominator by $\cos^2 \alpha$. For the last step we use the identity $\sec^2 \alpha = 1 + \tan^2 \alpha$ (Section 4.6).

(ii) l.h.s. $\qquad \cos 3\theta = \cos (\theta + 2\theta)$

$\qquad\qquad\qquad = \cos \theta \cos 2\theta - \sin \theta \sin 2\theta$

$\qquad\qquad\qquad = \cos \theta \cos 2\theta - \sin \theta (2 \sin \theta \cos \theta)$

To obtain an expression involving $\cos \theta$ only we now substitute $\cos 2\theta = 2 \cos^2 \theta - 1$ into the first term and $\sin^2 \theta = 1 - \cos^2 \theta$ into the second term, i.e.

$\qquad \cos 3\theta = \cos \theta (2 \cos^2 \theta - 1) - 2 (1 - \cos^2 \theta) \cos \theta$

$\qquad\qquad = 2 \cos^3 \theta - \cos \theta - 2 \cos \theta + 2 \cos^3 \theta$

$\qquad\qquad = 4 \cos^3 \theta - 3 \cos \theta \qquad$ r.h.s.

Example   67

Solve the following equations for values of θ in the range $0 \leqslant \theta \leqslant 360°$:
(i) $\sin 2\theta = 3 \cos^2\theta$ (ii) $3 \cos 2\theta + \sin \theta = 1$

(i) For this first equation we simply substitute the formula for $\sin 2\theta$ and then remove the common factor $\cos \theta$, i.e.

$$\sin 2\theta = 3 \cos^2\theta$$
$$\Rightarrow 2 \sin \theta \cos \theta - 3 \cos^2\theta = 0$$
$$\cos \theta (2 \sin \theta - 3 \cos \theta) = 0$$
$$\cos \theta = 0 \quad \text{or} \quad 2 \sin \theta - 3 \cos \theta = 0$$
$$\cos \theta = 0 \quad \text{or} \quad \tan \theta = \frac{3}{2}$$
$$\Rightarrow \theta = 90°, 270°, 56.3° \text{ or } 236.3°$$

(ii) In the second equation we have a choice of formulae for $\cos 2\theta$. We choose $\cos 2\theta = 1 - 2 \sin^2\theta$ so that the equation then involves $\sin \theta$ only, i.e.

$$3 \cos 2\theta + \sin \theta = 1$$
$$3(1 - 2 \sin^2\theta) + \sin \theta = 1$$
$$\Rightarrow \quad 0 = 6 \sin^2\theta - \sin \theta - 2$$
$$0 = (3 \sin \theta - 2)(2 \sin \theta + 1)$$
$$\sin \theta = \frac{2}{3} \quad \text{or} \quad \sin \theta = -\frac{1}{2}$$
$$\Rightarrow \quad \theta = 41.8°, 138.2°, 210° \text{ or } 330°$$

Exercise 10(e)

1. Prove that $\sin 2\alpha = \dfrac{2 \tan \alpha}{1 + \tan^2\alpha}$

2. Prove that $\cot 2\alpha = \dfrac{\cot^2\alpha - 1}{2 \cot \alpha}$

3. Obtain a formula for $\sin 3A$ in terms of $\sin A$ only.

4. Prove that $\tan 3A = \dfrac{3 \tan A - \tan^3 A}{1 - 3 \tan^2 A}$

5. Write $\cos 4\theta$ in terms of $\cos 2\theta$ and hence prove the identity $\cos 4\theta = 8 \cos^4\theta - 8 \cos^2\theta + 1$.

In questions 6–15 solve the equations for values of θ in the range $0 \leqslant \theta \leqslant 360°$.

6. $\sin 2\theta = \cos \theta$
7. $\cos 2\theta + \cos \theta = 0$
8. $2 \sin 2\theta - \sin^2\theta = 0$
9. $\cos 2\theta = 3 \sin^2\theta$
10. $2 \cos 2\theta - \sin \theta + 1 = 0$
11. $3 \cos 2\theta = 4 \cos \theta - 1$
12. $3 \tan 2\theta = 2 \cot \theta$

13. $\tan 2\theta = 8 \tan \theta$
14. $\sin 2\theta - \cos 2\theta = 1$
15. $\sin 2\theta - \cos \theta + 2 \sin \theta = 1$.
16. Prove that there is no non-zero angle X such that $\tan 2X = \tan X$.
17. Prove that there are no angles α such that

$$\cos 2\alpha = 2 \cos \alpha - 2.$$

18. Prove that

$$\sin (A + B + C) = \sin A \cos B \cos C + \cos A \sin B \cos C$$
$$+ \cos A \cos B \sin C - \sin A \sin B \sin C$$

19. Prove that

$$\cos (A + B + C) = \cos A \cos B \cos C - \sin A \sin B \cos C$$
$$- \sin A \cos B \sin C - \cos A \sin B \sin C$$

20. Prove that

$$\tan (A + B + C) = \frac{\tan A + \tan B + \tan C - \tan A \tan B \tan C}{1 - \tan A \tan B - \tan B \tan C - \tan C \tan A}$$

Deduce that if A, B and C are the angles of a triangle then

$$\tan A + \tan B + \tan C = \tan A \tan B \tan C.$$

11

The Binomial Expansion

11.1 Pascal's triangle

The expansion $(1 + x)^2 = 1 + 2x + x^2$ should be well known. In the working that follows we obtain similar expansions for $(1 + x)^3$ and $(1 + x)^4$

$$(1 + x)^2 = \underline{1 + 2x + \ x^2}$$

multiply by 1 $1 + 2x + \ x^2$

multiply by x $\underline{\ \ \ \ \ \ x + 2x^2 + \ x^3}$

$$\Rightarrow (1 + x)^3 = \underline{1 + 3x + 3x^2 + \ x^3}$$

multiply by 1 $1 + 3x + 3x^2 + \ x^3$

multiply by x $\underline{\ \ \ \ \ \ x + 3x^2 + 3x^3 + x^4}$

$$\Rightarrow (1 + x)^4 = \ 1 + 4x + 6x^2 + 4x^3 + x^4$$

The student should continue this process to obtain the results for $(1 + x)^5$ and $(1 + x)^6$.

If we take out the **coefficients** of the various powers of x in these expansions we may arrange them in a triangular array as follows

coefficients

power 2					1		2		1	
power 3				1		3		3		1
power 4			1		4		6		4		1
power 5		1		5		10		10		5	1
power 6	1		6		15		20		15	6	1

This is known as **Pascal's Triangle**. It is evident that each line in this triangle may be obtained by adding pairs of consecutive numbers in the preceding line. The triangle may easily be continued to find the coefficients for the expansion of $(1 + x)^7$, $(1 + x)^8$ etc.

Pascal's Triangle provides the quickest method by which many expansions related to powers of $(1 + x)$ may be written down. This is illustrated in the following example.

Example 68

Expand   (i) $(1 + 3a)^5$ (ii) $(1 - \frac{1}{2}b)^4$

(i) The coefficients for a power 5 expansion are first taken from Pascal's Triangle, i.e. 1, 5, 10, 10, 5, 1. In the expansion of $(1 + x)^5$ the second, third, fourth terms would involve x, x^2, x^3 ... respectively. Here they involve the corresponding powers of $3a$, i.e. $(3a)$, $(3a)^2$, $(3a)^3$ ... etc.

So $\quad (1+3a)^5 = 1 + 5(3a) + 10(3a)^2 + 10(3a)^3 + 5(3a)^4 + (3a)^5$
$$= 1 + 15a + 90a^2 + 270a^3 + 405a^4 + 243a^5$$

(ii) This is obtained in the same way, each power of x being replaced by the corresponding power of $(-\frac{1}{2}b)$

$$(1 - \tfrac{1}{2}b)^4 = 1 + 4(-\tfrac{1}{2}b) + 6(-\tfrac{1}{2}b)^2 + 4(-\tfrac{1}{2}b)^3 + (-\tfrac{1}{2}b)^4$$
$$= 1 - 2b \qquad +\frac{3}{2}b^2 \qquad -\frac{1}{2}b^3 \qquad +\frac{1}{16}b^4$$

Note: Throughout the second expansion the minus sign is attached to the $\frac{1}{2}b$. This is because if we are to relate this expansion to one involving $1 + x$ we must regard it as $1 + (-\frac{1}{2}b)$.

Example 69

Find the coefficient of y^3 in the expansion of $(1 - 2y)^8$.

The term involving y^3 is the fourth term in the expansion. By continuing Pascal's Triangle the coefficient for the fourth term in the basic expansion of $(1 + x)^8$ is found to be 56. The fourth term in our expansion is therefore

$$56(-2y)^3$$

$$= -448 y^3 \qquad \Rightarrow \text{coefficient} = -448$$

Exercise 11 (a)

1. By continuing Pascal's Triangle, write out the complete expansions of
   (i) $(1 + x)^7$ (ii) $(1 + x)^8$
2. Write out the complete expansions of
   (i) $(1 + x)^3$ and $(1 - x)^3$
   (ii) $(1 + x)^6$ and $(1 - x)^6$
3. Expand each of the following
   (i) $(1 + 2a)^4$ (ii) $(1 - 3b)^3$ (iii) $(1 - 4x)^5$
   (iv) $(1 + 2y)^6$ (v) $(1 + \frac{1}{3}a)^3$ (vi) $(1 - \frac{1}{2}b)^5$
4. Find the first four terms in each of the following expansions
   (i) $(1 + 5r)^6$ (ii) $(1 + \frac{1}{2}s)^8$ (iii) $(1 - 6a)^5$
   (iv) $(1 - \frac{1}{10}b)^7$
5. Find the coefficients of
   (i) a^2 in the expansion of $(1 + a)^5$
   (ii) b^3 in the expansion of $(1 - b)^7$
   (iii) c^3 in the expansion of $(1 + 3c)^4$
   (iv) d^4 in the expansion of $(1 - \frac{1}{3}d)^6$
6. Write out the following expansions in full
   (i) $(1 + x^2)^3$ (ii) $(1 - x^2)^4$
7. (i) Prove that $(1 + \sqrt{3})^4 = 28 + 16\sqrt{3}$.
   (ii) Obtain a similar expression for $(1 - \sqrt{2})^5$

11.2 The expansion $(a+b)^n$

We now consider expansions of the **binomial** $(a+b)$. A binomial, literally, is an expression consisting of two numbers. We begin, as in the previous section, by considering $(a+b)^2$, $(a+b)^3$ and $(a+b)^4$

$$(a+b)^2 = a^2 + 2ab + b^2$$

multiply by a $\quad a^3 + 2a^2b + ab^2$
multiply by b $\qquad\quad a^2b + 2ab^2 + b^3$

$$\Rightarrow (a+b)^3 = a^3 + 3a^2b + 3ab^2 + b^3$$

multiply by a $\quad a^4 + 3a^3b + 3a^2b^2 + ab^3$
multiply by b $\qquad\quad a^3b + 3a^2b^2 + ab^3 + b^4$

$$\Rightarrow (a+b)^4 = a^4 + 4a^3b + 6a^2b^2 + 4ab^3 + b^4$$

These results are very similar to those obtained in Section 11.1. The coefficients are again given by Pascal's Triangle and powers of the second number, b, increase term by term as do the powers of x in the expansions of $(1+x)^n$. Powers of the first number, a, decrease term by term. So if we wish to write out the expansion $(a+b)^5$ we could proceed as follows
(i)   Obtain coefficients from Pascal's Triangle

$\quad$ 1 $\quad$ 5 $\quad$ 10 $\quad$ 10 $\quad$ 5 $\quad$ 1

(ii)   Insert increasing powers of b (starting in second term)

$\quad$ 1 $\quad$ $5b$ $\quad$ $10b^2$ $\quad$ $10b^3$ $\quad$ $5b^4$ $\quad$ b^5

(iii)   Insert decreasing powers of a

$\quad a^5 \quad 5a^4b \quad 10a^3b^2 \quad 10a^2b^3 \quad 5ab^4 \quad b^5$

(Notice that the sum of the powers is 5 in each term.)
Thus

$$(a+b)^5 = a^5 + 5a^4b + 10a^3b^2 + 10a^2b^3 + 5ab^4 + b^5$$

More involved expansions, as in the example which follows, may be tackled in exactly the same way.

Example   70

Expand (i) $(3x+\tfrac{1}{2}y)^4$ $\qquad$ (ii) $\left(x-\dfrac{1}{x}\right)^6$

(i)   Here we have

power 4 coefficients $\quad$ 1 $\quad$ 4 $\quad$ 6 $\quad$ 4 $\quad$ 1
increasing powers of $(\tfrac{1}{2}y)$
decreasing powers of $(3x)$
sum of powers in each term equals 4

Thus

$$(3x+\tfrac{1}{2}y)^4 = (3x)^4 + 4(3x)^3(\tfrac{1}{2}y) + 6(3x)^2(\tfrac{1}{2}y)^2 + 4(3x)(\tfrac{1}{2}y)^3 + (\tfrac{1}{2}y)^4$$
$$= 81x^4 + 54x^3y + \tfrac{27}{2}x^2y^2 + \tfrac{3}{2}xy^3 + \tfrac{1}{16}y^4$$

(ii) We must have

power 6 coefficients   1 6 15 20 15 6 1

increasing powers of $\left(-\dfrac{1}{x}\right)$

decreasing powers of x

sum of powers in each term equals 6

$$\left(x-\frac{1}{x}\right)^6 = x^6 + 6x^5\left(-\frac{1}{x}\right) + 15x^4\left(-\frac{1}{x}\right)^2 + 20x^3\left(-\frac{1}{x}\right)^3 + 15x^2\left(-\frac{1}{x}\right)^4$$
$$+ 6x\left(-\frac{1}{x}\right) + \left(-\frac{1}{x}\right)^6$$
$$= x^6 - 6x^4 + 15x^2 - 20 + \frac{15}{x^2} - \frac{6}{x^4} + \frac{1}{x^6}$$

The x's cancel from the middle term. This term is said to be independent of x.

Exercise 11(b)

1. Write out the expansions of
   (i) $(a+b)^6$ (ii) $(a+b)^7$ (iii) $(a-b)^3$ (iv) $(a-b)^4$

2. Expand the following
   (i) $(a+2b)^3$ (ii) $(3x-y)^4$ (iii) $(2+3p)^5$
   (iv) $(3r-4s)^3$ (v) $(2r-\frac{1}{2}s)^6$ (vi) $(2q-1)^7$
   (vii) $(x+\frac{1}{x})^4$ (viii) $(x^2-\frac{1}{x})^5$

3. Find the coefficients of
   (i) x^2 in the expansion of $(2+x)^6$
   (ii) a^3 in the expansion of $(a-5)^4$
   (iii) p^3q^2 in the expansion of $(2p-3q)^5$
   (iv) x in the expansion of $(3x+\frac{1}{x})^7$

4. Find the terms independent of x in the expansions of
   (i) $\left(2x-\dfrac{1}{x}\right)^4$ (ii) $\left(x^2+\dfrac{1}{x}\right)^6$

*5. Expand the following as far as the term in x^3
   (i) $(1+x+x^2)^6$ (ii) $(2+x-x^2)^4$

11.3 The Binomial Theorem

An alternative method of obtaining the expansion of $(1+x)^n$ is by means of the following result, known as the **Binomial Theorem**

$$(1+x)^n = 1 + nx + \frac{n(n-1)}{2!}x^2 + \frac{n(n-1)(n-2)}{3!}x^3 + \ldots$$

Note: **Factorial 4** or 4! is the product of 4 with all the positive integers lower than 4, i.e.

$$4! = 4 \times 3 \times 2 \times 1 \qquad = 24$$

similarly $6! = 6 \times 5 \times 4 \times 3 \times 2 \times 1 = 720$

A proof of this result is outlined in Section 22.3. For the moment we shall only demonstrate its validity for some of the expansions already considered in this chapter. With $n = 6$, for example, we obtain

$$(1+x)^6 = 1 + 6x + \frac{6 \cdot 5}{2 \cdot 1}x^2 + \frac{6 \cdot 5 \cdot 4}{3 \cdot 2 \cdot 1}x^3 + \frac{6 \cdot 5 \cdot 4 \cdot 3}{4 \cdot 3 \cdot 2 \cdot 1}x^4 + \cdots$$

$$= 1 + 6x + 15x^2 + 20x^3 + 15x^4 + \cdots$$

With the example just considered we could write down the expansion more simply by using Pascal's Triangle. This is not the case when the power of the expansion is higher and it is then that the Binomial Theorem becomes useful. We consider next the first terms in the expansion of $(1+x)^{15}$. Here we take $n = 15$

$$(1+x)^{15} = 1 + 15x + \frac{15 \cdot 14}{2 \cdot 1}x^2 + \frac{15 \cdot 14 \cdot 13}{3 \cdot 2 \cdot 1}x^3 + \frac{15 \cdot 14 \cdot 13 \cdot 12}{4 \cdot 3 \cdot 2 \cdot 1}x^4 + \cdots$$

$$= 1 + 15x + 105x^2 + 455x^3 + 1365x^4 + \cdots$$

Succeeding terms may be calculated, if needed, by continuing this process. After the halfway point in the expansion has been passed the coefficients are reversed and the expansion terminates with the terms

$$\ldots + 105x^{13} + 15x^{14} + x^{15}$$

An exactly similar formula applies for the expansion of $(a+b)^n$. Here the powers of a decrease, starting with a^n in the first term.

$$(a+b)^n = a^n + na^{n-1}b + \frac{n(n-1)}{2!}a^{n-2}b^2 + \frac{n(n-1)(n-2)}{3!}a^{n-3}b^3 + \cdots$$

Example   71

Find the first five terms in each of the following expansions:

(i) $\left(1+\dfrac{r}{3}\right)^{12}$ (ii) $(p-2q)^{11}$

(i)   Powers of x in the $(1+x)^n$ formula are replaced by the corresponding powers of $\dfrac{r}{3}$

$$\left(1+\frac{r}{3}\right)^{12} = 1 + 12\left(\frac{r}{3}\right) + \frac{12 \cdot 11}{2 \cdot 1}\left(\frac{r}{3}\right)^2 + \frac{12 \cdot 11 \cdot 10}{3 \cdot 2 \cdot 1}\left(\frac{r}{3}\right)^3 + \frac{12 \cdot 11 \cdot 10 \cdot 9}{4 \cdot 3 \cdot 2 \cdot 1}\left(\frac{r}{3}\right)^4 +$$

$$= 1 + 12 \cdot \frac{r}{3} + 66 \cdot \frac{r^2}{9} + 2 \cdot 11 \cdot 10 \cdot \frac{r^3}{27} + 11 \cdot 5 \cdot 9 \cdot \frac{r^4}{81} + \cdots$$

$$= 1 + 4r + \frac{22}{3}r^2 + \frac{220}{27}r^3 + \frac{55}{9}r^4 + \cdots$$

(ii) Powers of $(-2q)$ increase while powers of p decrease from 11 in the first term. The sum of the powers in each term is 11

$$(p-2q)^{11} = p^{11} + 11 \cdot p^{10}(-2q) + \frac{11 \cdot 10}{2 \cdot 1} \cdot p^9(-2q)^2$$

$$+ \frac{11 \cdot 10 \cdot 9}{3 \cdot 2 \cdot 1} \cdot p^8(-2q)^3 + \frac{11 \cdot 10 \cdot 9 \cdot 8}{4 \cdot 3 \cdot 2 \cdot 1} \cdot p^7(-2q)^4 + \ldots$$

$$= p^{11} - 22p^{10}q + 55 \cdot 4p^9q^2 - 165 \cdot 8p^8q^3 + 330 \cdot 16p^7q^4 + \ldots$$

$$= p^{11} - 22p^{10}q + 220p^9q^2 - 1320p^8q^3 + 5280p^7q^4 + \ldots$$

Exercise 11(c)

1. Expand $(1 + x)^7$ by the method of this section and verify that the coefficients agree with those predicted by Pascal's Triangle.
2. Use the Binomial Theorem to find the first four terms in each of the following expansions
   (i) $(1 - x)^{10}$ (ii) $(a + b)^8$
3. Expand $(1 + x)^9$ as far as the term in x^4. By substituting $x = 0.01$ into your result obtain the value of $(1.01)^9$ correct to five decimal places.
4. Expand $(1 - x)^{13}$ as far as the term in x^4. Hence obtain the value of $(0.99)^{13}$ correct to five decimal places.
5. Find the first four terms in each of the following expansions
   (i) $(1 - 3b)^9$ (ii) $(1 + \frac{1}{2}x)^{12}$
   (iii) $(a + 2b)^{14}$ (iv) $\left(x - \frac{1}{x}\right)^{20}$
6. Find (i) the coefficients of x^3 and x^5 in the expansion of $(1 + x)^{16}$.
   (ii) the coefficients of x^2 and x^4 in the expansion of $(1 + \frac{1}{2}x)^{11}$.
7. Find (i) the fifth term in the expansion of $(a - \frac{1}{3}b)^{12}$.
   (ii) the sixth term in the expansion of $(2 - \frac{1}{4}x)^{14}$.
8. Find the first four terms in the expansion of $(1 + x)^{17}$. Hence find, as far as the term in x^3, an expansion in ascending powers of x for the function $(1 - 2x)(1 + x)^{17}$.

11.4 The infinite binomial series

Terminating binomial series

At the start of the previous section the Binomial Theorem was given in the form of a continuing series, i.e. a series which may be continued to as many terms as one requires. This series **terminates** at the correct point when the power n in the expansion of $(1 + x)^n$ is a positive integer. This is because there will come a point, in such a series, where a zero is introduced into the coefficient of a particular term (and all succeeding terms). Consider, for example, the case $n = 3$

$$(1 + x)^3 = 1 + 3x + \frac{3 \cdot 2}{2 \cdot 1} \cdot x^2 + \frac{3 \cdot 2 \cdot 1}{3 \cdot 2 \cdot 1} \cdot x^3 + \frac{3 \cdot 2 \cdot 1 \cdot 0}{4 \cdot 3 \cdot 2 \cdot 1} \cdot x^4 + \frac{3 \cdot 2 \cdot 1 \cdot 0 \cdot (-1)}{5 \cdot 4 \cdot 3 \cdot 2 \cdot 1} \cdot x^5$$

$$= 1 + 3x + 3x^2 + x^3 \quad \text{series terminates.}$$

In all cases where n is a positive integer the series terminates in this way. These terminating series always agree with the results obtained by direct multiplication or by using Pascal's Triangle.

Infinite binomial series

We are naturally led to wonder about cases where n is not an integer, e.g. $n = 1\frac{1}{2}$, or where n is negative, e.g. $n = -2$. Can we obtain expansions for $(1 + x)^{1\frac{1}{2}}$ and $(1 + x)^{-2}$? Certainly the form of the Binomial Theorem is such that it may apparently be applied to any value of n. Can we therefore substitute $n = 1\frac{1}{2}$ (or $\frac{3}{2}$) and obtain the following expansion?

$$(1+x)^{1\frac{1}{2}} = 1 + (\tfrac{3}{2})x + \frac{(\tfrac{3}{2})(\tfrac{1}{2})}{2 \cdot 1}x^2 + \frac{(\tfrac{3}{2})(\tfrac{1}{2})(-\tfrac{1}{2})}{3 \cdot 2 \cdot 1}x^3 + \frac{(\tfrac{3}{2})(\tfrac{1}{2})(-\tfrac{1}{2})(-\tfrac{3}{2})}{4 \cdot 3 \cdot 2 \cdot 1}x^4 + \dots$$

$$= 1 + \tfrac{3}{2}x + \tfrac{3}{8}x^2 \quad - \tfrac{1}{16}x^3 \quad + \tfrac{3}{128}x^4 + \dots$$

When writing out this expansion we notice that it is impossible for a zero to be introduced into any coefficient. The series will therefore never terminate.

If we substitute $n = -2$ into the Binomial Theorem the following series is found. This is also an **infinite** series

$$(1+x)^{-2} = 1 + (-2)x + \frac{(-2)(-3)}{2 \cdot 1}x^2 + \frac{(-2)(-3)(-4)}{3 \cdot 2 \cdot 1}x^3$$

$$+ \frac{(-2)(-3)(-4)(-5)}{4 \cdot 3 \cdot 2 \cdot 1}x^4 + \dots$$

$$= 1 - 2x + 3x^2 - 4x^3 + 5x^4 - \dots$$

Validity of the infinite series

Infinite series are obtained in all cases where n is not a positive integer. Are such series correct? There is no way that they can be verified by direct multiplication; $(1 + x)^{1\frac{1}{2}}$, for example, cannot be multiplied out in the same way as $(1 + x)^3$ and $(1 + x)^4$ were at the start of this chapter.

The validity of these results is a rather difficult question which we shall leave until the next section. The answer, briefly, is that they are valid under certain circumstances but not all the time. The following exercise is intended to give practice in the actual process by which these series are found.

Example   72

Find the first five terms of the expansion in ascending powers of x of the function $\dfrac{(1 - x)}{(1 + x)^2}$

This function is equivalent to $(1 - x)(1 + x)^{-2}$. We therefore find the expansion for $(1 + x)^{-2}$ and then multiply the result by $(1 - x)$.

from above	$(1+x)^{-2} = 1 - 2x + 3x^2 - 4x^3 + 5x^4 - \ldots$
multiply by 1	$1 - 2x + 3x^2 - 4x^3 + 5x^4 - \ldots$
multiply by $-x$	$\underline{\quad - x + 2x^2 - 3x^3 + 4x^4 \quad}$
	$\quad\quad\quad\quad\quad\quad\quad - \ldots$
add	$1 - 3x + 5x^2 - 7x^3 + 9x^4 - \ldots$
so	$\dfrac{(1-x)}{(1+x)^2} = 1 - 3x + 5x^2 - 7x^3 + 9x^4 - \ldots$

Exercise 11(d)

1. Expand the following as far as the term in x^4
   (i) $(1+x)^{\frac{1}{2}}$ (ii) $(1+x)^{-1}$ (iii) $(1+x)^{2\frac{1}{2}}$
   (iv) $(1+x)^{-3}$ (v) $(1-x)^{-4}$ (vi) $(1-x)^{-\frac{1}{3}}$
2. We may write $(1+x)^{1\frac{1}{2}} = (1+x)(1+x)^{\frac{1}{2}}$. Multiply the result of question 1(i) by $(1+x)$ and verify that the series given in the text above for $(1+x)^{1\frac{1}{2}}$ is obtained. Check also that multiplying a second time by $(1+x)$ gives the result of question 1(iii).
3. Find the first four terms in each of the following expansions
   (i) $(1-x)^{\frac{2}{3}}$ (ii) $(1+\frac{1}{2}x)^{-4}$ (iii) $\sqrt[4]{1+4x}$
   (iv) $\dfrac{1}{(1-3x)}$ (v) $\dfrac{1}{(1+2x)^3}$ (vi) $\dfrac{1}{\sqrt{1+x^2}}$
4. Find, in ascending powers of x, the first four terms in each of the following expansions:
   (i) $(1+x)\sqrt{1-4x}$ (ii) $\dfrac{1-x}{(1-2x)^2}$

11.5 Convergence of the binomial series

In the previous section we saw that when n is not a positive integer an infinite binomial series is obtained. We now investigate the validity of these series. As examples we shall use the series of Exercise 11(d), question 1, parts (i) and (ii). Here the following expansions should have been obtained. (One extra term is given in each.)

$$(1+x)^{\frac{1}{2}} = 1 + \frac{1}{2}x - \frac{1}{8}x^2 + \frac{1}{16}x^3 - \frac{5}{128}x^4 + \frac{7}{256}x^5 \ldots$$

$$(1+x)^{-1} = 1 - x + x^2 - x^3 + x^4 - x^5 + \ldots$$

The first of these series should give us $\sqrt{5} \approx 2.236$ when $x = 4$ and $\sqrt{3} \approx 1.732$ when $x = 2$, since $(1+x)^{\frac{1}{2}}$ is equivalent to $\sqrt{1+x}$

$$(1+x)^{\frac{1}{2}} = 1 + \frac{1}{2}x - \frac{1}{8}x^2 + \frac{1}{16}x^3 - \frac{5}{128}x^4 + \frac{7}{256}x^5 - \ldots$$

when $x = 4$	$1 + 2 - 2 + 4 - 10 + 28 - \ldots = ?$
when $x = 2$	$1 + 1 - 0.5 + 0.5 - 0.625 + 0.875 \quad \ldots = ?$

The terms in the $x = 4$ expansion are increasing in magnitude and it is extremely unlikely that the sum of this series can ever approach a limiting value of around 2.236. This behaviour is less marked for $x = 2$ but the terms are again increasing in magnitude and the sum fluctuates as further terms are considered. These series **diverge** and the expansion is *not valid* for these values of x.

If, however, we take values of x which are less than 1 in magnitude, then the powers of x involved must necessarily decrease from term to term so that convergence may be possible. Consider $x = 0.4$ and $x = 0.2$. (The terms may be obtained by dividing those for $x = 4$ and $x = 2$ by the appropriate powers of 10.)

when $x = 0.4$ $1 + 0.2 - 0.02 + 0.004 - 0.0010$ $\ldots \approx 1.183$

when $x = 0.2$ $1 + 0.1 - 0.005 + 0.0005 - 0.000\,062\,5\ldots \approx 1.095$

These series are converging onto the correct values for $\sqrt{1.4}$ (≈ 1.183) and $\sqrt{1.2}$ (≈ 1.095) respectively.

If we can draw a rather loose conclusion from this, it is that infinite binomial series are likely to diverge for *large* values of x and converge only for sufficiently *small* values of x. (The words large and small are at present undefined.) Similar behaviour is exhibited by the second of the series we have chosen as examples: the expansion for $(1 + x)^{-1}$ should give $\frac{1}{3}$ when $x = 2$ and $\frac{1}{1.2}$ or $\frac{5}{6}$ (≈ 0.8333) when $x = 0.2$

$(1 + x)^{-1} = 1 - x + x^2 - x^3 + x^4 - x^5 + \ldots$

when $x = 2$ $1 - 2 + 4 - 8 + 16 - 32 \ldots = ?$

when $x = 0.2$ $1 - 0.2 + 0.04 - 0.008 + 0.0016 - 0.000\,32 \ldots \approx 0.833$

The series is valid for $x = 0.2$ but diverges for $x = 2$.

We now take a closer look at the series for $(1 + x)^{-1}$. By coincidence (this is by no means a general result) this series happens also to be a geometric progression with common ratio $-x$. We have seen in Chapter 8 that the infinite geometric series converges when $|r| < 1$. So this establishes that the series for $(1 + x)^{-1}$ converges if $|x| < 1$, i.e. if the magnitude of x is less than 1.

It can be shown that the same criterion for convergence applies to *all* infinite binomial series $(1 + x)^n$: they are valid (i.e. converge) when $|x| < 1$. A rigorous proof of this result is beyond the scope of this book.

Note: Returning to the expansion of $(1 + x)^{-1}$ it is interesting to observe that, when convergent, the sum of this series, as given by the formula for the sum of an infinite geometric series, is

$$\frac{a}{1 - r} = \frac{1}{1 - (-x)} = \frac{1}{1 + x} = (1 + x)^{-1} \qquad !$$

Summary

$$(1 + x)^n = 1 + nx + \frac{n(n - 1)}{2!}x^2 + \frac{n(n - 1)(n - 2)}{3!}x^3 + \ldots$$

Terminating series (n positive integer): always valid
Infinite series: valid for $|x| < 1$

Example 73

State the values of a for which the expansions of each of the following are valid:

(i) $\dfrac{1}{(1+a)^2}$ (ii) $\dfrac{1}{\sqrt{1-2a}}$ (iii) $\left(1+\dfrac{1}{5}a\right)^{-3}$

We must compare each of these with the basic form $(1+x)^n$. Consider them therefore as

(i) $(1+a)^{-2}$ valid for $|a| < 1$ $-1 < a < 1$

(ii) $[1+(-2a)]^{-\frac{1}{2}}$ valid for $|-2a| < 1$ $\Rightarrow -\frac{1}{2} < a < \frac{1}{2}$
$-1 < 2a < 1$

(iii) $[1+(\frac{1}{5}a)]^{-3}$ valid for $|\frac{1}{5}a| < 1$ $\Rightarrow -5 < a < 5$
$-1 < \frac{1}{5}a < 1$

Example 74

Find, correct to 4 decimal places, the value of $\sqrt{4.16}$.

We would like to use the expansion for $(1+x)^{\frac{1}{2}}$ which is given at the start of this section, i.e.

$$(1+x)^{\frac{1}{2}} = 1 + \frac{1}{2}x - \frac{1}{8}x^2 + \frac{1}{16}x^3 - \frac{5}{128}x^4 \dots$$

However, this expansion is valid only for $|x| < 1$ and to obtain $\sqrt{4.16}$ directly we would need to substitute $x = 3.16$. To find a way round this difficulty proceed as follows:

$$\sqrt{4.16} = \sqrt{4(1.04)} = 2\sqrt{1.04}$$

We therefore use the above series with $x = 0.04$ (a small value of x such as this is necessary for rapid convergence) and then double the result so obtained.

with $x = 0.04$, $(1+x)^{\frac{1}{2}} = 1 + 0.02 - 0.000\,2 + 0.000\,004 - \dots$

hence $\sqrt{4.16} = 2 + 0.04 - 0.000\,4 + 0.000\,008 - \dots$
$$\approx 2.039\,6(08)$$

To four decimal places the answer is 2.0396

Exercise 11(e)

1. State the values of x for which each of the expansions in Exercise 11(d) question 3 is valid.
2. State the values of x for which each of the expansions in Exercise 11(d) question 4 is valid.
3. Expand $(1-x)^{-2}$ and hence obtain the value of $\dfrac{1}{(0.997)^2}$ correct to seven decimal places.
4. Use the first four terms of the expansion for $(1+x)^{\frac{1}{2}}$ to find the square roots of the following numbers correct to four decimal places:
   (i) 1.08   (ii) 27   (iii) 102

5. Find the first four terms in the expansion of $(1 + 3x)^{\frac{1}{3}}$. For what values of x is this expansion valid? Deduce the cube roots of (i) 1.06 (ii) 8.24 correct to four places of decimals.

6. Find the first four terms in the expansion of $(1 - x)^{\frac{1}{2}}$.

   (i) By substituting $x = 0.02$ find $\sqrt{2}$ correct to four decimal places.

$$\left(\text{Hint: } 0.98 = \frac{2 \times 49}{100}. \right)$$

   (ii) By substituting $x = 0.01$ find $\sqrt{11}$ correct to four decimal places.

7. Obtain expansions in ascending powers of x, as far as the term in x^3, for each of the following. State the values of x for which your results are valid.

   (i) $\dfrac{1-x}{(1 - \frac{1}{2}x)^2}$ (ii) $\dfrac{2+x}{\sqrt{1+4x}}$

8. Find the first four terms in the expansions of $(1 + 2x)^{\frac{1}{2}}$ and $(1 - 2x)^{-\frac{1}{2}}$. By multiplying these series together show that if x is small enough for x^4 and higher powers to be neglected then

$$\sqrt{\frac{1 + 2x}{1 - 2x}} \approx 1 + 2x + 2x^2 + 4x^3$$

By substituting $x = 0.01$ into this result, obtain $\sqrt{51}$ correct to four places of decimals.

12

Logarithms

Note: It is probably reasonable to assume that most students will obtain the values of logarithms from scientific calculators. The bar notation is not therefore used in this text, e.g. $\log 0.5$ is written -0.3010 and not $\bar{1}.6990$. Logarithmic values are, however, corrected to 4 decimal places so that they should be consistent with values obtained from tables.

12.1 Common logarithms

The advent of the slide rule and, more recently, of the pocket calculator has meant that many students starting A level courses have little or no experience of using logarithms. Such experience is a great help in the understanding of the laws of logarithms (Section 12.3). This section is intended as an aid to students who have not used logarithms before.

Powers of 10

Logarithms are concerned with powers of 10. The following numbers are exact powers of 10

$$10 = 10^1, \quad 100 = 10^2, \quad 1000 = 10^3$$
$$1 = 10^0, \quad 0.1 = 10^{-1}, \quad 0.01 = 10^{-2} \quad \text{etc.}$$

In fact any number may be written as a power of 10. Numbers between 1 and 10 lie between 10^0 and 10^1: (an example is 3.1623 which is close to $\sqrt{10}$ and is therefore approximately $10^{\frac{1}{2}}$ or $10^{0.5}$). Numbers between 10 and 100 lie between 10^1 and 10^2 and so on. When we look up the logarithm of a certain number we are in effect converting it to a power of 10. For example, we find from a calculator that

$$\log 7 \approx 0.8451, \quad \log 26.4 \approx 1.4216, \quad \log 0.19 \approx -0.7212$$

This tells us that

$$7 \approx 10^{0.8451}, \quad 26.4 \approx 10^{1.4216}, \quad 0.19 \approx 10^{-0.7212}$$

Numbers less than 1 correspond to negative powers of 10 and we therefore find that their logarithms are negative.

The **inverse log** function on a calculator enables us to convert powers of 10 back to ordinary numbers. Thus **inverse log 2** gives the result 100 because we are effectively asking the calculator which number is equivalent to 10 to power 2. Similarly

$$10^{2.5} \approx 316.2 \qquad (\text{inverse log} \quad 2.5 \quad = 316.2)$$
$$10^{0.756} \approx 5.702 \qquad (\text{inverse log} \quad 0.756 = 5.702)$$
$$10^{-1.34} \approx 0.04571 \qquad (\text{inverse log} \quad -1.34 = 0.04571)$$

Use of logarithms

Logarithms have long been used as an aid to calculation. The use of logarithms is based upon the laws of indices (Section 1.1), i.e.

$$a^m \times a^n = a^{m+n} \qquad \text{add indices}$$
$$a^m \div a^n = a^{m-n} \qquad \text{subtract indices}$$

Consider for example the simple calculations 32×8 and $32 \div 8$. The logarithms of 32 and 8 (corrected to 4 decimal places) are 1.5051 and 0.9031 respectively. We may therefore write

$$32 \times 8 \approx 10^{1.5051} \times 10^{0.9031} \qquad (1)$$
$$32 \div 8 \approx 10^{1.5051} \div 10^{0.9031} \qquad (2)$$

We proceed by adding the powers in (1) and subtracting them in (2), i.e.

$$32 \times 8 \approx 10^{2.4082} \quad \text{or} \quad 255.98$$
$$32 \div 8 \approx 10^{0.6020} \quad \text{or} \quad 3.9994$$

The final answers (obtained from inverse log 2.4082 and inverse log 0.6020) are not exact. If the logarithms are taken to 4 decimal places then our answers should be corrected to 4 figures, i.e. 256.0 and 3.999. The error in the second answer should serve to remind the student of the limitations of any approximate method of calculation. (Greater accuracy can of course be achieved if further decimal places are considered for the logarithms.)

When calculations such as these are performed using logarithms it is customary to write down the logarithms only rather than the full method in powers of 10. Thus a multiplication such as 15.37×6.951 could be set out as follows:

	log
15.37	1.1867
6.951	0.8420

add logs   2.0287   Answer: 106.8

In this way difficult multiplications and divisions can be replaced by the far quicker operations of addition and subtraction of logarithms. Although the electronic calculator has now rendered such use of logarithms rather superfluous, they remain of great importance in mathematical theory and in the solution of a great number of physical problems.

Exercise 12(a)

1. Use a calculator to write each of the following numbers as a power of 10. (Give each power correct to 4 decimal places.)
   (i) 37, 214.6, 4.93, 5247, 1.83, 99.74
   (ii) 0.84, 0.0521, 0.00087, 0.1071, $\frac{1}{4}$, $\frac{1}{50}$

2. Convert the following powers of 10 back to ordinary numbers:
   (i) $10^{1.7}$, $10^{2.541}$, $10^{0.692}$, $10^{5.125}$, $10^{0.08}$
   (ii) $10^{-2.1}$, $10^{-1.07}$, $10^{-0.723}$, $10^{-0.003}$, $10^{-4.69}$

3. Find the logarithms of the following numbers:
   (i) 5.23, 52.3, 523, 5230
   (ii) 3.47, 347, 34700, 3470000
   (iii) 15.85, 1.585, 0.1585, 0.01585

4. Use logarithms to perform the following calculations and hence check the accuracy of the method:
   (i) 25×8 (ii) 1.6×200 (iii) $180 \div 6$
   (iv) $4800 \div 120$ (v) $(30)^2$ (vi) $(6)^3$

5. Proceed as for question 4, but be careful with negative logarithms.
   (i) 36×0.5 (ii) $2.4 \div 0.03$ (iii) 0.06×0.12
   (iv) $0.9 \div 0.15$ (v) $(0.4)^2$ (vi) $(0.5)^3$

*6. Use logarithms to find the values of
   (i) $(49.7)^2$ (ii) $(0.984)^4$ (iii) $\sqrt{63.8}$ (iv) $\sqrt[3]{63.8}$
   (v) $\sqrt[3]{1753}$ (vi) $\sqrt[4]{1000}$ (vii) $\sqrt[6]{0.347}$ (viii) $\sqrt[10]{85.9}$

12.2 Logarithms to other bases

Common logarithms are based on powers of 10. In the previous section we saw how the simple calculations 32×8 and $32 \div 8$ could be effected in powers of 10. But there is no reason why we should not use powers of some other number. For example these same calculations could also be performed very simply in powers of 2

$$32 \times 8 = 2^5 \times 2^3 = 2^8 = 256$$
$$32 \div 8 = 2^5 \div 2^3 = 2^2 = 4$$

In lines (1) and (2) of Section 12.1 the logarithms of 32 and 8 are 1.5051 and 0.9031 (i.e. the indices when the numbers are written as powers of 10). Here, where we are using powers of 2, the logarithms of 32 and 8 are 5 and 3 respectively but these are said to be **logarithms to base 2**. 'Common' logarithms are **logarithms to base 10**. In fact any base number may be used. Another important class of logarithms are **natural** or **Napierian logarithms**: these are logarithms to the base e (approximately 2.7183 – see Chapter 18).

Definition

The logarithm of a number n to base a is the index when the number n is expressed as a power of the base a, i.e.

if $n = a^x$ then $\log_a n = x$

Note: $\log_a n$ means the logarithm of n to base a. If no base is specified then the logarithm may be taken as a common logarithm, i.e. base 10.

Example   75

Find the logarithms to base 5 of each of the following numbers:

(i) 125   (ii) $\sqrt{5}$ (iii) $\dfrac{1}{25}$ (iv) 0.2

In order to find the logarithms we must write each number as a power of 5

(i) $125 = 5^3$ so $\log_5 125 = 3$

(ii) $\sqrt{5} = 5^{\frac{1}{2}}$ so $\log_5 \sqrt{5} = \frac{1}{2}$

(iii) $\dfrac{1}{25} = 5^{-2}$ so $\log_5 \dfrac{1}{25} = -2$

(iv) $0.2 = \dfrac{1}{5}$ or 5^{-1} so $\log_5 0.2 = -1$

Exercise 12(b)

1. Express the following numbers as powers of 2 and hence obtain their logarithms to base 2
    (i) 16   (ii) 64   (iii) $\frac{1}{4}$ (iv) $\sqrt{2}$ (v) 0.125
2. Find the logarithms to base 4 of the numbers in question 1.
3. Find the logarithms to base 3 of
    (i) 27   (ii) 243   (iii) 1   (iv) $\frac{1}{81}$ (v) $3\sqrt{3}$
4. Find the values of
    (i) $\log_8 64$ (ii) $\log_6 216$ (iii) $\log_5 625$
    (iv) $\log_2 128$ (v) $\log_4 \frac{1}{64}$ (vi) $\log_{0.1} (0.01)$
    (vii) $\log_9 3$ (viii) $\log_4 \frac{1}{2}$ (ix) $\log_{27} 9$
5. Write down the values of
    (i) $\log_4 16$ and $\log_{16} 4$
    (ii) $\log_2 8$ and $\log_8 2$
    (iii) $\log_{100} 1000$ and $\log_{1000} 100$
    What do you notice?
6. Find, in each case, the value of x
    (i) $\log_x 512 = 3$ (ii) $\log_3 x = -2$ (iii) $\log_x 7 = \frac{1}{2}$
    (iv) $\log_7 343 = x$ (v) $\log_4 x = 2.5$ (vi) $\log_x 4 = 4$
    (vii) $\log_8 x = \frac{2}{3}$ (viii) $\log_{\frac{1}{2}} 16 = x$ (ix) $\log_x 256 = x$
7. If $\log_4 x = z$ prove that $\log_2 x = 2z$. Hence find x if $\log_2 x + \log_4 x = 6$.
8. (i)   If $a = \log_3 25$ and $b = \log_9 5$ write down the values of 3^a and 9^b and show that $a = 4b$.
    (ii) Write down also the values of 9^a, $3^{\frac{1}{2}a}$, 3^b.

12.3 The laws of logarithms

The following laws are of use in the simplification of expressions involving logarithms. They are valid for any base a.

$$\log_a m + \log_a n = \log_a (mn) \tag{1}$$
$$\log_a m - \log_a n = \log_a (m/n) \tag{2}$$
$$n \log_a m = \log_a (m^n) \tag{3}$$

These laws are less complicated than they appear. To remember law (1), for example, it is only necessary to ask oneself under what circumstances two logarithms are added together. Clearly this is when we wish to multiply the two numbers concerned so that the result is the logarithm of the product, e.g.

$$\log 5 + \log 3 = \log 15$$
$$\log 8 + \log 7 = \log 56$$

in general $\log m + \log n = \log (mn)$.

Similarly if $\log m$ and $\log n$ are subtracted then we must be dividing the numbers m and n so that the result is the logarithm of (m/n), i.e. law (2). If $\log m$ is multiplied by n then we are raising the number m to power n so the result is $\log (m^n)$, i.e. law (3), e.g.

$$3 \log 5 = \log(5^3) = \log 125$$
$$4 \log 2 = \log(2^4) = \log 16$$

Whenever three numbers are connected by a multiplicative relation then there exists a corresponding relation between their logarithms, e.g.

(i) the relation $a = bc$

$\Rightarrow$ logarithmic relation $\log a = \log b + \log c$

(ii) the relation $p = qr^2$

$\Rightarrow$ logarithmic relation $\log p = \log q + \log r^2$
$$= \log q + 2 \log r$$

Example   76

Simplify (i) $\log 27 + \log 9$ (ii) $\log 27 - \log 9$
(iii) $3 \log 2 + \frac{1}{2} \log 9$ (iv) $1 + \log 9$

(i) Here we are multiplying 27 and 9. The result is $\log 243$.
(ii) We are dividing 27 by 9. The result is $\log 3$.
(iii) We would multiply $\log 2$ by 3 when using logarithms to find 2^3, and take one half of $\log 9$ when finding the square root of 9. Hence

$$3 \log 2 + \frac{1}{2} \log 9 = \log 8 + \log 3 = \log 24$$

(iv) As a general rule one should avoid expressions which contain both logarithms and plain numbers. Here we convert the number 1 into a logarithm. Since no base is specified we take the logarithms to be common logarithms (i.e. base 10) so that $1 = \log 10$. We then have

$$1 + \log 9 = \log 10 + \log 9 = \log 90$$

Example   77

Given $\log 2 = 0.3010$ and $\log 3 = 0.4771$ find the logarithms of 18, 27, $33\frac{1}{3}$, $2\frac{1}{4}$, 15.

In this question we find means by which the numbers given may be generated by multiplying or dividing the numbers 2 and 3. The logarithms are then found from the corresponding logarithmic relations.

(i) $18 = 2 \times 3^2$
$$\begin{aligned} \Rightarrow \log 18 &= \log 2 + \log 3^2 \\ &= \log 2 + 2\log 3 \\ &= 0.3010 + 0.9542 \\ &= \underline{1.2552} \end{aligned}$$

(ii) $27 = 3^3$
$$\begin{aligned} \Rightarrow \log 27 &= 3\log 3 \\ &= \underline{1.4313} \end{aligned}$$

(iii) $33\frac{1}{3} = 100 \div 3$
$$\begin{aligned} \Rightarrow \log 33\frac{1}{3} &= \log 100 - \log 3 \\ &= 2 - 0.4771 \\ &= \underline{1.5229} \end{aligned}$$

(iv) $2\frac{1}{4} = 3^2 \div 2^2$
$$\begin{aligned} \Rightarrow \log 2\frac{1}{4} &= 2.\log 3 - 2.\log 2 \\ &= 0.9542 - 0.6020 \\ &= \underline{0.3522} \end{aligned}$$

(v) $15 = \dfrac{10 \times 3}{2}$
$$\begin{aligned} \Rightarrow \log 15 &= \log 10 + \log 3 - \log 2 \\ &= 1 + 0.4771 - 0.3010 \\ &= \underline{1.1761} \end{aligned}$$

Notice that powers of 10 may also be used, as in parts (iii) and (v).

Exercise 12(c)

Logarithms are to base 10 unless otherwise stated.

1. Express as single logarithms
   - (i) $\log 5 + \log 6$
   - (ii) $2\log 3 + \log 4$
   - (iii) $\log 40 - \log 8$
   - (iv) $2\log 8 - \log 16$
   - (v) $\frac{1}{2}\log 64$
   - (vi) $\log 3 + 2\log 4 - \log 6$
   - (vii) $1 + \frac{1}{2}\log 4$
   - (viii) $\frac{1}{3}(\log 40 - \log 5)$

2. Express in terms of $\log a$, $\log b$ and $\log c$
   - (i) $\log abc$
   - (ii) $\log \dfrac{ab}{c}$
   - (iii) $\log \sqrt[3]{a}$
   - (iv) $\log ab^3$
   - (v) $\log \sqrt{\dfrac{b}{c}}$
   - (vi) $\log \dfrac{1}{c}$

3. Express as single logarithms
   - (i) $\log_2 3 + \log_2 7$
   - (ii) $3\log_5 4 - \log_5 8$
   - (iii) $2(\log 12 - \log 3)$
   - (iv) $\frac{1}{3}\log_2 125$
   - (v) $\log 6 + \log 8 - 2\log 4$
   - (vi) $\log_3 5 + \log_3 6 - 1$
   - (vii) $2 - \log_{10} 50$
   - (viii) $\frac{1}{2}(\log 2 + \log 8 + \log 9)$

4. For each of the following write down the corresponding relation between $\log a$, $\log b$ and $\log c$:
   - (i) $a = b^3$
   - (ii) $a = \dfrac{b^2}{c}$
   - (iii) $abc = 1$
   - (iv) $a = \sqrt{bc}$
   - (v) $a = \dfrac{1}{b}$
   - (vi) $a = b^c$

5. Given $\log 3 = 0.4771$ and $\log 5 = 0.6990$, find the logarithms of 15, 25, 45, 75, 7.5, $\frac{1}{3}$, 0.6, 1.8.

6. Given $\log 2 = 0.30103$, write down $\log 4$, $\log 8$ and $\log 20$. Find also $\log 5$ and hence obtain the logarithms of 25, 2.5, 1.25 and 1.6.

7. Simplify
    (i) $\log_5 75 - \log_5 3$ (ii) $2\log_3 6 - \log_3 4$
    (iii) $\frac{1}{2}\log_{10} 25 + \frac{1}{4}\log_{10} 16$ (iv) $\log 125 - 3\log 5$
    (v) $\log (x^2 - 1) - \log (x + 1)$ (vi) $\log a^3 - \log a^2 + \log a$
    (vii) $\log pq + \log \dfrac{p}{q} - 2\log p$ (viii) $\dfrac{\log 32}{\log 4}$

8. If $\log_2 a = b$, find the values of
    (i) $\log_2 a^2$ (ii) $\log_2 2a$ (iii) $\log_2 \sqrt{a}$ (iv) $\log_2 \left(\dfrac{4}{a^2}\right)$

9. Given $\log 4 = 0.602$, write down $\log 2$, $\log 16$ and $\log 32$. Find also $\log 25$ and hence obtain $\log 5$, $\log 125$ and $\log 80$.

*10. Solve the pairs of simultaneous equations
    (i) $\log_2 x + \log_2 y = 3$ and $\log_x y = 2$
    (ii) $2\log_3 x - \log_3 y = 3$ and $\log_3 (x - 3y + 1) = 1$

11. Given $\log 2 = 0.3010$ and $\log 3 = 0.4771$, find $\log(\tan 60°)$, $\log(\cos 30°)$, $\log(\cos 60°)$, $\log(\sin 45°)$.

12. Prove that $\displaystyle\sum_{r=1}^{n} \log x^r = \frac{1}{2}n(n+1)\log x$.

12.4 Compound interest and mortgages

We shall consider first the case where interest is charged to the account annually and none of the **principal** (i.e. the total sum due for repayment) is repaid. Let the original sum borrowed be P and the rate of interest $R\%$ per annum. Then

principal due after 1 yr $P_1 \quad = P + \dfrac{R}{100}\cdot P \;= P\left(1 + \dfrac{R}{100}\right)$

principal due after 2 yrs $P_2 \;= P_1 + \dfrac{R}{100}\cdot P_1 = P\left(1 + \dfrac{R}{100}\right)^2$

principal due after 3 yrs $P_3 \;= P_2 + \dfrac{R}{100}\cdot P_2 = P\left(1 + \dfrac{R}{100}\right)^3$

Thus the principal due after n yrs is given by

$$P_n = P\left(1 + \dfrac{R}{100}\right)^n \tag{1}$$

This is sometimes called the 'Compound Interest Formula'. The money due increases annually in geometric progression. If the rate of interest is 12% p.a., for example, the principal increases by a factor of 1.12 each year so that for a loan of £5000 the money owing is

    $5000 \times 1.12 = £5600$ after 1 yr
    $5600 \times 1.12 = £6272$ after 2 yrs
    $6272 \times 1.12 = £7024.64$ after 3 yrs, etc.

After 10 years the value of this loan would be

$$5000 \times (1.12)^{10} \approx 5000 \times 3.106 \text{ or } \pounds15\,530.$$

This shows how rapidly the interest accumulates for if interest were paid on the original loan only (i.e. Simple Interest) then $\pounds600$ interest would be paid each year and the principal after 10 years would be $\pounds5000 + 10\,(\pounds600) = \pounds11\,000$.

Six-monthly interest

Consider a loan of $\pounds5000$ borrowed at 12 % p.a. with interest charged to the account six-monthly. After six months, interest is charged for half a year (i.e. 6 % or $\pounds300$). At the end of the first year interest is again charged at 6 % but on a principal of $\pounds5300$ (i.e. $\pounds318$). So the money due after 1 year is $\pounds5618$.

The principal after 10 years may be found using the Compound Interest formula if we substitute $n = 20$ and $R = 6$ since there are 20 payments of 6 %, i.e.

$$5000(1.06)^{20} \approx 5000 \times 3.207 \text{ or } \pounds16\,035$$

Example   78

After how many years will a deposit double in value if interest is added annually at 8 %?

If the original deposit is P and it has doubled in value to $2P$ after n years then the formula (1) gives

$$2P = P\left(1 + \frac{R}{100}\right)^n = P(1.08)^n$$
$$\Rightarrow (1.08)^n = 2$$

The value of n can be found by taking logarithms on both sides

$$n\log 1.08 = \log 2$$

$$n = \frac{\log 2}{\log 1.08} = \frac{0.3010}{0.0334} \approx 9.01$$

The deposit will almost have doubled in value after 9 years. The implication of the answer of 9.01 is that just over 9 years would be needed but since interest will not be paid until the end of the year the answer should, strictly speaking, be 10 years.

Repayment loan (or mortgage)

Normally when a loan is made the borrower undertakes to repay the loan by making a fixed monthly (or annual) repayment over the period or 'term' of the loan. For example, a man obtaining a mortgage of $\pounds8000$ at 11 % p.a. interest may be required to repay about $\pounds1005$ annually (i.e. approximately $\pounds83.75$ per month) over a 20 year term. Notice that to clear the loan he will have to repay over $\pounds20\,000$. How is the annual repayment calculated and why does the total repayment seem so large?

First we must understand how the account operates. At the end of each year the interest due for that year is added to the account and any repayment made during the year is subtracted. So for the example given we have

	Loan at start of year	+	Interest for year (11%)	− Repayment =	Loan at end of year
1st Year	8000	+	880	− 1005 =	7875
2nd Year	7875	+	866.25	− 1005 =	7736.25
3rd Year	7736.25	+	850.99	− 1005 =	7582.24

And so on. It is interesting to observe that after 3 years little more than £400 has been repaid although the total payment is over £3000! This is because in the first few years the repayment does little more than cover the interest due. The amount of interest paid decreases slightly each year so that a progressively greater part of the annual repayment goes towards repaying the loan itself. The bulk of the repayment is made over the last few years when the interest due is low.

The calculation of the correct annual repayment is an interesting problem on series. Let P be the principal and A the annual repayment. Then the amount of the loan outstanding is

after 1 yr. $P\left(1+\dfrac{R}{100}\right)-A \qquad = Pr - A \qquad$ where $r=\left(1+\dfrac{R}{100}\right)$

after 2 yrs. $(Pr-A)r-A \qquad = Pr^2 - Ar - A$

after 3 yrs. $(Pr^2-Ar-A)r-A \ = Pr^3 - Ar^2 - Ar - A$

after n yrs. $Pr^n - (Ar^{n-1} + Ar^{n-2} + \ldots + Ar^2 + Ar + A)$

If the loan is exactly repaid after n years then this expression must equal zero, i.e.

i.e. $\quad A + Ar + Ar^2 + \ldots + Ar^{n-1} = Pr^n$

$\Rightarrow \dfrac{A(r^n-1)}{r-1} = Pr^n \qquad$ (using the sum of a G.P.)

$A = \dfrac{r^n}{r^n-1} \cdot P(r-1)$

or $\qquad \boxed{A = \dfrac{r^n}{r^n-1} \cdot \dfrac{P \cdot R}{100} \qquad \text{where} \quad r=\left(1+\dfrac{R}{100}\right)}$

For the example quoted, i.e. a 20 year mortgage of £8000 at 11% p.a. we have $P = 8000$, $n = 20$ and $R = 11$ (so that $r = 1.11$)

$$A = \frac{(1.11)^{20}}{(1.11)^{20}-1} \cdot 880 \approx \frac{8.062}{7.062} \times 880 \approx 1005$$

In the formula deduced above, the quantity $\dfrac{PR}{100}$ may be interpreted as the first year's interest (i.e. £880) and the factor $r^n/(r^n-1)$ converts this into the annual repayment.

Exercise 12(d)

1. A man borrows £2500 at 10% p.a. compound interest. If no money is repaid, find the amount he owes at the end of (i) 1 year (ii) 2 years (iii) 3 years (iv) 4 years.
2. £1200 is deposited in a savings account which credits interest annually at 9%. Use a calculator to find the value of the deposit to the nearest pound after (i) 3 years (ii) 6 years (iii) 10 years.
3. After how many years will the deposit of question 2 first exceed £4000?
4. An old man remembers that 60 years previously he had been given a £5 post office savings bond by a relative. If this bond accumulates interest at 5% p.a. how much is it now worth?
5. Compare the amounts owing after 8 years on a loan of £2000 if interest is charged
   (i) annually at $12\frac{1}{4}$% p.a.
   (ii) six-monthly at 12% p.a.
   (Give answers to the nearest pound.)
6. A man has £600 in a building society account which pays interest six-monthly at 8% p.a. How much are these savings worth after 3 years? If the rate of interest is then increased to 9% p.a., what is their value after a further 2 years?
7. A man owes £1500 and interest is added yearly at 16% p.a. After how many years will his debt reach (i) £4000 (ii) £6000, if no repayment is made?
8. A man obtains a £12000 mortgage from a building society which charges interest annually at 10% p.a. His total annual repayment is fixed at £1410. How much does he owe the building society after (i) 1 year (ii) 2 years (iii) 3 years? (iv) The term of the mortgage is 20 years. After 5 years he sells his house and, reckoning that he should have repaid one quarter of the loan in this time, he expects to repay £9000 to the building society from the proceeds of the sale. How much does he owe (to the nearest pound)?
9. Calculate the total annual repayment on each of the following mortgages:
   (i) £6000 at 8% for 20 years
   (ii) £6000 at 12% for 20 years
   (iii) £6000 at 12% for 25 years.
   (Give answers to the nearest pound.)
10. (i) A certain savings scheme offers the advantageous rate of R% p.a. to savers who contract to pay an amount A into the scheme at the beginning of each year for a minimum of n years. If interest is credited at the end of each year, prove that the total value of savings and interest after n years is $Ar(r^n-1)/(r-1)$ where $r=\left(1+\dfrac{R}{100}\right)$.
    (ii) A man contracts to save £300 a year for 5 years on such a scheme. If the rate of interest is 14% per annum, how much will his £1500 savings be worth at the end of the 5 years?

12.5 Change of base

Example 79

Using a table of logarithms to base 10, calculate $\log_4 9$.

The required logarithm tells us what power of the base 4 gives the number 9. Suppose $4^x = 9$: then we require x. Taking logarithms to base 10 we have

$$x \log_{10} 4 = \log_{10} 9$$
$$\Rightarrow x = \frac{\log_{10} 9}{\log_{10} 4} \approx \frac{0.9542}{0.6021} \quad \text{or} \quad 1.585$$

i.e. $\log_4 9 \approx 1.585$

Note: Any logarithm may be found by this method. We see from the above example that

$$\log_4 9 = \frac{\log_{10} 9}{\log_{10} 4}$$

In the same way

$$\log_3 7 = \frac{\log_{10} 7}{\log_{10} 3}, \quad \text{i.e.} \quad \frac{\log \text{ of number}}{\log \text{ of base}}$$

General case

Suppose we know logarithms to base a and we require logarithms to a different base z. Consider the logarithm of a particular number N to base z. This tells us what power of z gives the number N, i.e.

if $z^x = N$ then $\log_z N = x$

taking logarithms to base a

$$x \log_a z = \log_a N$$

$$\Rightarrow \log_z N = \frac{\log_a N}{\log_a z}$$

This result can be rather confusing to remember and is best derived from first principals, as above, if required. An interesting special case is obtained when $a = N$ so that $\log_a N = 1$. We then have

$$\log_z a = \frac{1}{\log_a z}$$

So that if we wish to interchange the number and the base we take the reciprocal of the logarithm, for example

$$\log_2 8 = 3 \quad \Rightarrow \log_8 2 = \frac{1}{3}$$

$$\log_4 9 \approx 1.585 \quad \Rightarrow \log_9 4 \approx \frac{1}{1.585} \quad \text{or} \quad 0.631$$

Exercise 12(e)

1. Find the value of x correct to 3 significant figures when
   (i) $5^x = 8$ (ii) $(2.7)^x = 14.2$ (iii) $7^x = 10$ (iv) $3^{x+1} = 2^{x-1}$
*2. Solve the following equations:
   (i) $2(2^{2x}) - 9(2^x) + 4 = 0$ (Hint: let $2^x = y$.)
   (ii) $10^{2x} + 10^x = 20$
   (iii) $3^{2x} - 3^{x+1} + 2 = 0$
3. Find, correct to 3 decimal places, the values of
   (i) $\log_2 7$ (ii) $\log_8 27$ (iii) $\log_{12} (5.6)$ (iv) $\log_5 (3.7)^2$
4. Write down the values of $\log_5 125$, $\log_{\sqrt{2}} 4$, $\log_a a^2$.

   Hence write down also $\log_{125} 5$, $\log_4 \sqrt{2}$, $\log_{a^2} a$.
5. Given $\log_{10} 5 = 0.6990$, find $\log_5 10$ to 3 significant figures. Hence find $\log_5 2$ and $\log_2 5$.
*6. Solve the equation $2 \log_2 x + \log_x 2 = 3$.
7. Given $\log_{10} 4 = 0.6021$, find $\log_4 10$ to 3 significant figures. Find also $\log_{10} 2$, $\log_2 10$, $\log_8 10$ and $\log_8 100$.
8. Given that $\log_{10} e = 0.4343$, solve the equation $\log_{10} x + \log_e x = 1$.
9. Given that $\log_a x = y$ and $\log_x b = z$, find $\log_a b$.

10. If $\log_a x = r$ and $\log_b x = s$, prove that $\log_a b = \dfrac{r}{s}$. Find also $\log_x (ab)$ and hence $\log_{ab} x$.

12.6 Further linear laws

In Section 2.2 we saw how a linear relationship between two variables may be demonstrated graphically. The method may be applied to relationships of the form $y = ab^x$ (a, b constants) and $y = cx^n$ (c, n constants). In order to reduce these equations to a linear form it is necessary to use logarithms.

(i) $y = ab^x \Rightarrow \log y = \log a + \log (b^x)$
     $\log y = \log a + x \log b$

A graph of $\log y$ against x should therefore be linear with gradient $(\log b)$ and y intercept $(\log a)$.

(ii) $y = cx^n \Rightarrow \log y = \log c + \log (x^n)$
     $\log y = \log c + n \log x$

Here a graph of $\log y$ against $\log x$ should be used. This will have gradient n and y intercept $(\log c)$.

In both cases logarithms to any base may be used but common logarithms will be the usual choice.

Exercise 12(f)

1. Variables x and y are thought to be related by a law of the form $y = ax^n$. Using the following experimental values, plot a suitable graph and determine the values of the constants a and n.

x	2	5	8	12	16
y	11.3	44.7	90.5	166.3	256.0

2. The strength of an electric field (H units) is measured at various distances (r units) from the centre of the field O. The following results are obtained:

H	75.0	18.8	8.3	3.0	1.3
r	2	4	6	10	15

Obtain graphically a law of the form $H = kr^n$.

3. The following experimental results are obtained for two variables x and y:

x	1	3	5	8	10	13
y	6	8.6	12.4	21.5	31.0	53.5

By drawing a suitable graph obtain an approximate law of the form $y = ab^x$.

4. In a chemical reaction the mass (m gm) of a certain reagent which remains at time t mins after the start of the reaction is found to be as follows:

t	5	10	12	15	20	25
m	164	54	34	17.6	5.8	1.9

Use a graphical method to find a relation of the form $m = Ab^t$ where A and b are constants.

5. The following data shows the orbital periods P (in days) of certain planets and their distances d (in millions of km) from the sun

	Mercury	Venus	Earth	Mars	Jupiter
Period P	88.0	224.7	365.3	687.0	4333
distance d	58	108	150	228	778

Obtain a law of the form $P = kd^n$ where k and n are constants. Use your result to estimate the distance of the planet Saturn from the sun, given that its period is 10 760 days:

6. Show that the following values satisfy an approximate relation of the form $A = k(1 + x)^n$ and find values for the constants k and n.

A	0.3	5.0	21	70	135
x	1	4	7	11	14

13

Further Trigonometry

13.1 The function *a* sin *x* + *b* cos *x* (graphical)

Example 80

Draw the graph of $2 \sin x + 3 \cos x$ for $0° \leqslant x \leqslant 360°$.
Hence (i) find the maximum and minimum values of the function
(ii) solve the equation $2 \sin x + 3 \cos x = 1$.

It is convenient to consider values of the angle x in steps of $30°$ since the sines and cosines of these angles are well known (e.g. $\sin 30° = \frac{1}{2}$, $\cos 30° = \sqrt{3}/2 \approx 0.866$). The table of values, part of which is shown below, is easily completed column by column (e.g. the values of $\sin x$ are entered by increasing to a value of 1 at $90°$, then running back through the same values to 0 at $180°$, then continuing to -1 at $270°$, and so on). The values shown for $2 \sin x$ and for $3 \cos x$ have been corrected to 2 decimal places.

Angle $x°$	$\sin x$	$\cos x$	$2 \sin x$	$3 \cos x$	$2 \sin x + 3 \cos x$
0	0	1	0	3	3
30	0.5	0.866	1	2.60	3.60
60	0.866	0.5	1.73	1.5	3.23
90	1	0	2	0	2
120	0.866	−0.5	1.73	−1.5	0.23
150	0.5	−0.866	1	−2.60	−1.60
180	0	−1	0	−3	−3
210	−0.5	−0.866	−1	−2.60	−3.60
240	−0.866	−0.5	−1.73	−1.5	−3.23
etc.					

When these values are plotted the graph of Fig. 1 is obtained. From the graph we see that
(i) the maximum value of the function is approximately <u>3.6</u> the minimum value of the function is approximately <u>− 3.6</u>
(ii) the function takes the value 1 when the angle x is approximately 108 or 109° and again at 320°,
i.e. solutions of $2 \sin x + 3 \cos x = 1$ are $x \approx 108°, \quad 320°$

Note: The most important feature of this graph is its shape. We have seen in Chapter 4 that the graphs of both $\sin x$ and $\cos x$ have a characteristic wave shape which is periodic over intervals of $360°$. This graph demonstrates the

$2 \sin x + 3 \cos x$

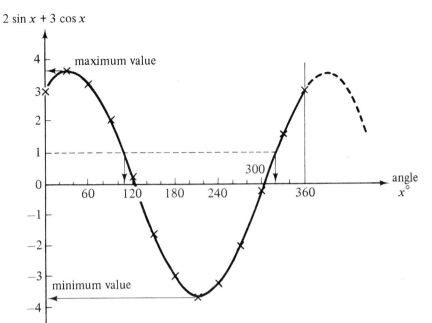

Fig. 1

rather surprising fact that a linear combination of these functions (i.e. $a \sin x + b \cos x$ where a and b are constants) has the same wave form, again periodic over 360°. The values of the function, however, do not vary between 1 and -1 (as do those of $\sin x$ and $\cos x$) but, in this case, between 3.6 and -3.6.

Exercise 13(a)

1. Draw the graph of the function $3 \cos x - \sin x$ for $0 \leqslant x \leqslant 360°$.
   (i) State the maximum and minimum values of the function.
   (ii) Solve the equation $3 \cos x - \sin x = 2$.
2. Draw the graph of the function $\sin x - \cos x$ for $0 \leqslant x \leqslant 360°$.
   (i) State the maximum and minimum values of the function.
   (ii) Solve the equation $\sin x - \cos x = -0.6$.

13.2 The function $a \sin x + b \cos x$ (theoretical)

We now show that functions of the form $a \sin x + b \cos x$ (a, b constants) are of wave form and that their characteristics may be determined theoretically.

The function $R \sin (x + \alpha)$

We begin by considering the functions illustrated in Figs. 2a and 2b. The function $2 \sin x$ clearly has the basic sine wave shape but varies between $+2$

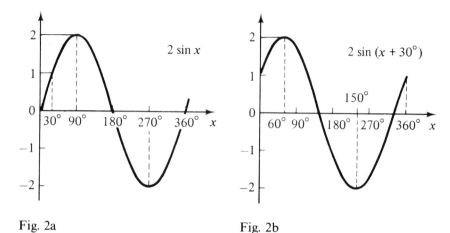

Fig. 2a   Fig. 2b

and -2 (Fig. 2a). Fig. 2b shows an example of the type of function we shall be concerned with shortly. This function, $2 \sin (x + 30°)$, has a very similar graph to $2 \sin x$ except that at $x = 0$ we plot the value $2 \sin 30° = 1$, at $x = 30°$ we plot $2 \sin 60°$ (≈ 1.73) and at $x = 60°$ we plot the first peak value of $2 \sin 90° = 2$. In effect, then, the graph shows the same wave shape as $2 \sin x$ but is shifted by $30°$ on the horizontal axis.

The most general function of this form may be written $R \sin (x + \alpha)$ where R is a constant number and α is a constant angle. All functions of this form exhibit the basic wave shape. So too do functions of the forms $R \sin (x - \alpha)$ and $R \cos (x + \alpha)$, $R \cos (x - \alpha)$.

These functions, however, are easily shown to be equivalent to linear combinations of $\sin x$ and $\cos x$. This is done by using the compound angle formulae (Chapter 10). For example

$$R \sin (x + \alpha) = R (\sin x \cos \alpha + \cos x \sin \alpha)$$
$$= (R \cos \alpha) \sin x + (R \sin \alpha) \cos x$$

i.e. the function is of the form $a \sin x + b \cos x$ since $R \cos \alpha$ and $R \sin \alpha$ are constants.

Transformation to 'wave form'

We now demonstrate a method by which any function of the form $a \sin x + b \cos x$ may be transformed into **wave form**, i.e. into one of the forms $R \sin (x \pm \alpha)$ or $R \cos (x \pm \alpha)$.

Consider first the function $2 \sin x + 3 \cos x$ whose graph was drawn in Example 80. This function may be written in the form $R \sin (x + \alpha)$ by the method which follows.

If $2 \sin x + 3 \cos x = R \sin (x + \alpha)$

$$= R (\sin x \cos \alpha + \cos x \sin \alpha)$$
$$= (R \cos \alpha) \sin x + (R \sin \alpha) \cos x$$

then $R \cos \alpha = 2$ and $R \sin \alpha = 3$

We now draw a triangle with hypotenuse R to contain an angle α (Fig. 3) and mark on the values of $R\cos\alpha$ (adjacent side) and $R\sin\alpha$ (opposite side). From this triangle we see that

$$R^2 = 3^2 + 2^2 \Rightarrow R = \sqrt{13}$$

$$\tan\alpha = \frac{3}{2} \qquad \Rightarrow \alpha \approx 56.3°$$

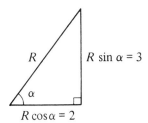

$R\sin\alpha = 3$

$R\cos\alpha = 2$

Fig. 3

Thus $2\sin x + 3\cos x \equiv \sqrt{13}\sin(x + 56.3°)$

The function therefore has sine wave shape and takes values between $\pm\sqrt{13}$ ($\approx \pm 3.606$). The maximum value $+\sqrt{13}$ occurs when $\sin(x + 56.3°) = 1$ which is when the angle $(x + 56.3°) = 90°$, i.e. $x = 33.7°$. Similarly the minimum value occurs when $(x + 56.3°) = 270° \Rightarrow x = 213.7°$. All of these details agree with the graph of Fig. 1.

Choice of wave form

Consider the function $3\cos x - \sin x$ of Exercise 13(a), question 1. If we are to transform this to wave form then we must pick one of the cosine forms, i.e. $R\cos(x \pm \alpha)$, since these give $\cos x$ in the first term. But to obtain the minus sign between the terms our choice is restricted to $R\cos(x + \alpha)$. The working is set out in the following example.

Example 81

Write $3\cos x - \sin x$ in the form $R\cos(x + \alpha)$ where R and α are constants. Hence determine the maximum and minimum values of the function and the values of x for which these occur ($0 \leqslant x \leqslant 360°$).

Let $3\cos x - \sin x = R\cos(x + \alpha)$

$$= R(\cos x \cos\alpha - \sin x \sin\alpha)$$

$$= (R\cos\alpha)\cos x - (R\sin\alpha)\sin x$$

then $R\cos\alpha = 3$ and $R\sin\alpha = 1$.

From Fig. 4 $R = \sqrt{10}$ and $\alpha = \arctan\frac{1}{3} \approx 18.4°$

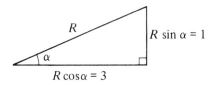

Fig. 4

Hence $3 \cos x - \sin x \equiv \sqrt{10} \cos (x + 18.4°)$

The maximum value is $+ \sqrt{10}$ when $x + 18.4° = 0°$ or $360° \Rightarrow x = 341.6°$

The minimum value is $- \sqrt{10}$ when $x + 18.4° = 180°$ $\Rightarrow x = 161.6°$

Exercise 13(b)

Give answers for x in the range of $0 \leqslant x \leqslant 360°$.

1. Write $\sin x - \cos x$ in the form $R \sin (x - \alpha)$. Hence determine the maximum and minimum values of the function and the values of x for which these occur. Check that your results agree with the graph of Exercise 13(a) question 2.
2. Write the following in the form $R \sin (x + \alpha)$. Hence find the value of x for which each function takes its maximum value and state this value
    (i) $2 \sin x + \cos x$ (ii) $4 \sin x + 3 \cos x$
3. Write the following in the form $R \cos (x + \alpha)$. Hence find the value of x for which each function takes its minimum value and state this value.
    (i) $4 \cos x - \sin x$ (ii) $\cos x - \sqrt{3} \sin x$
4. Write the function $2 \cos x + 5 \sin x$ in the form $R \cos (x - \alpha)$. Hence determine the values of x for which the function takes the value zero.
5. Show that if $a \sin x + b \cos x \equiv R \sin (x + \alpha)$ then $R = \sqrt{a^2 + b^2}$ and $\alpha = \arctan (b/a)$. State, without calculation, the maximum and minimum values of the following functions
    (i) $12 \sin x + 5 \cos x$ (ii) $\cos x + \sin x$
    (iii)· $\sqrt{5} \sin x - 2 \cos x$ (iv) $\cos x - 7 \sin x$

13.3 Equations of the form $a \sin x + b \cos x = c$

In Example 80 we solved the equation $2 \sin x + 3 \cos x = 1$ graphically. How can such an equation be solved by calculation? There are two methods in common use. For convenience these are often referred to as the '*R*-method' and the '*t*-method'.

The *R*-method

Consider the equation $2 \sin x + 3 \cos x = 1$. The method is based on the work of the previous section where we saw that the function $2 \sin x + 3 \cos x$ could be written in the form $R \sin (x + \alpha)$; in fact $\sqrt{13} \sin (x + 56.3°)$. We may therefore write the equation as

$$\sqrt{13} \sin (x + 56.3°) = 1$$

$$\Rightarrow \qquad \sin (x + 56.3°) = \frac{1}{\sqrt{13}} \approx 0.2774$$

Hence $\qquad x + 56.3° \approx 16.1°$ (or $376.1°$) or $163.9°$

$$x \approx \underline{319.8°} \quad \text{or} \quad \underline{107.6°}$$

Solutions are found initially for the angle $(x + 56.3°)$ whose sine is $1/\sqrt{13}$. The answers for x then follow by subtracting $56.3°$.

The complete procedure for solving an equation by the R-method is illustrated by the following example.

Example   82

Solve the equation $\cos x + 3 \sin x = 2$ for $0 \leqslant x \leqslant 360°$.

We choose to write the function $\cos x + 3 \sin x$ in the form $R \cos (x - \alpha)$. The equation will then be

$$R \cos (x - \alpha) = 2 \qquad\qquad (1)$$

or $\quad R (\cos x \cos \alpha + \sin x \sin \alpha) = 2$

$$(R \cos \alpha) \cos x + (R \sin \alpha) \sin x = 2$$

So we must have $R \sin \alpha = 3, \qquad R \cos \alpha = 1$

$$\Rightarrow R = \sqrt{10} \quad \text{and} \quad \alpha = \arctan(3) \approx 71.6°$$

Rewriting line (1) $\qquad \sqrt{10} \cos (x - 71.6°) = 2$

$$\Rightarrow \qquad \cos (x - 71.6°) = \frac{2}{\sqrt{10}} \approx 0.6325$$

$$x - 71.6° \approx 50.8° \quad \text{or} \quad 309.2°$$

$$x \approx 122.4° \quad \text{or} \quad 380.8°$$

In the range $0 \leqslant x \leqslant 360°$ $\qquad x \approx \underline{122.4°} \quad \text{or} \quad \underline{20.8°}$

The t-method

t stands for $\tan \frac{1}{2}x$ and the 't-method' is based on formulae, which we shall now derive, for $\sin x$ and $\cos x$ in terms of t (i.e. in terms of $\tan \frac{1}{2}x$).

We have, from Section 10.4,

$$\tan x = \frac{2 \tan \frac{1}{2}x}{1 - \tan^2 \frac{1}{2}x} = \frac{2t}{1 - t^2}$$

If we draw the triangle of Fig. 5 to represent the angle x then the length of the hypotenuse, h, is given by

$$h^2 = (1 - t^2)^2 + (2t)^2$$
$$= 1 - 2t^2 + t^4 + 4t^2$$
$$= 1 + 2t^2 + t^4 \quad \text{or} \quad (1 + t^2)^2$$

Thus $h = 1 + t^2$ and we may write

$$\sin x = \frac{2t}{1+t^2} \qquad \cos x = \frac{1-t^2}{1+t^2} \tag{2}$$

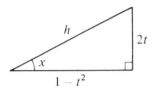

Fig. 5

Equations of the form $a \sin x + b \cos x = c$ may be solved by substituting these expressions for $\sin x$ and $\cos x$ and then solving first for t. We now repeat Example 82 by this method.

Example   83

Solve the equation $\cos x + 3 \sin x = 2$ for $0 \leqslant x \leqslant 360°$.

Substituting the results (2) we obtain

$$\frac{1-t^2}{1+t^2} + \frac{3(2t)}{1+t^2} = 2$$

$$\Rightarrow \quad 1 - t^2 + 6t = 2(1+t^2)$$

$$\Rightarrow \quad 0 = 3t^2 - 6t + 1$$

This quadratic equation is solved by the formula

$$t = \frac{6 \pm \sqrt{36-12}}{6} \approx \frac{6 \pm 4.899}{6}$$

i.e. $\quad \tan \tfrac{1}{2}x \approx 1.8165 \quad$ or $\quad 0.1835$

$\qquad \tfrac{1}{2}x \approx 61.2° \quad$ or $\quad 10.4°$

$\quad \Rightarrow x \approx 122.4° \quad$ or $\quad 20.8°$

Note: If $0 \leqslant x \leqslant 360°$ then we need only consider solutions for $\tfrac{1}{2}x$ in the range $0 \leqslant \tfrac{1}{2}x \leqslant 180°$.

Summary

$$\tan x = \frac{2t}{1-t^2} \qquad \sin x = \frac{2t}{1+t^2} \qquad \cos x = \frac{1-t^2}{1+t^2}$$

$$\text{where } t = \tan \tfrac{1}{2}x$$

Exercise 13(c)

Give answers for x in the range $0 \leqslant x \leqslant 360°$.

1. Solve the equations of Exercise 13(a), questions 1(ii) and 2(ii). Check that your answers agree with these obtained graphically.

2. Solve the following equations by the *R*-method:
   (i) $3 \cos x + 4 \sin x = 2$ (ii) $2 \sin x + \sqrt{3} \cos x = 1$
   (iii) $7 \tan x + 2 \sec x = 1$ (iv) $\sin 2x = \sin x - \sin^2 x$
3. Solve by the *t*-method
   (i) $2 \cos x + 2 \sin x = 1$ (ii) $5 \sin x - 3 \cos x = 4$
   *(iii) $3 \sin x - 2 \cos x = 2$ (iv) $5 \sin 2x + 2 \cos 2x = 5$
4. (i) Solve the equation $5 \sin x + \cos x = 4$.
   (ii) State the range of values of x for which $5 \sin x + \cos x > 4$.
5. Find the range of values for which the function $3 \sin x - 4 \cos x$ exceeds one half of its maximum value.
6. Write the function $f(x) = \sqrt{3} \cos x + \sin x$ in the form $R \cos (x - \alpha)$. Hence determine the values of x for which
   (i) the maximum and minimum values of $f(x)$ occur.
   (ii) $f(x) = 0$.
   (iii) $f(x) = -1$.
   Sketch the function and state the values of x for which $-1 < f(x) < 0$.

13.4 The factor formulae

Expressions such as $\sin A + \sin B$ or $\cos A - \cos B$ which involve the sines or cosines of two *different* angles A and B are frequently encountered and it is often helpful to write such expressions as the **product** of factors (rather than leave them as the sum or difference of two separate terms). This may be achieved with the help of results which are known as the **factor formulae**.

The sum and difference of two sines

We consider first how the expressions $\sin A + \sin B$ and $\sin A - \sin B$ may be written in factors. If we can find angles X and Y such that $X + Y = $ angle A and $X - Y = $ angle B then we can use the compound angle formulae in the following way

$$\sin A = \sin (X + Y) = \sin X \cos Y + \cos X \sin Y \tag{1}$$
$$\sin B = \sin (X - Y) = \sin X \cos Y - \cos X \sin Y \tag{2}$$

Adding (1) and (2), $\sin A + \sin B = 2 \sin X \cos Y$ (3)
Subtracting (1) & (2), $\sin A - \sin B = 2 \cos X \sin Y$ (4)

These results are in factors as required. All that remains to be done is to express X and Y in terms of the original angles A and B.

Since $\left. \begin{array}{l} X + Y = A \\ X - Y = B \end{array} \right\}$ we have $\begin{array}{l} 2X = A + B \\ 2Y = A - B \end{array}$ $\Rightarrow$ $\begin{array}{l} X = \frac{1}{2}(A + B) \\ Y = \frac{1}{2}(A - B) \end{array}$

So the results (3) and (4) may now be written as follows

$$\sin A + \sin B = 2 \sin \frac{A+B}{2} \cos \frac{A-B}{2}$$
$$\sin A - \sin B = 2 \cos \frac{A+B}{2} \sin \frac{A-B}{2}$$

These results are best remembered in words

Sum of two sines = Twice sine (half the sum) cos (half the difference)
Difference of two sines = Twice cos (half the sum) sine (half the difference)

The sum and difference of two cosines

The factor formulae for $\cos A + \cos B$ and $\cos A - \cos B$ may be obtained in an exactly similar way using the compound angle formulae for $\cos(X + Y)$ and $\cos(X - Y)$. This is left as an exercise for the reader. The results are

$$\cos A + \cos B = 2 \cos \frac{A+B}{2} \cos \frac{A-B}{2}$$

$$\cos A - \cos B = -2 \sin \frac{A+B}{2} \sin \frac{A-B}{2}$$

Sum of two cosines = Twice cos (half the sum) cos (half the difference)
Difference of two cosines = *Minus* twice sine (half the sum) sine (half the difference)

Notes: (i) In order that the angle $\frac{A-B}{2}$ (i.e. 'half the difference') may be positive it is usual to ensure that the first of the two angles, A, is larger than the second, B. See also Example 84 part (iii). (ii) It is important not to forget the minus sign in the result for the difference of two cosines. With first quadrant angles this arises because the larger angle, A, will have the smaller cosine.

Example 84

Factorize (i) $\sin 50° + \sin 20°$ (ii) $\cos 4\theta + \cos 2\theta$ (iii) $\sin \phi - \sin 2\phi$

(i) $\sin 50° + \sin 20° = 2 \sin \dfrac{50° + 20°}{2} \cos \dfrac{50° - 20°}{2} = \underline{2 \sin 35° \cos 15°}$

(ii) $\cos 4\theta + \cos 2\theta = 2 \cos \dfrac{4\theta + 2\theta}{2} \cos \dfrac{4\theta - 2\theta}{2} = \underline{2 \cos 3\theta \cos \theta}$

(iii) Here we change the order so that the larger angle is first.
$$\sin \phi - \sin 2\phi = -(\sin 2\phi - \sin \phi) = \underline{-2 \cos \tfrac{3}{2}\phi \sin \tfrac{1}{2}\phi}$$

Example 85

Prove that $\dfrac{\cos 3A - \cos 2A}{\sin 3A + \sin 2A} = -\tan \tfrac{1}{2} A.$

This proof is achieved by factorizing both the numerator and the denominator of the fraction

l.h.s. $\dfrac{\cos 3A - \cos 2A}{\sin 3A + \sin 2A} = \dfrac{-2 \sin \tfrac{5}{2}A \sin \tfrac{1}{2}A}{2 \sin \tfrac{5}{2}A \cos \tfrac{1}{2}A} = -\tan \tfrac{1}{2}A$ r.h.s.

Example   86

Solve the equation $\sin 5x - \sin x = 0$ giving all solutions in the range $0 \leqslant x \leqslant 180°$.

$$\sin 5x - \sin x = 0$$

Factorizing $\qquad 2 \cos 3x \sin 2x = 0$

It then follows that $\qquad \cos 3x = 0 \quad$ or $\quad \sin 2x = 0$

$\Rightarrow 3x = 90°, 270°, 450° \qquad$ or $\quad 2x = 0, 180°, 360°$

$\qquad x = 30°, \quad 90°, \; 150° \qquad\qquad\quad x = 0, \quad 90°, \; 180°$

So the solutions are: $0°, 30°, 90°, 150°, 180°$

Note: In order to find all solutions for x up to $180°$ it is necessary to find solutions for $3x$ up to $540°$ and for $2x$ up to $360°$.

Exercise   13(d)

1. Factorize
   (i) $\sin 30° + \sin 20°$ $\qquad$ (ii) $\cos 65° + \cos 25°$
   (iii) $\sin 4A - \sin 2A$ $\qquad$ (iv) $\cos 5A - \cos 3A$
   (v) $\cos 3B + \cos 2B$ $\qquad$ (vi) $\sin 2B - \sin 6B$
   (vii) $\sin 2\alpha + \sin 2\beta$ $\qquad$ (viii) $\cos (\alpha + \beta) + \cos (\alpha - \beta)$
2. (i) Factorize $\sin 60° - \sin 30°$ and hence find the exact value of $\sin 15°$.
   (ii) Factorize $\cos 60° + \cos 30°$ and hence find the exact value of $\cos 15°$.
3. Simplify the following fractions:
   (i) $\dfrac{\sin 3x + \sin x}{\sin 2x}$ $\qquad$ (ii) $\dfrac{\sin 2\theta - \sin \theta}{\cos 2\theta + \cos \theta}$
   (iii) $\dfrac{\sin A + \sin (A + B)}{\cos A - \cos (A + B)}$ $\qquad$ (iv) $\dfrac{\sin \frac{5}{2}\phi + \sin \frac{3}{2}\phi}{\cos \frac{3}{2}\phi + \cos \frac{1}{2}\phi}$
4. Factorize $\cos 3A + \cos A$ and hence prove that
   $$\cos 3A = 4 \cos^3 A - 3 \cos A.$$
5. Factorize $\sin 3A - \sin A$ and hence prove that
   $$\sin 3A = 3 \sin A - 4 \sin^3 A$$
6. Prove the identities
   (i) $\dfrac{\sin A + \sin B}{\cos A + \cos B} = \tan \frac{1}{2}(A + B)$

   (ii) $\dfrac{\cos \theta + \cos 3\theta}{\cos \theta - \cos 3\theta} = \cot 2\theta \cot \theta$
7. Solve the following equations for $0 \leqslant x \leqslant 180°$:
   (i) $\cos 4x + \cos 2x = 0$ $\qquad$ (ii) $\sin 5x = \sin 3x$
   (iii) $\cos \frac{5}{2}x - \cos \frac{x}{2} = 0$ $\qquad$ (iv) $\sin 3x + \sin x = \cos x$
8. (i) Show that $\sin x + \sin 2x + \sin 3x = \sin 2x (2 \cos x + 1)$ and hence solve the equation $\sin x + \sin 2x + \sin 3x = 0$.
   (ii) Solve the equation $\cos x + \cos 3x + \cos 5x = 0$ by a similar method. (Give answers in the range $0 \leqslant x \leqslant 180°$.)

9. Prove that

(i) $\dfrac{\sin 3x + \sin x}{1 + \cos 2x} = 2 \sin x$

(ii) $(\sin A + \sin B)(\sin A - \sin B) = \sin (A + B) \sin (A - B)$

10. (i) Factorize $\cos 4A + \cos 2A$ and hence prove that

$$\cos 4A = 8 \cos^4 A - 8 \cos^2 A + 1$$

(Use the result of question 4.)

(ii) Factorize $\cos 5A + \cos 3A$ and hence find a formula for $\cos 5A$ in terms of $\cos A$ only.

13.5 Radian measure

Definition

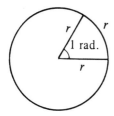

Fig. 6

In any circle **one radian** is the angle subtended at the centre by an arc equal in length to the radius (Fig. 6).

Comparison with an equilateral triangle indicates that 1 radian is slightly less than 60°. (In fact 57.3° – see below.)

Conversion of degrees to radians

Since the complete circumference of a circle is $2\pi r$, (i.e. $2\pi \times r$) it must subtend 2π radians at the centre, i.e.

$$360° \equiv 2\pi \text{ radians}$$

hence $\qquad 180° \equiv \pi \text{ radians}$

This is the result to remember when converting degrees to radians or vice-versa. For example

degrees to radians $\qquad 90° = \dfrac{\pi}{2} \text{ rad}$

$$60° = \dfrac{\pi}{3} \text{ rad}$$

$$1° = \dfrac{\pi}{180} \text{ rad}$$

$$35° = 35 \times \dfrac{\pi}{180} \qquad = \dfrac{7\pi}{36} \text{ rad} \quad (\approx 0.611 \text{ rad})$$

radians to degrees

$$\frac{\pi}{4}\ \text{rad} = \frac{180°}{4} \qquad = \ 45°$$

$$\frac{2\pi}{5}\ \text{rad} = \frac{2}{5} \times 180° \qquad = \ 72°$$

$$1\ \text{rad} = \frac{180°}{\pi} \qquad \approx \ 57.3°$$

$$2.2\ \text{rad} = 2.2 \times \frac{180°}{\pi} \ \approx 126.1°$$

In this book angles measured in degrees will always carry the $°$ sign. Where there is a possibility of confusion the symbol r is used to indicate an angle in radians (e.g. $\sin 2.2^r = \sin 2.2$ rad or $\sin 126.1°$). In a situation such as $\sin \frac{\pi}{4}$ it should be clear that the angle is in radians. Thus $\sin \frac{\pi}{4} = \sin 45° = \frac{1}{\sqrt{2}}$.

Arcs and sectors

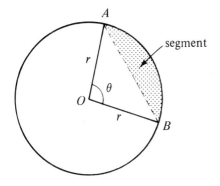

Fig. 7

The following formulae may be used when the angle θ of Fig. 7 is in radians. Both results are obtained by expressing the angle θ as a fraction of one complete revolution or 2π radians.

Length of arc AB $\qquad \frac{\theta}{2\pi} \times \text{circumference } 2\pi r = r\theta$ $\qquad$ (1)

Area of sector OAB $\qquad \frac{\theta}{2\pi} \times \text{area } \pi r^2 \qquad = \frac{1}{2}r^2\theta$ $\qquad$ (2)

The area of the segment cut off by the chord AB (shaded area in Fig. 7) may be found by subtracting the area of the triangle AOB from that of the sector AOB, i.e. segment $= \frac{1}{2}r^2\theta - \frac{1}{2}r^2\sin \theta$. (The area of the triangle is found using the formula $\frac{1}{2}ab \sin C$ for two sides and an included angle – Section 7.1.)

Example 87

Find the area of the minor segment bounded on one side by a 7 cm arc in a circle of radius 5 cm.

Let the angle subtended by the 7 cm arc at the centre of the circle be θ rads.

By (1) $\text{arc} = r\theta$ or $7 = 5\theta$ $\Rightarrow \theta = 1.4^r$

By (2) $\text{area sector} = \frac{1}{2}r^2\theta$ $= \frac{1}{2} \times 25 \times 1.4$ $= 17.5 \text{ cm}^2$

$\text{area triangle} = \frac{1}{2}r^2 \sin\theta = \frac{1}{2} \times 25 \times \sin 1.4^r$ $\approx 12.32 \text{ cm}^2$

(This last result is best found using a scientific calculator.) The area of the segment is approximately $17.5 - 12.32 = \underline{5.18 \text{ cm}^2}$

Exercise 13(e)

1. Convert from radians to degrees
   (i) $\frac{1}{6}\pi$, $\frac{2}{3}\pi$, $\frac{3}{2}\pi$, 4π, $\frac{1}{8}\pi$, $\frac{7}{10}\pi$ (exact)
   (ii) 2,   1.5, $\frac{1}{3}$,   0.63   (approximate)
2. Convert from degrees to radians
   (i) $45°$, $135°$, $60°$, $15°$, $36°$, $100°$ (exact)
   (ii) $8.3°$, $77°$, $109°$, $212.4°$ (approximate)
3. Write down the exact values of
   $\sin\frac{1}{6}\pi$, $\tan\frac{1}{4}\pi$, $\cos\frac{2}{3}\pi$, $\sin\frac{3}{2}\pi$, $\tan\frac{4}{3}\pi$, $\cos 3\pi$
4. Find the approximate values of
   $\cos\frac{1}{12}\pi$, $\sin\frac{1}{5}\pi$, $\tan\frac{7}{9}\pi$, $\sin 0.6^r$, $\cos 1.8^r$, $\tan 2.1^r$
5. Find the length of the arc and the area of the corresponding sector in each of the following cases
   (i) Circle radius 10 cm, angle subtended at centre 1.22 rad.
   (ii) Circle radius 6 cm, angle subtended at centre 0.8 rad.
6. If an arc of length 14 cm subtends an angle of 1.75 radians at the centre of a circle, find the radius of the circle and the area of the sector bounded by this arc.
7. Find the area of a sector bounded by a 12 cm arc in a circle of radius 9 cm. Find also the length of the chord joining the ends of the arc.
8. In a certain circle a 5 cm arc bounds a sector of area 12 cm². Find the radius of the circle and the angle subtending the arc (i) in radians   (ii) in degrees.
9. Find the areas of the following minor segments
   (i) subtended by an angle of 1.2 rad in a circle of radius 9 cm.
   (ii) bounded by a 12 cm arc in a circle of radius 16 cm.
10. What angle in radians does a 10 cm chord subtend at the centre of a circle of radius 8 cm? Find the perimeter of the minor segment cut off by the chord.
11. A wheel turns through 5 radians each second. How many revolutions is it making per minute? If the diameter of the wheel is 0.8 metre find the speed of a point on the rim in ms^{-1}.
12. Two circles of radius 10 cm have their centres, A and B, 16 cm apart. If the circles intersect at P and Q find
   (i) the length of the common chord PQ.

(ii) the area of the rhombus $APBQ$.
(iii) the angle PAQ in radians.
Hence find the area which is common to both circles. Calculate also the perimeter of this area.

13.6 Small angles

Tables of sines and of tangents show that for angles θ below $5°$ or $6°$ there is little difference between the values of $\sin\theta$ and $\tan\theta$ and that these values are almost identical for angles below about $2°$. Furthermore we find that almost the same values are found for the angle θ itself when measured in radians, e.g. for angle $5°$, $\theta = 0.0873$ rad, $\sin\theta = 0.0872$, $\tan\theta = 0.0875$ and for angle $1°$, $\theta = 0.0175$ rad, $\sin\theta = 0.0175$, $\tan\theta = 0.0175$. These values are, of course, correct only to 4 decimal places and are not exactly equal in the $1°$ case. We can prove, however, that as the angle θ approaches zero the values of $\sin\theta$, $\tan\theta$ and θ (in radians) become almost identical, i.e.

$$\text{Lim}_{\theta \to 0} \frac{\theta}{\sin\theta} = 1 \qquad \text{Lim}_{\theta \to 0} \frac{\theta}{\tan\theta} = 1 \qquad (1)$$

These results are particularly important in the differentiation of $\sin x$ and $\cos x$ which we consider in the next chapter.

Proof

In Fig. 8 the line BT is a tangent to the circle. Providing θ is acute, as in the diagram, it must be true that

area triangle AOB < area sector AOB < area triangle OBT

i.e. $\qquad \frac{1}{2}r^2 \sin\theta < \qquad \frac{1}{2}r^2\theta \qquad < \frac{1}{2}r^2 \tan\theta$

$\Rightarrow \qquad \sin\theta < \theta < \tan\theta \qquad (2)$

This result is borne out by the figures for a $5°$ angle quoted above. It is evident for the $1°$ figures only if further places of decimals are considered.

Divide (2) by $\sin\theta \qquad 1 < \dfrac{\theta}{\sin\theta} < \dfrac{1}{\cos\theta}$

Hence as $\theta \to 0$, $\dfrac{1}{\cos\theta} \to 1$ and so $\dfrac{\theta}{\sin\theta} \to 1$ also.

Divide (2) by $\tan\theta \qquad \cos\theta < \dfrac{\theta}{\tan\theta} < 1$

As $\theta \to 0$, $\cos\theta \to 1$ and so $\dfrac{\theta}{\tan\theta} \to 1$

The results (1) are therefore proved.

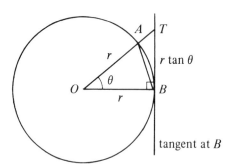

Fig. 8

Exercise 13(f)

1. With the help of a scientific calculator, complete the following table to as great a degree of accuracy as is possible:

Angle	$\sin \theta$	θ (radians)	$\tan \theta$
$1°$			
$0.5°$			
$0.2°$			
$0.1°$			

2. If θ is a small angle (i.e. $\theta \approx 0$) state the approximate values of the following:

$$\frac{\tan \theta}{\sin \theta}, \quad \frac{\sin \frac{1}{2}\theta}{\frac{1}{2}\theta}, \quad \frac{3\theta}{\tan \theta}, \quad \frac{\sin 2\theta}{\theta}, \quad \frac{\sin^2 \theta}{\theta}$$

*3. Use the half-angle formula $\cos \theta = 1 - 2\sin^2 \frac{1}{2}\theta$ to prove that if θ is small then an approximate value for $\cos \theta$ is given by

$$\cos \theta \approx 1 - \tfrac{1}{2}\theta^2 \tag{3}$$

4. Using a scientific calculator convert the angles $2°$, $4°$, $6°$, $8°$ to radians. Then use formula (3) to obtain values for the cosines of these angles. Compare your results with those printed in four figure tables.

> **Summary**
>
> (i) $\displaystyle \lim_{\theta \to 0} \frac{\theta}{\sin \theta} = 1 \quad \lim_{\theta \to 0} \frac{\theta}{\tan \theta} = 1$
>
> (ii) If $\theta \approx 0$ then $\sin \theta \approx \theta$, $\tan \theta \approx \theta$
>
> $$\cos \theta \approx 1 - \tfrac{1}{2}\theta^2$$

14

Further Calculus

14.1 Differentiation of sin x and cos x

To find the gradient of sin x

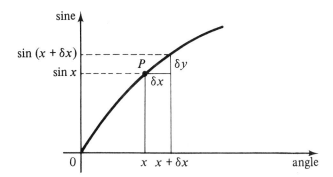

Fig. 1

Consider a general point P corresponding to angle x. The y coordinate of P gives the value of $\sin x$ (Fig. 1). If the angle x is increased by δx then the increase in the y coordinate is

$$\delta y = \sin(x + \delta x) - \sin x$$

$$= 2 \cos\left(x + \frac{\delta x}{2}\right) \sin\left(\frac{\delta x}{2}\right) \quad \text{(by the factor formulae)}$$

$$\Rightarrow \quad \frac{\delta y}{\delta x} = \frac{2 \cos\left(x + \frac{\delta x}{2}\right) \sin\left(\frac{\delta x}{2}\right)}{\delta x}$$

$$= \cos\left(x + \frac{\delta x}{2}\right) \cdot \frac{\sin\left(\frac{\delta x}{2}\right)}{\left(\frac{\delta x}{2}\right)}$$

We now let $\delta x \to 0$. (Clearly the angle $\dfrac{\delta x}{2} \to 0$ also.)

Providing the angles are measured in radians we may then use the results of Section 13.6, i.e.

as $\dfrac{\delta x}{2} \to 0$ $\dfrac{\sin\left(\dfrac{\delta x}{2}\right)}{\left(\dfrac{\delta x}{2}\right)} \to 1$

Since $\cos\left(x + \dfrac{\delta x}{2}\right) \to \cos x$ we obtain the result $\dfrac{dy}{dx} = \cos x.$

i.e. $\dfrac{d}{dx}(\sin x) = \cos x$

Note: It is interesting to observe how the behaviour of the function $\cos x$ is consistent with the results we would expect for the gradient of $\sin x$, i.e.

gradient positive but decreasing for 1st quadrant angles

gradient zero at $x = \dfrac{\pi}{2}$ (or $90°$)

gradient negative for 2nd quadrant angles etc.

Exercise 14(a)

1. Prove that the gradient of $\cos x$, where x is in radians, is given by $-\sin x$. Do not draw a diagram since the decreasing cosine graph may be confusing. Start from $\delta y = \cos(x + \delta x) - \cos x$ and use the same method as above.

*2. Prove that the gradient of $\tan x$, where x is in radians, is given by $\sec^2 x$. This is more difficult. Start from

$$\delta y = \tan(x + \delta x) - \tan x = \frac{\sin(x + \delta x)}{\cos(x + \delta x)} - \frac{\sin x}{\cos x}$$

and proceed by putting the fractions over a common denominator. (An alternative method of obtaining this result is indicated in Exercise 16(e) question 3.)

14.2 Problems

The results of the preceding section may be summarised as follows:

$$\frac{d}{dx}(\sin x) = \cos x$$

$$\frac{d}{dx}(\cos x) = -\sin x$$

$$\frac{d}{dx}(\tan x) = \sec^2 x$$

where the angle x must be measured in radians.

The derivatives of multiples of these functions and of combinations of these functions are obtained in the usual way, e.g.

(i) if $y = 5 \cos x$ $\qquad\qquad\qquad \dfrac{dy}{dx} = -5 \sin x$

$\qquad\qquad\qquad\qquad\qquad\qquad \dfrac{d^2 y}{dx^2} = -5 \cos x$

(ii) if $y = 2 \sin x - \tan x$ $\qquad \dfrac{dy}{dx} = 2 \cos x - \sec^2 x$

We cannot, as yet, find the second derivative of any function involving $\tan x$.

Example 88

Find any maximum and minimum points for the function $x + \sqrt{2} \cos x$ in the range $0 \leqslant x \leqslant 2\pi$ (i.e. $0°$ to $360°$).

Maximum and minimum points occur where the gradient is zero.

Let $\qquad\qquad\qquad y = x + \sqrt{2} \cos x$

gradient $\qquad\quad \dfrac{dy}{dx} = 1 - \sqrt{2} \sin x$

gradient $= 0$ when $\sin x = \dfrac{1}{\sqrt{2}}$

$\qquad\qquad\qquad \Rightarrow \qquad x = \dfrac{\pi}{4}(45°) \quad$ or $\quad \dfrac{3\pi}{4}(135°)$

at $x = \dfrac{\pi}{4}, \quad y = \dfrac{\pi}{4} + \sqrt{2}\left(\dfrac{1}{\sqrt{2}}\right) = \dfrac{\pi}{4} + 1$

at $x = \dfrac{3\pi}{4}, \quad y = \dfrac{3\pi}{4} + \sqrt{2}\left(\dfrac{-1}{\sqrt{2}}\right) = \dfrac{3\pi}{4} - 1$

To determine whether these are maxima or minima we use the second derivative

$\dfrac{d^2 y}{dx^2} = -\sqrt{2} \cos x$

at $x = \dfrac{\pi}{4} \quad \dfrac{d^2 y}{dx^2}$ is negative $\Rightarrow$ Maximum point

at $x = \dfrac{3\pi}{4} \quad \dfrac{d^2 y}{dx^2}$ is positive $\Rightarrow$ Minimum point

The answers are therefore   Max $\left(\dfrac{\pi}{4}, \dfrac{\pi}{4} + 1\right)$,   Min $\left(\dfrac{3\pi}{4}, \dfrac{3\pi}{4} - 1\right)$

Fig. 2b shows a rough sketch of the function. This is obtained by adding the two constituent functions x and $\sqrt{2} \cos x$, whose graphs are shown in Fig. 2a.

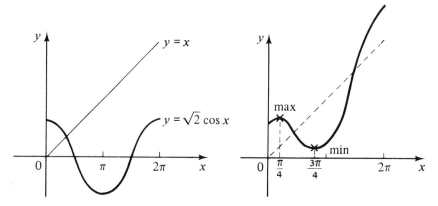

Fig. 2a   Fig. 2b

Exercise 14(b)

1. Differentiate
   (i) $3 \sin x$
   (ii) $2 \tan x$
   (iii) $\frac{1}{2} \cos x$
   (iv) $\sin x - \cos x$
   (v) $x - 5 \tan x$
   (vi) $3 \cos x - 2 \sin x$
   (vii) $\dfrac{2 \sin x + \tan x}{3}$
   (viii) $\dfrac{\sin x}{\cos x}$
   (ix) $\sec x (\cos x - \sin x)$

2. Find the gradients of the following functions at the points indicated:
   (i) $y = \sin x$ at $x = 0$ and $x = \frac{1}{3}\pi$
   (ii) $y = \cos x$ at $x = \frac{1}{3}\pi$ and $x = \pi$
   (iii) $y = \tan x$ at $x = \frac{1}{4}\pi$ and $x = \frac{2}{3}\pi$
   (iv) $y = 2 \sin x + 3 \cos x$ at $x = \frac{1}{2}\pi$
   (v) $y = \tan x - 2 \cos x$ at $x = \frac{1}{6}\pi$
   (vii) $y = x + \tan x$ at $x = \pi$

3. Find $\dfrac{dr}{d\theta}$ and $\dfrac{d^2 r}{d\theta^2}$ when   (i) $r = 5 \cos \theta$
   (ii) $r = 3 \sin \theta - 4 \cos \theta$ (iii) $r = \cos \theta (1 - \tan \theta)$

4. Find the angles x between 0 and 2π for which
   (i)   the gradient of $\cos x$ is 1
   (ii) the gradient of $\tan x$ is 4
   (iii) the gradient of $\sin x$ is 0.2
   (iv) the gradient of $x + \cos x$ is 0.6

5. Find the maximum and minimum points of the function $x - 2 \sin x$ in the range $0 \leqslant x \leqslant 2\pi$.

*6. Write down, without calculation, the maximum values of the following functions (see Exercise 13(b), question 5). By differentiation determine the values of x between 0 and 2π for which these occur.
   (i) $2 \sin x + \cos x$ (ii) $5 \cos x - 3 \sin x$.

*7. Show that the function $x + \sin x$ is always increasing and hence prove that it has a point of inflexion at $x = \pi$. Sketch the function for $0 \leqslant x \leqslant 2\pi$.

8. Find the coordinates of the turning points of $2x - \tan x$ in the range $0 \leqslant x \leqslant 2\pi$. By sketching (i) $2x$ and (ii) $-\tan x$ gain a rough idea of the behaviour of the function and hence determine whether these are maximum or minimum points. (We cannot yet find the second derivative.)

14.3 Integration of sin *x* and cos *x*

A straightforward reversal of the results set out at the start of Section 14.2 gives

$$\int \cos x \, dx = \sin x + c$$
$$\int \sin x \, dx = -\cos x + c$$
$$\int \sec^2 x \, dx = \tan x + c$$

Notice that although we can differentiate tan *x* we cannot, as yet, integrate it. The integral of tan *x* is effected by the method of Section 18.4.

Example   89

Find the area under one loop of the six *x* curve (e.g. $0 \leqslant x \leqslant \pi$). Deduce the mean value of sin *x* for $0 \leqslant x \leqslant \pi$.

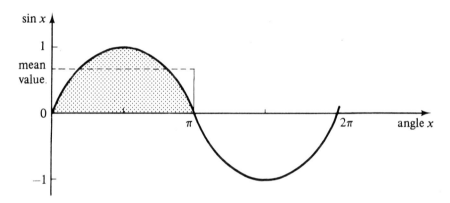

Fig. 3

The area required is shown in Fig. 3.

$$\text{Area} = \int_0^\pi y \, dx = \int_0^\pi \sin x \, dx$$
$$= \left[-\cos x \right]_0^\pi$$
$$= (-\cos \pi) - (-\cos 0)$$
$$= +1 - (-1) = 2 \text{ sq. units}$$

The mean value, as we saw in Section 9.6, may be thought of as the average height of this area. It is therefore obtained by dividing by the width π, i.e.

$$\text{mean value of sin } x \text{ for } 0 \leqslant x \leqslant \pi \quad = \quad \frac{2}{\pi}$$

Note: The mean value of sin *x* over one complete period i.e. $0 \leqslant x \leqslant 2\pi$ is zero since this involves equal areas above and below the *x*-axis. Alternatively it is clear that for each positive value of sin x in the range of $0 \leqslant x \leqslant \pi$ there is a corresponding negative value in the range $\pi \leqslant x \leqslant 2\pi$.

Exercise 14(c)

1. Integrate the following. (Simplify first where necessary.)
   (i) $4 \sin x$ (ii) $\frac{1}{3} \cos x$ (iii) $2 \sec^2 x$
   (iv) $3 \sin x - 2 \cos x$ (v) $x + 5 \sin x$ (vi) $\frac{1}{2}(\cos x - \sin x)$
   (vi) $\tan x \cos x$ (viii) $\sin x (1 + \cot x)$ (ix) $\dfrac{\tan x}{\sin 2x}$

2. Evaluate the following integrals:
   (i) $\displaystyle\int_{\frac{1}{6}\pi}^{\frac{1}{2}\pi} \cos x \, dx$ (ii) $\displaystyle\int_0^{\frac{1}{4}\pi} (3 \cos x - \sin x) dx$

   (iii) $\displaystyle\int_0^{\frac{1}{3}\pi} (1 + 2 \sin x) dx$ (iv) $\displaystyle\int_0^{\frac{1}{3}\pi} (1 + \tan^2 x) dx$

3. Find the areas bounded by the x-axis and the curves
   (i) $y = 2 + \cos x$ from $x = 0$ to $x = \frac{1}{2}\pi$
   (ii) $y = \cos x + 3 \sin x$ from $x = \frac{1}{4}\pi$ to $x = \frac{3}{4}\pi$
4. Find the volumes of the solids of revolution formed when the following curve sections are rotated about the x-axis
   (i) $y = \sec x$ from $x = 0$ to $x = \frac{1}{4}\pi$
   (ii) $y = 2\sqrt{\cos x}$ from $x = \frac{1}{6}\pi$ to $x = \frac{1}{3}\pi$
   *(iii) $y = \tan x$ from $x = 0$ to $x = \frac{1}{4}\pi$
5. Find the mean values of
   (i) $\cos x$ for $0 \leqslant x \leqslant \frac{1}{2}\pi$
   (ii) $1 + \sec^2 x$ for $0 \leqslant x \leqslant \frac{1}{4}\pi$
   (iii) $\sqrt{3} \sin x - \cos x$ for $\frac{1}{6}\pi \leqslant x \leqslant \frac{1}{2}\pi$
6. The section of the curve $y = \sin\frac{1}{2}x + \cos\frac{1}{2}x$ from $x = 0$ to $x = \pi$ is rotated about the x-axis. Prove that the volume of the solid generated is $\pi(\pi + 2)$ cu. units.

14.4 Differentiation of a function of a function (the chain rule)

In order to differentiate a function such as $(2x^2 + 1)^3$ we are at present obliged to multiply out the function (the method of Section 11.2 could be used) and then differentiate term by term, i.e.

$$y = (2x^2 + 1)^3$$
$$= (2x^2)^3 + 3(2x^2)^2 + 3(2x^2) + 1$$
$$= 8x^6 + 12x^4 + 6x^2 + 1$$
$$\Rightarrow \frac{dy}{dx} = 48x^5 + 48x^3 + 12x \tag{1}$$

This method is lengthy, particularly when a higher power than a cube is involved, and we therefore look for a more convenient approach.

The basic idea behind the method we are about to introduce is as follows. If we regard the function considered above as being of the form $(\text{bracket})^3$, then are we correct in supposing the derived function to be of the form $3(\text{bracket})^2$, just as x^3 has derived function $3x^2$?

i.e. since $\qquad x^3 \xrightarrow{\text{diff}} 3x^2$

does $\qquad (\quad)^3 \longrightarrow 3(\quad)^2 \quad ?$

In fact this is not correct because we have not performed our differentiation in terms of the variable x, but in terms of the more involved variable $(\quad)$. If we can permit ourselves the use of rather unconventional notation, then we have found $\dfrac{dy}{d(\quad)}$ rather than $\dfrac{dy}{dx}$ as required.

This new approach therefore needs some modification.

The chain rule

This is conveniently set down as follows

$$\frac{dy}{dx} = \frac{dy}{d(\quad)} \cdot \frac{d(\quad)}{dx}$$

A justification of this rule is given at the end of the section. To begin with we shall concentrate on the *application* of this result. We first illustrate the complete procedure as applied to the function $(2x^2 + 1)^3$.

(i) Regard the function as $y = (\quad)^3$

(ii) Write down the result of the 'intuitive' differentiation, i.e. $3(\quad)^2$; this is $\dfrac{dy}{d(\quad)}$ in our notation.

(iii) Now look at *the contents* of the bracket and differentiate this with respect to x. Hence $\dfrac{d(\quad)}{dx} = \dfrac{d(2x^2 + 1)}{dx} = 4x$

(iv) The derived function $\dfrac{dy}{dx}$ is found by multiplying these two results together, i.e.

$$\frac{dy}{dx} = 3(\quad)^2 4x = 12x(2x^2 + 1)^2 \tag{2}$$

Once familiarity with the method has been gained the only working which need be put down is that of line (2). The result is identical to that of line (1) above and is also in a more convenient form.

This method may be applied to a wide variety of functions. Some of the more important types are considered in the following example and some further applications are introduced in the next section.

Example   90

Differentiate the following functions:

(i) $(x^3 - 4)^5$ (ii) $\dfrac{1}{(3x - 2)^2}$ (iii) $\dfrac{1}{\sqrt{1 + 2x^2}}$

(iv) $\cos 3x$ (v) $\tan \frac{1}{2}x$ (vi) $(1 - \cos x)^2$

The working of these examples is set out in a table for convenience.

Function			$\dfrac{dy}{d(\ )} \cdot \dfrac{d(\ )}{dx}$		$\dfrac{dy}{dx}$
(i) $y = (x^3 - 4)^5$	or	$(\ )^5$	$5(\ )^4$	$\cdot \quad 3x^2$	$15x^2(x^3 - 4)^4$
(ii) $y = \dfrac{1}{(3x - 2)^2}$	or	$(\ )^{-2}$	$-2(\ )^{-3}$	$\cdot \quad 3$	$-\dfrac{6}{(3x - 2)^3}$
(iii) $y = \dfrac{1}{\sqrt{1 + 2x^2}}$	or	$(\ )^{-\frac{1}{2}}$	$-\frac{1}{2}(\ )^{-\frac{3}{2}}$	$\cdot \quad 4x$	$-\dfrac{2x}{(1 + 2x^2)^{\frac{3}{2}}}$
(iv) $y = \cos 3x$	or	$\cos(\ )$	$-\sin(\ )$	$\cdot \quad 3$	$-3 \sin 3x$
(v) $y = \tan \frac{1}{2}x$	or	$\tan(\ )$	$\sec^2(\ )$	$\cdot \quad \frac{1}{2}$	$\frac{1}{2} \sec^2 \frac{1}{2}x$
(vi) $y = (1 - \cos x)^2$	or	$(\ )^2$	$2(\ )$	$\cdot \quad \sin x$	$2 \sin x(1 - \cos x)$

Justification of result

We regard the function as being a function of some bracket (   ), which is itself a function of x: hence the origin of the name **function of a function**. Denote the bracket by b. Then we have to show that

$$\frac{dy}{dx} = \frac{dy}{db} \cdot \frac{db}{dx}$$

Imagine that a small change δx in the value of x causes the value of the bracket b to change by δb. This in turn will cause a change δy in the value of the function itself. If δx is sufficiently small then both δb and δy will be small. As $\delta x \to 0$ the limiting value of the ratio $\dfrac{\delta y}{\delta x}$ gives us $\dfrac{dy}{dx}$.

But $$\frac{\delta y}{\delta x} = \frac{\delta y}{\delta b} \cdot \frac{\delta b}{\delta x} \tag{3}$$

so $\text{Lim} \left(\dfrac{\delta y}{\delta x} \right) = \text{Lim} \left(\dfrac{\delta y}{\delta b} \cdot \dfrac{\delta b}{\delta x} \right) = \left(\text{Lim} \dfrac{\delta y}{\delta b} \right) \cdot \left(\text{Lim} \dfrac{\delta b}{\delta x} \right)$ $\tag{4}$

i.e. $$\frac{dy}{dx} = \frac{dy}{db} \cdot \frac{db}{dx}$$

Line (3) is always true exactly. Hence the limiting value of the ratio $\delta y / \delta x$ is equal to the product of the two limiting values of line (4). From this the result follows.

Exercise 14(d)

1. Differentiate
   (i) $(x^2 + 3)^4$ (ii) $(1 - 3x)^7$ (iii) $(x - 5)^3$
   (iv) $(x^3 - x)^2$ (v) $(1 + \sin x)^3$ (vi) $(x - \cos x)^2$
2. Differentiate

   (i) $\dfrac{1}{(2x + 1)^2}$ (ii) $\dfrac{1}{(3x - 5)}$ (iii) $\dfrac{1}{(1 - 4x)^3}$

   (iv) $\sqrt{2x + 1}$ (v) $\sqrt[3]{3x^2 - 2}$ (vi) $\dfrac{1}{\sqrt{4x - 1}}$

3. Differentiate
   (i) $\sin 3x$ (ii) $\tan 2x$ (iii) $\cos\frac{1}{2}x$
   (iv) $\cos 5x$ (v) $\sin 4x - \cos 2x$ (vi) $3 \sin 2x$
   (vii) $\frac{1}{2}\tan 4x$ (viii) $6 \sin\frac{1}{2}x$ (ix) $2 \cos 3x - 3 \cos x$
4. Find the gradients of the following functions at the points indicated:
   (i) $y = (2x - 5)^3$ at $x = 4$

   (ii) $y = \dfrac{1}{2x - 1}$ at $x = -1$

   (iii) $y = \tan 2x$ at $x = \frac{1}{8}\pi$
   (iv) $y = x - 3 \sin\frac{1}{2}x$ at $x = 2\pi$
5. Show that the gradient of the curve $y = (1 - \sin x)^2$ is given by $\sin 2x - 2 \cos x$ and hence find the second derivative.
6. Find the turning points on the curve $y = x - \sin 2x$ for $0 \leqslant x \leqslant \pi$ and determine their nature.

7. Find the equation of the tangent to the curve $y = \dfrac{1}{(x - 2)^2}$ at the point

   where $x = 5$.

8. If $r = 2 \sin \theta + \cos 2\theta$ find $\dfrac{dr}{d\theta}$ and $\dfrac{d^2 r}{d\theta^2}$. Hence prove that the function

   has three turning points for $0 \leqslant \theta \leqslant \pi$ and determine their nature, stating also the values of r at these points.

9. Prove that the function $\dfrac{1}{x - x^2}$ increases for all values of $x > \frac{1}{2}$.

10. Prove that the gradient of $(\sin x + \cos x)^2$ is given by $2 \cos 2x$
    (i) by squaring and simplifying before differentiation
    (ii) by direct differentiation using the chain rule.

14.5 Further examples on the chain rule

In the following example we see how (i) powers of $\sin x$, $\cos x$ and $\tan x$ (ii) functions of the form $R \sin (x \pm \alpha)$ or $R \cos (x \pm \alpha)$ may be differentiated by means of the chain rule.

Example 91

Differentiate with respect to x
(i) $\sin^2 x$ (ii) $2 \tan^3 x$ (iii) $5 \cos (2x - \frac{1}{4}\pi)$ (iv) $\cos^3 \frac{1}{2}x$

Function		$\dfrac{dy}{d(\ )} \cdot \dfrac{d(\ )}{dx}$		$\dfrac{dy}{dx}$
(i)	$y = \sin^2 x$	or $(\sin x)^2$	$2(\sin x)\ \cdot\ \cos x$	$2\sin x \cos x$
(ii)	$y = 2\tan^3 x$	or $2(\tan x)^3$	$6(\tan x)^2\ \cdot\ \sec^2 x$	$6\tan^2 x \sec^2 x$
(iii)	$y = 5\cos(2x - \frac{1}{4}\pi)$	or $5\cos(\ )$	$-5\sin(\ )\ \cdot\ 2$	$-10\sin(2x - \frac{1}{4}\pi)$
(iv)	$y = \cos^3\frac{1}{2}x$	or $[\cos\frac{1}{2}x]^3$	$3[\ ]^2\ \cdot\ -\frac{1}{2}\sin\frac{1}{2}x$	$-\frac{3}{2}\cos^2\frac{1}{2}x \sin\frac{1}{2}x$

Notice that the $\frac{1}{4}\pi$ in example (iii) is a constant and so does not affect the differentiation.

To differentiate cot x

Having established that the derived function of $\tan x$ is $\sec^2 x$ we may deduce the derived function of $\cot x$ by regarding it as $(\tan x)^{-1}$.

i.e. if $\qquad y = \cot x = \dfrac{1}{\tan x} = (\tan x)^{-1}$

then $\qquad \dfrac{dy}{dx} = -1(\tan x)^{-2}\sec^2 x$

$$= -\frac{\cos^2 x}{\sin^2 x} \cdot \frac{1}{\cos^2 x} = \underline{-\operatorname{cosec}^2 x}$$

The derivatives of $\sec x$ and $\operatorname{cosec} x$ may be found by a similar method using the results for $\cos x$ and $\sin x$ respectively. This is left as an exercise for the student.

Exercise 14(e)

1. Differentiate with respect to x
   (i) $\cos^2 x$ (ii) $\sin^3 x$ (iii) $\tan^2 x$
   (iv) $\sin^5 x$ (v) $\frac{1}{2}\cos^4 x$ (vi) $3\sin^2 x$
   (vii) $\cos(x + \frac{1}{2}\pi)$ (viii) $\sin(2x - \alpha)$ (ix) $\tan(\frac{1}{2}x + \frac{1}{4}\pi)$
2. Differentiate with respect to x
   (i) $\sin^2 2x$ (ii) $\cos^2 \frac{1}{2}x$ (iii) $\tan^3 4x$
   (iv) $\cos^2(x - \alpha)$ (v) $2\sin^4 3x$ (vi) $3\tan^2 \frac{1}{4}x$
   (vii) $5\sin^2(\frac{1}{2}x - \alpha)$ (viii) $\sqrt{\sin x}$ (ix) $\sqrt{\tan x}$
3. Show that the gradient of $\cos^3 x$ may be written in the form $3\sin^3 x - 3\sin x$. Hence find the second derivative.
4. Show that the gradient of the curve $y = (1 - \cos 2x)^2$ is given by $4\sin 2x - 2\sin 4x$. Hence show that

$$\frac{d^2 y}{dx^2} = 16\sin 3x \sin x$$

5. By regarding $\sec x$ as $(\cos x)^{-1}$ and $\operatorname{cosec} x$ as $(\sin x)^{-1}$ prove that

$$\frac{d}{dx}(\sec x) = \sec x \tan x \qquad \frac{d}{dx}(\operatorname{cosec} x) = -\operatorname{cosec} x \cot x$$

6. Show that the second derivative of $\tan x$ is $2\tan x \sec^2 x$. By writing $\sec^2 x = 1 + \tan^2 x$ find the third derivative.
7. Find the angles x between 0 and 2π for which the gradient of the curve $y = \sin^3 x + \cos^3 x$ is zero.
8. Show that the curve $y = \sin x - \sin^2 x$ has four turning points for values of x between 0 and 2π. Prove that the second derivative is $-\sin x - 2\cos 2x$ and hence determine the nature of these points.

14.6 Integration of sin 2x and other associated integrals

Integral of sin 2x

We look for a function which gives $\sin 2x$ when differentiated. We try $\cos 2x$ as a first attempt. But on differentiation $\cos 2x \rightarrow -2\sin 2x$. The required integral is therefore $-\frac{1}{2}\cos 2x$, i.e.

$$\int \sin 2x \, dx = -\frac{1}{2}\cos 2x + c$$

Integral of sin (2x + α)

If α is a constant angle then it does not affect differentiation or integration. Therefore, by the same reasoning as above

$$\int \sin(2x + \alpha) \, dx = -\frac{1}{2}\cos(2x + \alpha) + c$$

Some further examples of this type are

$$\int \cos 5x \, dx = \frac{1}{5}\sin 5x + c \qquad \text{since } \sin 5x \rightarrow 5\cos 5x$$

$$\int \sec^2 \frac{1}{3}x \, dx = 3\tan\frac{1}{3}x + c \qquad \text{since } \tan\frac{1}{3}x \rightarrow \frac{1}{3}\sec^2\frac{1}{3}x$$

$$\int \sin\left(3x - \frac{1}{2}\pi\right) dx = -\frac{1}{3}\cos\left(3x - \frac{1}{2}\pi\right) + c$$

$$\text{since } \cos\left(3x - \frac{1}{2}\pi\right) \rightarrow -3\sin\left(3x - \frac{1}{2}\pi\right)$$

Note: In these examples the symbol $\rightarrow$ is used to indicate the result of differentiation.

Example 92

Evaluate the definite integral $\displaystyle\int_{\frac{1}{6}\pi}^{\frac{1}{3}\pi} (1 - 2\cos 3x) \, dx$

$$\int_{\frac{1}{6}\pi}^{\frac{1}{3}\pi} (1 - 2\cos 3x) \, dx = \left[x - \frac{2}{3}\sin 3x\right]_{\frac{1}{6}\pi}^{\frac{1}{3}\pi}$$

$$= \left(\frac{1}{3}\pi - \frac{2}{3}\sin\pi\right) - \left(\frac{1}{6}\pi - \frac{2}{3}\sin\frac{1}{2}\pi\right)$$

$$= \left(\frac{1}{3}\pi - 0\right) - \left(\frac{1}{6}\pi - \frac{2}{3}\right)$$

$$= \frac{1}{6}\pi + \frac{2}{3} \quad \text{or} \quad \frac{1}{6}(\pi + 4)$$

Example 93

Find the following integral: $\int \sin 4x \cos x \, dx$

This type of integral may be solved by using the appropriate factor formula (Section 13.4) – but in reverse. Here we use

sum of two sines = twice sine (half the sum) cos (half the difference)

The sum of the two angles concerned is $8x$ (half the sum being $4x$) and their difference is $2x$. The angles are therefore $5x$ and $3x$. Thus

$$\int \sin 4x \cos x \, dx = \frac{1}{2}\int 2 \sin 4x \cos x \, dx$$

$$= \frac{1}{2}\int (\sin 5x + \sin 3x) \, dx$$

$$= \frac{1}{2}\left(-\frac{1}{5}\cos 5x - \frac{1}{3}\cos 3x\right) + c$$

$$= -\frac{1}{10}\cos 5x - \frac{1}{6}\cos 3x + c$$

Exercise 14(f)

1. Integrate the following with respect to x:
   - (i) $\cos 2x$
   - (ii) $\sin 3x$
   - (iii) $\cos \frac{1}{2}x$
   - (iv) $\sec^2 4x$
   - (v) $2 \sin 4x$
   - (vi) $4 \sec^2 \frac{1}{2}x$
   - (vii) $\frac{1}{2}\sin\frac{1}{3}x$
   - (viii) $\sin(2x - \frac{1}{2}\pi)$
   - (ix) $\frac{1}{2}\cos(5x + 1)$

2. Evaluate the following definite integrals:

   (i) $\displaystyle\int_0^{\frac{1}{6}\pi} \sec^2 2x \, dx$ (ii) $\displaystyle\int_{2\pi}^{3\pi} \left(1 - \cos\frac{1}{3}x\right) dx$

   (iii) $\displaystyle\int_0^{\frac{1}{2}\pi} 2 \cos(2x - \frac{1}{4}\pi) \, dx$ (iv) $\displaystyle\int_{-\alpha}^{\alpha} R \sin(x + \alpha) \, dx$

3. Sketch the curve $y = 1 + \sin 2x$ for $0 \leqslant x \leqslant \pi$. Find the area bounded by this curve and the two coordinate axes.

4. Find the volume of the solid generated when the section of $y = \tan 2x$ between $x = 0$ and $x = \frac{1}{6}\pi$ is rotated about the x-axis. (Hint: use the identity $\sec^2\theta = 1 + \tan^2\theta$.)

5. Considering values of x between 0 and $\frac{1}{2}\pi$ only, find the point of intersection of $y = \cos 2x$ and $y = \sin x$. Find the areas bounded by
   - (i) $y = \cos 2x$, $y = \sin x$ and the y-axis
   - (ii) $y = \cos 2x$, $y = \sin x$ and the x-axis.

6. Find the following integrals by first expressing the functions concerned as the sum of two sines (see Example 93).

(i) $\displaystyle\int 2 \sin 3x \cos x \, dx$ (ii) $\displaystyle\int \sin\frac{3x}{2} \cos\frac{x}{2} \, dx$

7. Find the following integrals:

(i) $\displaystyle\int 4 \cos 3x \cos 2x \, dx$ (ii) $\displaystyle\int \sin 5x \sin 2x \, dx$

14.7 Integration of sin²x, sin³x etc.

In this section the symbol $\rightarrow$ is again used to indicate the result of differentiation.

We begin by recalling the differentiation results of Section 14.5. These enable us to solve without difficulty a certain type of integral. For example

Since $\sin^3 x \rightarrow 3 \sin^2 x \cos x$ we have $\displaystyle\int \sin^2 x \cos x \, dx = \frac{1}{3} \sin^3 x + c$

Since $\cos^5 x \rightarrow -5 \cos^4 x \sin x$ we have $\displaystyle\int \cos^4 x \sin x \, dx = -\frac{1}{5} \cos^5 x + c$

Any combination of $\sin x$ and $\cos x$ in which one of the two is to power one only may be integrated in this way, e.g.

$$\int \cos x \sin^3 x \, dx = \frac{1}{4} \sin^4 x + c \quad \text{since } \sin^4 x \rightarrow 4 \sin^3 x \cos x$$

When the student has grasped the idea behind this type of integral he will understand that

(i) $\displaystyle\int \sin^2 x \, dx$ is *not* $\dfrac{1}{3} \sin^3 x + c$ $\left(\text{although } \displaystyle\int x^2 \, dx = \dfrac{1}{3} x^3 + c\right)$

(ii) $\displaystyle\int \sin^3 x \, dx$ is *not* $\dfrac{1}{4} \sin^4 x + c$ $\left(\text{although } \displaystyle\int x^3 \, dx = \dfrac{1}{4} x^4 + c\right)$

These two integrals are more difficult than the type we have just considered and require special methods.

Integration of sin² x and cos² x

Both $\sin^2 x$ and $\cos^2 x$ may be written in terms of $\cos 2x$. This provides a method of integration.

$$\cos 2x = 2 \cos^2 x - 1 = 1 - 2 \sin^2 x$$

$$\Rightarrow \sin^2 x = \frac{1}{2}(1 - \cos 2x), \quad \cos^2 x = \frac{1}{2}(1 + \cos 2x)$$

Thus $\displaystyle\int \sin^2 x \, dx = \frac{1}{2} \int (1 - \cos 2x) \, dx$

$$= \frac{1}{2}\left(x - \frac{1}{2} \sin 2x\right) + c$$

$$= \frac{1}{2}x - \frac{1}{4}\sin 2x + c$$

The integral of $\cos^2 x$ is achieved in the same manner.

Integration of $\sin^3 x$ and $\cos^3 x$

Here the identity $\sin^2 x + \cos^2 x = 1$ enables us to transform the integrals into the type considered at the start of this section. We take the integral of $\cos^3 x$ as our example

$$\int \cos^3 x \, dx = \int \cos x (1 - \sin^2 x) \, dx$$

$$= \int (\cos x - \cos x \sin^2 x) \, dx$$

$$= \sin x - \frac{1}{3}\sin^3 x + c$$

Exercise 14(g)

1. Find the following integrals:

(i) $\int \sin^3 x \cos x \, dx$ (ii) $\int \sin x \cos^2 x \, dx$

(iii) $\int \sin x \cos x \, dx$ (iv) $\int \sin^2 3x \cos 3x \, dx$

2. Find the following integrals:

(i) $\int \cos^2 x \, dx$ (ii) $\int \sin^3 x \, dx$

(iii) $\int \sin^2 \frac{1}{2}x \, dx$ (iv) $\int \cos^3 2x \, dx$

3. Find the mean value of $\sin^2 x$ for $0 \leqslant x \leqslant 2\pi$. Deduce the **root-mean-square value** of $\sin x$ for $0 \leqslant x \leqslant 2\pi$.
4. The section of $y = \cos x$ from $x = 0$ to $x = \frac{1}{4}\pi$ is rotated about the x-axis. Find the volume of the solid generated.
5. Find the following integrals:

(i) $\int \cos^2 x + \sin^2 x \, dx$ (ii) $\int \cos^2 x - \sin^2 x \, dx$

(iii) $\int \cos x (1 + \sin x)^2 \, dx$ (iv) $\int (1 + \sin x)^2 \, dx$

(v) $\int \sin 2x \cos^2 x \, dx$ (vi) $\int \cos x \sqrt{\sin x} \, dx$

*(vii) $\int \sin^2 x \cos^2 x \, dx$ *(viii) $\int \sin^2 x \cos^3 x \, dx$

15

Miscellaneous I

15.1 Basic inequalities

The first rule for handling inequalities is that equal quantities may be added or subtracted from both sides without changing the direction of the inequality sign, e.g.

$7 > 5 \Rightarrow 10 > 8$ (adding three to both sides)
$7 > 5 \Rightarrow 1 > -1$ (subtracting six from both sides).

In practice this means that terms can be moved from one side of the inequality to the other in the usual way, e.g.

if $3x - 5 > x$
then $3x > x + 5$ (adding five)
    $3x - x > 5$ (subtracting x)
$\Rightarrow$ $x > 2\frac{1}{2}$

The solution of the inequality $3x - 5 > x$ is therefore the set of values $x > 2\frac{1}{2}$.

Quadratic and cubic inequalities

The simplest method for dealing with quadratic inequalities was introduced in Section 5.3. A further example is given here. A similar method may be used for cubic inequalities.

Example 94

Solve the inequalities
(i) $2x^2 - 7x < 4$ (ii) $x^3 > 4x$ (iii) $3x^2 - 2x^3 \geqslant 1$

(i) $2x^2 - 7x < 4 \Rightarrow$ $2x^2 - 7x - 4 < 0$
    $(2x + 1)(x - 4) < 0$

The function $2x^2 - 7x - 4$ is zero when $x = -\frac{1}{2}$ and $x = 4$. A simple sketch (Fig. 1a) shows that it is negative for $-\frac{1}{2} < x < 4$

(ii) $x^3 > 4x \Rightarrow$ $x^3 - 4x > 0$
        $x(x^2 - 4) > 0$
      $x(x + 2)(x - 2) > 0$

The function $x^3 - 4x$ is zero for $x = 0, x = -2$ and $x = +2$. From Fig. 1b we see that the values of x for which it is greater than zero are $-2 < x < 0$ and $x > 2$

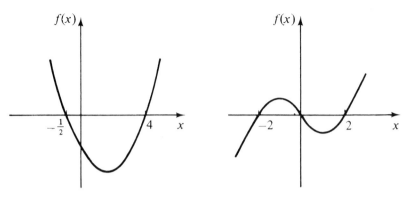

Fig. 1a   Fig. 1b

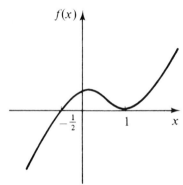

Fig. 1c

(iii) $3x^2 - 2x^3 \geqslant 1 \Rightarrow \quad 0 \geqslant 2x^3 - 3x^2 + 1$

(It is convenient to put terms on the right hand side so that the x^3 term is positive.) By the remainder theorem (Section 5.7) we see that $(x-1)$ is a factor of $2x^3 - 3x^2 + 1$.

$$0 \geqslant (x-1)(2x^2 - x - 1)$$
$$0 \geqslant (x-1)(2x+1)(x-1)$$

The function is zero for $x = -\frac{1}{2}$ and $x = 1$ (repeated); Fig. 1c is a sketch of the graph. The function is less than or equal to zero for $x \leqslant -\frac{1}{2}$ and for the single value $x = 1$

The modulus of a function

By the modulus of a function we simply mean the magnitude of the function irrespective of whether it is positive or negative. The modulus of $f(x)$ is denoted by $|f(x)|$, e.g.

if $f(x) = 3x - 5$

then, when $x = 4$ $f(x) = \quad 7$ and $|f(x)| = 7$

but, when $x = 1$ $f(x) = -2$ and $|f(x)| = 2$

i.e. the modulus has the same *numerical* value as the function but ignores the sign.

The modulus notation can sometimes be useful in expressing inequalities; e.g. the infinite binomial series for $(1 + x)^{\frac{1}{2}}$ is valid providing x is numerically less than 1, i.e. if $|x| < 1$, the geometric progression $a + ar + ar^2 + ar^3 + \ldots$ is convergent if $|r| < 1$.

The following example shows how certain modulus inequalities may be handled.

Example 95

Find the values of x for which
(i) $|2x - 3| > 5$ (ii) $|x^2 - 7| < 2$

(i) The expression $2x - 3$ must be numerically greater than 5, i.e. if positive it must be larger than 5 and if negative it must be *less than* -5. We therefore have

$$2x - 3 > 5 \qquad \text{or} \qquad 2x - 3 < -5$$
$$\Rightarrow \qquad 2x > 8 \qquad\qquad\qquad 2x < -2$$

Hence the solutions are $x > 4$ and $x < -1$

(ii) If $x^2 - 7$ is numerically less than 2 then its value must lie between -2 and $+2$

$$-2 < x^2 - 7 < 2$$
$$\Rightarrow \quad 5 < \quad x^2 \quad < 9 \tag{1}$$
$$\Rightarrow \sqrt{5} < \quad |x| \quad < 3 \tag{2}$$

The inequality involving x^2 on line (1) has both positive solutions ($\sqrt{5} < x < 3$) and negative solutions ($-3 < x < -\sqrt{5}$). Notice that both sets of solutions are contained in the modulus inequality of line (2).

Exercise 15(a)

1. Solve the inequalities
   (i) $3x - 5 > 4$ (ii) $x - 1 > 3 - 7x$
   (iii) $2(5 - x) \geqslant x + 4$ (iv) $1 - x < 3(x + 5)$
2. Find the values of x for which
   (i) $x(x - 4) < 0$ (ii) $x^2 + x - 20 > 0$
   (iii) $3x^2 \geqslant 5x + 2$ (iv) $6 - 2x^2 \geqslant x$
   (v) $x(1 - 4x) > -3$ (vi) $(x + 3)^2 > 2(x + 3)$
3. Solve the inequalities
   (i) $4x^3 - x < 0$ (ii) $x^3 \geqslant 3x^2$ (iii) $x^3 \geqslant 7x + 6$
   (iv) $2x^3 + x^2 - 2x < 1$
4. Find the values of
   (i) $|5x - 3|$ when $x = 1$ and $x = -1$
   (ii) $|x^2 - 5x|$ when $x = 3$ and $x = -3$
   (iii) $\left|\dfrac{x + 3}{x - 2}\right|$ when $x = 7$ and $x = -2$

5. For each of the following functions calculate $f(x)$ and $|f(x)|$ when $x = 3, 2,$ 1, 0, -1 and -2
   (i) $f(x) = 2x - 1$ (ii) $f(x) = x^2 - x - 2$
   In each case sketch the graphs of $f(x)$ and $|f(x)|$. Comment on the relationship between the graphs.

6. Solve the inequalities
   (i) $|3x + 1| > 5$ (ii) $|2 - 5x| < 3$
   (iii) $|\frac{1}{2}x + 3| < 2$ (iv) $|x^2 - 9| < 5$
   (v) $|x^2 + 6| > 10$ *(vi) $|2x - x^2| > 3$

7. Sketch the graphs of $|x + 1|$ and $|3x - 2|$ on the same axes. Hence find the values of x for which $|3x - 2| > |x + 1|$.

15.2 Further inequalities

The second rule for handling inequalities is that when multiplying through by a negative quantity we must change the direction of the inequality sign. This rule is often overlooked which inevitably leads to error.

To illustrate the rule consider the simple inequality $5 > 3$. If we multiply both numbers by a positive number such as 2 then the direction of the inequality is preserved $(10 > 6)$ but if we multiply by -2, obtaining the numbers -10 and -6, the direction of the inequality is reversed $(-10 < -6)$.

The same rule applies when dividing the terms in an inequality.

Example   96

Solve the inequality $2x - 7 < \dfrac{4}{x}$.

It is tempting to multiply through by x, giving $2x^2 - 7x < 4$, and then proceed as in Example 94 part (i). But this will be incorrect if x is negative for then the direction of the inequality is changed as a result of the multiplication. We must therefore consider separate cases as follows.

Case (i) $x > 0$ then $2x^2 - 7x < 4$
$$\Rightarrow \quad 2x^2 - 7x - 4 < 0$$

Case (ii) $x < 0$ then $2x^2 - 7x > 4$ (inequality reversed)
$$\Rightarrow \quad 2x^2 - 7x - 4 > 0$$

We now sketch the function $2x^2 - 7x - 4$ or $(2x + 1)(x - 4)$. Looking first at the region $x > 0$ (unshaded in Fig. 2) we see that the function is negative for $0 < x < 4$. Secondly, looking at the region $x < 0$ (shaded in Fig. 2) we see that the function is positive for $x < -\frac{1}{2}$.

Case (iii) We must also consider the isolated value $x = 0$. For this value the function $4/x$ is not defined. Although 'infinite', it is not necessarily greater then $2x - 7$ since it may be negative (see also Fig. 3.) The solutions are therefore $x < -\frac{1}{2}$ and $0 < x < 4$

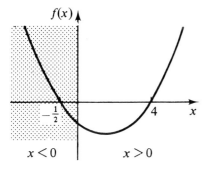

Fig. 2

Note: This inequality may also be solved by sketching $2x - 7$ and $4/x$ on the same axes as in Fig. 3. After finding the intersections of the graphs the solutions may be written down by inspection.

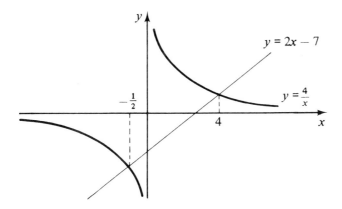

Fig. 3

Example 97

Find the values of x for which $\dfrac{x+1}{2-x} > 1$.

Here we multiply through by $(2 - x)$ and different cases must be considered as follows.

Case (i) $(2 - x)$ positive (i.e. $x < 2$)

$$x + 1 > 2 - x$$
$$\Rightarrow 2x > 1 \quad \text{or} \quad x > \tfrac{1}{2}$$

But this working was restricted to $x < 2$ so solutions are $\quad \tfrac{1}{2} < x < 2$

Case (ii) $(2 - x)$ negative (i.e. $x > 2$)

$$x + 1 < 2 - x \qquad \text{(inequality reversed)}$$
$$\Rightarrow 2x < 1 \quad \text{or} \quad x < \tfrac{1}{2} \quad \#$$

This contradicts the requirement that $x > 2$ so no solutions are obtained here. (# means contradiction).

Case (iii) $(2 - x)$ zero (i.e. $x = 2$). As with case (iii) in Example 96 the function is not defined uniquely and so $x = 2$ is not considered to be a solution

The solutions are therefore $\frac{1}{2} < x < 2$

Exercise (15(b)

Solve the following inequalities:

1. $2x - 5 > \dfrac{3}{x}$ 2. $\dfrac{x + 1}{x - 3} < 5$ 3. $\dfrac{x + 2}{4 - x} \geqslant \dfrac{1}{3}$

4. $\dfrac{x + 2}{x} > 3x$ 5. $x + 1 > \dfrac{3}{x - 1}$ 6. $3 - x \geqslant \dfrac{4}{x^2}$

*7. $\dfrac{1}{x} > \dfrac{1}{x - 2}$ *8. $\left|\dfrac{x}{x - 1}\right| > 3$ 9. $\left|\dfrac{2 + x}{x - 3}\right| > 4$

10. $\dfrac{1}{x} < \dfrac{1}{4 - x}$

*11. $1 + 2 \sin x < \operatorname{cosec} x$ (Give answers for x between $0°$ and $360°$.)

12. $\sec x - \cos x > \sin x$ (Hint: divide by $\cos x$.)

15.3 Sketching rational functions

A rational function is one which takes the form of a fraction, (just as a rational number is one which may be written as a fraction). When making simple sketches of these functions the first things to consider are
(i)   Intersections with the axes
(ii)   Values of x for which the function becomes infinite. (These give rise to vertical asymptotes.)
(iii) Behaviour of the function as $x \to \infty$ and $x \to -\infty$.

If necessary one can also investigate
(iv) The sign of the function (i.e. whether it is positive or negative for certain ranges of values of x).
(v) Turning points. (Calculation required.)
The calculation of turning points is at present beyond the scope of the student (see Section 16.5).

Example   98

Sketch the functions (i) $\dfrac{3 - x}{x + 2}$ (ii) $\dfrac{x^2 + x - 2}{x^2 - 2x - 3}$

(i) $f(x) = \dfrac{3 - x}{x + 2}$

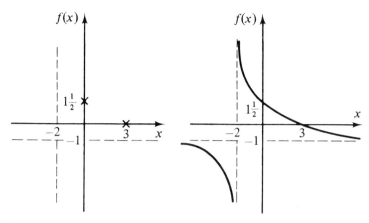

Fig. 4a   Fig. 4b

Fig. 4a is obtained by marking on the following features:

   intersection with x axis : $f(x) = 0$ when $x = 3$
   intersection with y axis : when $x = 0$ $f(x) = \frac{3}{2} = 1\frac{1}{2}$
   vertical asymptote   : $f(x)$ infinite when $x = -2$
   horizontal asymptote   : as $x \to \pm\infty$ $f(x) \to \dfrac{-x}{x}$ or -1

When x becomes very large the graph must approach the horizontal asymptote
and when x approaches the value -2 the graph must approach the vertical
asymptote. (These are marked as broken lines in Fig. 4a.) It is also important to
realise that there can be *no further intersections with the axes* other than those
which have been found. Bearing this in mind the function can only be sketched
as in Fig. 4b. (Notice that the section of the curve for $x < -2$ must go below
the horizontal asymptote rather than above, since this would involve a further
intersection with the x axis.)

(ii) $f(x) = \dfrac{x^2 + x - 2}{x^2 - 2x - 3}$ or $\dfrac{(x+2)(x-1)}{(x-3)(x+1)}$

Here we observe

   intersection with x-axis: $f(x) = 0$ when $x = -2$ and $x = 1$
   intersection with y-axis : when $x = 0$, $f(x) = \frac{-2}{-3} = +\frac{2}{3}$
   vertical asymptotes   : $f(x)$ infinite when $x = 3$ and $x = -1$
   horizontal asymptote : as $x \to \pm\infty$ $f(x) \to \dfrac{x^2}{x^2}$ or   1

Note: A strict justification of the behaviour as $x \to \pm\infty$ is obtained by
dividing the function top and bottom by x^2, i.e.

$$f(x) = \frac{x^2 + x - 2}{x^2 - 2x - 3} = \frac{1 + \dfrac{1}{x} - \dfrac{2}{x^2}}{1 - \dfrac{2}{x} - \dfrac{3}{x^2}}$$

Then when $x \to \pm\infty$, $\dfrac{1}{x}$ and $\dfrac{1}{x^2} \to 0$ so $f(x) \to \dfrac{1}{1}$ or   1

We now have Fig. 5a from which it is already possible to sketch the graph correctly if we remember that no further intersections with the axes are allowed. However, we shall use this example to demonstrate how consideration of the sign of the function may be used to restrict the curve to the shaded regions of Fig. 5b.

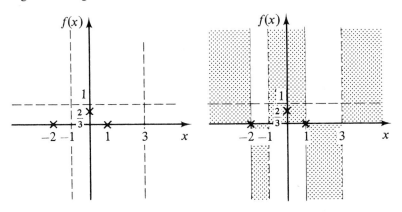

Fig. 5a   Fig. 5b

The best method is as follows. When x is large and positive all four factors in the function are positive so $f(x)$ is itself positive. Now imagine that x is decreased steadily (on the graph we move from right to left progressively).

As $x =$ 3 is passed $(x-3)$ becomes $-$ so $f(x)$ becomes $-$
     $x =$ 1 is passed $(x-1)$ becomes $-$ so $f(x)$ becomes $+$
     $x = -1$ is passed $(x+1)$ becomes $-$ so $f(x)$ becomes $-$
     $x = -2$ is passed $(x+2)$ becomes $-$ so $f(x)$ becomes $+$

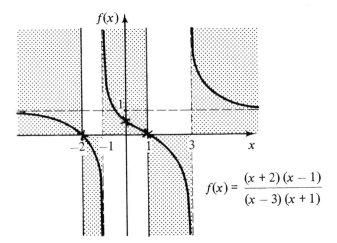

$$f(x) = \frac{(x+2)(x-1)}{(x-3)(x+1)}$$

Fig. 6

(i.e. consider the values of x at which each factor in turn changes sign.) In this way we can quickly shade in the regions through which the curve must pass (Fig. 5b). Remember that only the broken lines are asymptotes.

The final sketch is shown in Fig. 6.

Exercise 15(c)

1. Sketch the function $\dfrac{x-2}{x+3}$. Hence write down the values of x for which

   (i) $\dfrac{x-2}{x+3} > 1$ (ii) $\dfrac{x-2}{x+3} < -\dfrac{2}{3}$

2. Sketch the function $\dfrac{x}{x-1}$ and hence solve the inequality $\dfrac{x}{x-1} > 0$.

3. Sketch the function $\dfrac{x^2-2x-3}{x^2-4}$. Hence find the values of x for which

   $\dfrac{x^2-2x-3}{x^2-4} < 1$.

4. Sketch the function $\dfrac{x}{x^2-1}$

*5. Sketch the function $f(x) = \dfrac{(x-1)^2}{x^2-2x}$

   Your sketch should indicate that there is a range of values which the function $f(x)$ cannot take (for any value of x). What is this range of values?

*6. Sketch the function $f(x) = \dfrac{3x-9}{x^2-x-2}$. Show that $f(x)$ must take a maximum value in the range $x > 3$ and a minimum value in the range $0 < x < 2$.

15.4 Values taken by a rational function

In question 5 of Exercise 15(c) the function $f(x)$ does not take values between 0 and 1. The student who has successfully sketched the function of question 6 will see that the same sort of situation almost certainly arises. The function takes a maximum value (unknown) somewhere in $x > 3$ and a minimum (also unknown) somewhere in $0 < x < 2$. Between these maximum and minimum values is a range of values which the function cannot take. In this section we introduce a method by which the precise range of values taken (or not taken) by a rational function may be ascertained.

Example 99

Find the range of values which the function $f(x) = \dfrac{3x-9}{x^2-x-2}$ cannot take.

Let the value of the function $f(x)$ be k, i.e.

$$\frac{3x-9}{x^2-x-2} = k$$

then $3x-9 = k(x^2-x-2)$

$\Rightarrow \qquad 0 = kx^2 - (k+3)x + (9-2k)$

At this stage we have rearranged the terms into a quadratic equation in x. Solving this equation gives the values of x for which the function takes the particular value k. It follows that if this equation cannot be solved then the function cannot take the value k, (since no value of x exists which leads to this value). With the usual notation for quadratic equations we deduce that

$f(x)$ cannot take value k if $b^2 - 4ac < 0$

$\Rightarrow \quad (k+3)^2 - 4k(9-2k) < 0$

$\qquad k^2 + 6k + 9 - 36k + 8k^2 < 0$

$\qquad 9k^2 - 30k + 9 < 0$

or $\quad 3k^2 - 10k + 3 < 0 \qquad$ (dividing by 3)

A simple sketch of the quadratic function $3k^2 - 10k + 3$ or $(3k-1)(k-3)$ shows that it is zero for $k = \frac{1}{3}$ and $k = 3$ and less than zero for $\frac{1}{3} < k < 3$.

Hence the function cannot take values in the range $\frac{1}{3} < f(x) < 3$. A sketch of the function is shown in Fig. 7. (The x-axis is a horizontal asymptote.)

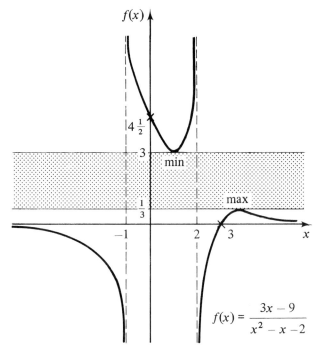

Fig. 7

Note: It follows that the function may take *all other values*, i.e. all values $f(x)$ such that $f(x) \geqslant 3$ and $f(x) \leqslant \frac{1}{3}$.

Exercise 15(d)

In numbers 1 and 2 find the values which the functions cannot take and sketch the functions.

1. $\dfrac{4}{x^2 - 4x + 3}$ 2. $\dfrac{3x - 6}{x^2 + 6x}$

In numbers 3 and 4 find the complete range of values taken by the functions and sketch the functions.

3. $\dfrac{(x - 3)(x - 1)}{(x - 2)^2}$ 4. $\dfrac{1}{x^2 + 1}$

*5. Show that the function $\dfrac{4x - p}{x^2 - 1}$ can take the value k providing

$$k^2 - pk + 4 \geqslant 0 \tag{1}$$

(i) For the case $p = 5$ find the complete range of values taken by the function.

(ii) For the case $p = 2$ show that the inequality (1) is always true. What can be deduced about the case $p = 2$?

(iii) Prove that the function can take all real values if $-4 \leqslant p \leqslant 4$.

6. Prove that, irrespective of the value of q, the function $f(x) = \dfrac{(x + q)^2}{x^2 + q^2}$

takes values in the range $0 \leqslant f(x) \leqslant 2$ only. Find the values of x for which $f(x) = 0$ and $f(x) = 2$. Sketch the curve.

*7. Prove that the function $\dfrac{ax + 1}{x(x + 1)}$ takes all real values if $a \geqslant 1$. Find also the range of values taken by the function when $a = -3$.

8. Show that if the function $f(x) = \dfrac{x^2 - 2rx + 1}{x^2 + 1}$ takes the value k then

$(k - 1)^2 \leqslant r^2$. Hence prove that the function takes only those values in the range $1 - r \leqslant f(x) \leqslant 1 + r$.

15.5 Polar coordinates

In polar coordinates (r, θ) the position of a point in two dimensions is specified by giving

(i) the distance of the point from the origin, r

(ii) the angle θ (Fig. 8a) measured *anti-clockwise* from the direction of the x axis (sometimes called the 'initial line').

Fig. 8b illustrates the position of the point P whose polar coordinates are $(3, 5\pi/6)$. Notice that the direction of the line OP could also be fixed by giving a negative value of θ, i.e. $-7\pi/6$ (or $-210°$). It is usual to give θ in the range $-\pi \leqslant \theta \leqslant \pi$, though $0 \leqslant \theta \leqslant 2\pi$ may often be encountered.

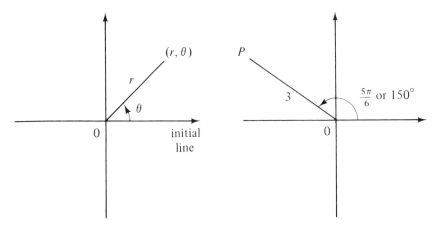

Fig. 8a   Fig. 8b

Conversion to cartesian coordinates (x, y)

If a rough sketch is drawn it is a simple matter to convert polar coordinates to Cartesian coordinates. For example, Fig. 8b shows us that the point P with polar coordinates $(3, 5\pi/6)$ has Cartesian coordinates (x, y) given by

$$x = -3 \cos 30° = -3\sqrt{3}/2$$
$$y = 3 \sin 30° = 1\tfrac{1}{2}$$

In general $x = r \cos \theta$ and $y = r \sin \theta$. (See fig. 8a).

To find the polar coordinates of a point specified in conventional Cartesian coordinates, find the distance r by Pythagoras, and obtain θ by using tangents. For example, the point $Q(-2, -4)$ in Fig. 9a has polar coordinates

$$r = \sqrt{20} = 2\sqrt{5} \quad (\approx 4.472)$$
$$\theta \approx -116.6° \quad \text{or} \quad -2.035 \,\text{rad}$$

(since $\tan \alpha = 2$ so that $\alpha \approx 63.4°$ – see Fig. 9a)

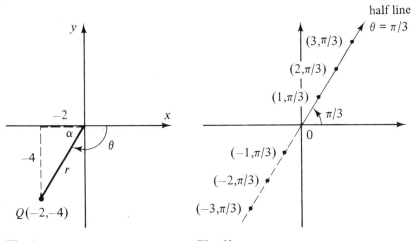

Fig. 9a   Fig. 9b

In general $r = \sqrt{x^2 + y^2}$ and $\theta = \arctan{(y/x)}$

Negative values of r

When plotting curves from their polar equations (see example 100) it is not uncommon to encounter points whose values of r are negative, e.g. $(-1, \pi/3)$ and $(-2, \pi/3)$. How are the positions of these points to be found?

Consider the points $(3, \pi/3)$, $(2, \pi/3)$ and $(1, \pi/3)$. These lie on the **half-line** $\theta = \pi/3$, i.e. the line outwards from the origin in the direction indicated by $\theta = \pi/3$ (see Fig. 9b). When considered in the order stated these three points lie progressively closer to the origin and the point $(0, \pi/3)$ is of course the origin itself. Continuing this sequence we see that $(-1, \pi/3)$ and $(-2, \pi/3)$ must be in the positions indicated in Fig. 9b, i.e. on the half-line leaving the origin in the *opposite* direction to $\theta = \pi/3$. Note that these positions could also be specified as $(1, -2\pi/3)$ and $(2, -2\pi/3)$.

Example 100

Sketch the curve whose polar equation is $r = a(1 + 2\cos\theta)$ where a is a constant.

We first complete the table below which gives approximate values for $(1 + 2\cos\theta)$ at steps of $30°$ for the angle θ. Strictly speaking the angle θ should be in radians but it is easier to use degrees for curve plotting.

θ	$\cos\theta$	$1 + 2\cos\theta$	θ	$\cos\theta$	$1 + 2\cos\theta$
0	1	3	210	-0.866	-0.732
30	0.866	2.732	240	-0.5	0
60	0.5	2	270	0	1
90	0	1	300	0.5	2
120	-0.5	0	330	0.866	2.732
150	-0.866	-0.732	360	1	3
180	-1	-1			

Using polar graph paper and taking units of a, the points may now be plotted and the curve of Fig. 10 obtained. Care is needed with the points for which r is negative. The point for $150°$, for example, is plotted in the position marked Z in Fig. 10

Exercise 15(e)

1. The following points are given in polar coordinates:
    (i) $A(2, 0)$, $B(2, 2\pi/3)$, $C(2, 4\pi/3)$
    (ii) $P(6, \pi/6)$, $Q(3, \pi/2)$, $R(6, -5\pi/6)$, $S(3, -\pi/2)$
    Draw diagrams to show these positions. Describe the figures ABC and $PQRS$ and find their areas.
2. Plot the positions of the following points, given in polar coordinates:
    (i) $(3, \frac{1}{4}\pi)$, $(2, \frac{1}{4}\pi)$, $(1, \frac{1}{4}\pi)$, $(-1, \frac{1}{4}\pi)$, $(-3, \frac{1}{4}\pi)$
    (ii) $(5, \frac{2}{3}\pi)$, $(3, \frac{2}{3}\pi)$, $(1, \frac{2}{3}\pi)$, $(-1, \frac{2}{3}\pi)$, $(-3, \frac{2}{3}\pi)$
    In each case suggest alternative polar coordinates for the last two points.

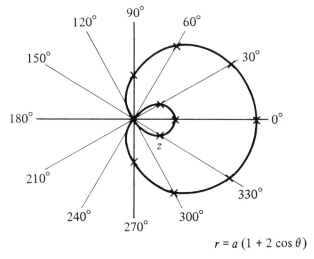

$r = a\,(1 + 2\cos\theta)$

Fig. 10

3. Show the approximate positions of the following points, given in polar coordinates $(r,\ \theta)$. Hence find the corresponding Cartesian coordinates $(x,\ y)$.

$(3,\ \tfrac{1}{2}\pi),\quad (4,\ \tfrac{1}{3}\pi),\quad (2,\ -\tfrac{1}{4}\pi),\quad (5,\ \pi),\quad (\sqrt{3},\ \tfrac{7}{6}\pi),\quad (10,\ 2).$

4. Find the polar coordinates $(r,\ \theta)$ of the following points given in Cartesian coordinates. (Give the values of θ in radians.)

$(0,\ -6),\quad (1,\ 1),\quad (-2,\ 0),\quad (3,\ 4),\quad (-5,\ -12),\quad (1,\ -\sqrt{3})$

5. Plot the following curves taking θ in $30°$ steps from 0 to $360°$:
   (i) $r = a(1 + \cos\theta)$ (ii) $r = a(1 + 3\sin\theta)$
   (iii) $r = a\sin\tfrac{1}{2}\theta$ (iv) $r = a(1 - \sin\theta)$
   In part (iii) add a further section of curve by considering values of θ from $360°$ to $720°$.

6. Plot the following curves taking θ in $15°$ steps from 0 to $180°$:
   (i) $r = 5\cos\theta$ (ii) $r = a\sin 2\theta$
   (iii) $r = \sec\theta$ *(iv) $r = a(1 + \sin 2\theta)$
   In each case consider whether any further sections of curve need be added for values of θ from $180°$ to $360°$.

7. Make rough sketches of the following curves:
   (i) $r = a\sin 3\theta$ (ii) $r = a\tan\theta$ (iii) $r = a\cos 2\theta$

15.6 Some special polar equations

(i) $r = a$ (constant) r takes the same value a for any angle θ (Fig. 11a). The result is a circle of radius a, centre the origin.

(ii) $\theta = \alpha$ (constant)   A 'half-line' as in Fig. 9b (though if negative values of r are permitted a complete line is obtained.).

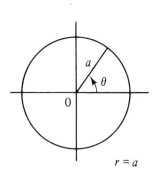

Fig. 11a

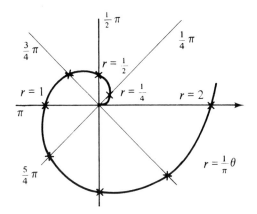

Fig. 11b

(iii) $r = k\theta$ (k constant)

A spiral, as in Fig. 11b (which sketches the curve $r = \frac{1}{\pi}\cdot\theta$). The spiral continues if values of θ above 2π are considered.

(iv) $r = a \cos \theta$

This is a circle of diameter a passing through the origin (as in Fig. 12a). This follows since the angle in a semi-circle is $90°$.

(v) $r = a \sec \theta$

Fig. 12b shows that this is a straight line parallel to the y-axis passing through $x = a$.

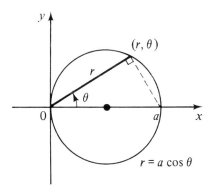

Fig. 12a

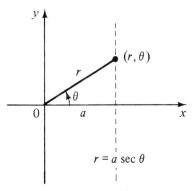

Fig. 12b

Conversion of equations (polar/cartesian coordinates)

The equation of a curve given in Cartesian form may be converted to polar form, or vice-versa, using the conversion results of Section 15.5. These are grouped here for convenience.

$$x = r\cos\theta \qquad r^2 = x^2 + y^2$$
$$y = r\sin\theta \qquad \tan\theta = \frac{y}{x}$$

Example 101

Convert the equations

(i) $x^2 + y^2 - 6x = 0$ to polar form
(ii) $r = a(1 + 2\cos\theta)$ to Cartesian form

(i) $x^2 + y^2 - 6x = 0 \Rightarrow r^2\cos^2\theta + r^2\sin^2\theta - 6r\cos\theta = 0$

$$r^2 = 6r\cos\theta$$

i.e. $r = 6\cos\theta$ (if $r \neq 0$)

This is a circle of diameter 6 units as in Fig. 12a.

(ii) In order that we may use the relation $x = r\cos\theta$ it is convenient to multiply both sides of this equation by r

$$r = a(1 + 2\cos\theta) \Rightarrow r^2 = ar + 2ar\cos\theta$$
$$x^2 + y^2 = a\sqrt{x^2 + y^2} + 2ax$$

We now isolate the square root term and square both sides

$$(x^2 + y^2 - 2ax)^2 = a^2(x^2 + y^2)$$

No simplification is achieved by proceeding further. (This curve is the one sketched in Fig. 10 and it is hardly surprising that its Cartesian equation is complicated.)

Exercise 15(f)

All the coordinates given in this exercise are Cartesian.

1. Find the polar equations of the following straight lines:
    (i)   through the origin inclined at angle α to the initial line
    (ii) perpendicular to the initial line and 5 units right of 0
    (iii) parallel to the initial line and 4 units above 0
2. Find the polar equations of the following circles:
    (i)   radius a, centre $(a, 0)$
    (ii) radius a, centre $(0, a)$
    (iii) radius a, centre $(2a, 0)$
3. Convert the following Cartesian equations into polar form:
    (i) $y = 3$ (ii) $x = 0$
    (iii) $x^2 + y^2 = 4$ (iv) $x^2 - y^2 = 4$
    (v) $y^2 = 4ax$ (vi) $x^2 + (y - 3)^2 = 9$
4. Find the Cartesian equations of the following curves:
    (i) $\theta = \frac{3}{4}\pi$ (ii) $r = 2\sin\theta$
    (iii) $r = a(1 + \cos\theta)$ (iv) $r^2 = \operatorname{cosec} 2\theta$
    (v) $r = a\cot\theta$ (vi) $\frac{1}{r} = 1 + \cos\theta$

5. Show that the polar equation of the circle centre (a, a) which passes through the origin is $r = 2a(\cos\theta + \sin\theta)$.

6. A point moves so that its distance from the origin is always equal to its distance from the line $x = a$. Show that the equation of its locus is $r = a/(1 + \cos\theta)$.

7. A point moves so that the sum of its distances from the origin and the point $(d, 0)$ is constant and equal to $2d$. Show that the polar equation of the locus is $r = 3d/(4 - 2\cos\theta)$.

*8. (i) By considering Fig. 13 show that the equation $r = p\sec(\theta - \alpha)$ represents a straight line for which the perpendicular from the origin is of length p and is inclined at angle α to the initial line.

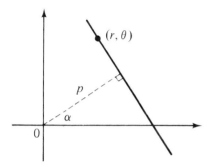

Fig. 13

(ii) Show that the corresponding Cartesian equation is $x\cos\alpha + y\sin\alpha = p$. (This is called the 'perpendicular form' for the equation of a straight line.)

(iii) Express the following straight lines in perpendicular form and hence state the distance of each from the origin:
$3x - 4y = 8$, $2x + y = 5$, $ax + by + c = 0$.

16

Methods of Differentiation

16.1 The product rule

We need to be able to differentiate functions such as $x^2 \cos 3x$ which is the product of two simpler functions. As *separate* terms each of these could be differentiated with ease, i.e.

$$\frac{d(x^2)}{dx} = 2x \qquad \frac{d}{dx}(\cos 3x) = -3 \sin 3x$$

but when multiplied together they form a *single* more complicated term which is harder to deal with.

All functions of this type may be written as $y = uv$ where u and v are functions of x. Let an increase δx in the value of x cause corresponding changes δu and δv in these functions. Then the new value for the product y is defined as follows:

$$y + \delta y = (u + \delta u)(v + \delta v)$$
$$\text{hence} \quad y + \delta y = uv + u \cdot \delta v + v \cdot \delta u + \delta u \cdot \delta v$$
$$\delta y = u \cdot \delta v + v \cdot \delta u + \delta u \cdot \delta v \qquad (y = uv)$$
$$\Rightarrow \quad \frac{\delta y}{\delta x} = u \cdot \frac{\delta v}{\delta x} + v \cdot \frac{\delta u}{\delta x} + \frac{\delta u \cdot \delta v}{\delta x}$$

When we take the limit of each term as $\delta x \to 0$ we obtain the following result

$$\boxed{\frac{d}{dx}(uv) = u \cdot \frac{dv}{dx} + v \cdot \frac{du}{dx}}$$

The last term vanishes since it may be regarded as either

$$\frac{du}{dx} \left\{ \underset{\delta x \to 0}{\text{Lim}} \delta v \right\} \qquad \text{or} \qquad \left\{ \underset{\delta x \to 0}{\text{Lim}} \delta u \right\} \frac{dv}{dx}$$

both of which are zero since $\delta v \to 0$ and $\delta u \to 0$.

Example 102

Differentiate each of the following functions:

(i) $x^2 \cos 3x$ (ii) $\dfrac{\sin x}{x^2}$ (iii) $2x \sqrt{1 - x^2}$

For ease of understanding the working has been set out in a table. In practice, of course, this is unnecessary.

$u.v$	$u \cdot \dfrac{dv}{dx} + v \cdot \dfrac{du}{dx}$
(i) $x^2.\cos 3x$	$x^2.(-3 \sin 3x) + (\cos 3x).2x$
(ii) $\dfrac{1}{x^2} \cdot \sin x$	$\dfrac{1}{x^2} \cdot \cos x + \sin x.\left(\dfrac{-2}{x^3}\right)$
(iii) $2x \cdot (1-x^2)^{\frac{1}{2}}$	$2x\left\{\dfrac{1}{2} \cdot \dfrac{-2x}{(1-x^2)^{\frac{1}{2}}}\right\} + 2 \cdot (1-x^2)^{\frac{1}{2}}$

The results for the first two functions may be written as

(i) $-3x^2 \sin 3x + 2x \cos 3x$ (ii) $\dfrac{\cos x}{x^2} - \dfrac{2 \sin x}{x^3}$

That obtained for function (iii) may be simplified by using a common denominator, i.e.

$$\dfrac{-2x^2}{(1-x^2)^{\frac{1}{2}}} + 2(1-x^2)^{\frac{1}{2}} = \dfrac{-2x^2 + 2(1-x^2)}{(1-x^2)^{\frac{1}{2}}} = \dfrac{2-4x^2}{\sqrt{1-x^2}}$$

Exercise 16(a)

1. Differentiate
   (i) $x^2 \sin x$ (ii) $x(3x-1)^4$ (iii) $2x \cos^2 x$
   (iv) $x\sqrt{1+x}$ (v) $\dfrac{\tan 2x}{x^2}$ (vi) $\sin^2 x \cos x$

2. Differentiate
   (i) $x \tan x$ (ii) $(2x-3)^2 (x+1)^3$ (iii) $\dfrac{\cos x}{x}$
   (iv) $\sin 2x \cos 3x$ (v) $(1+x)\sqrt{1+x^2}$ (vi) $3x \cot x$

3. Find the values of x for which the gradients of the following functions are zero. (In part (iii) consider $0 \leqslant x < 2\pi$ only.)
   (i) $y = (3x+1)^2 (x-2)^2$ (ii) $y = \dfrac{\sqrt{x}}{x+1}$ (iii) $y = \sin x \cos^3 x$

4. Find the second derivative for each of the following functions:
   (i) $x^3 \cos x$ (ii) $x^2 (2x+1)^4$ (iii) $\sin x \cos 3x$

5. Find the gradients of the following curves at the points specified:
   (i) $y = (x+1)^2 \tan x$ at $x = \pi$
   (ii) $y = x \sin x \cos x$ at $x = \frac{1}{2}\pi$
   (iii) $y = \dfrac{\sqrt{x-1}}{x^2}$ at the point $(5, +\frac{2}{25})$

6. Show that there are three points on the curve $y = (x+1)^3 (x-1)^2$ where the gradient is zero. Investigate the nature of these points.

16.2 Implicit differentiation

With curves such as $y^2 - 2xy + x^2 - y = 6$ it is not normally possible to obtain an expression for y in terms of x alone. In order to obtain the gradient of the curve $\dfrac{dy}{dx}$ a method known as **implicit differentiation** is used. Here we differentiate each term with respect to x, treating terms involving y in the way indicated by the following examples:

$$\frac{d}{dx}(y^2) = \frac{d}{dy}\cdot(y^2)\cdot\frac{dy}{dx} = 2y\cdot\frac{dy}{dx}$$

$$\frac{d}{dx}(3y) = \frac{d}{dy}(3y)\cdot\frac{dy}{dx} = 3\cdot\frac{dy}{dx}$$

$$\frac{d}{dx}\left(\frac{1}{y}\right) = \frac{d}{dy}\left(\frac{1}{y}\right)\cdot\frac{dy}{dx} = \frac{-1}{y^2}\cdot\frac{dy}{dx}$$

i.e. differentiate first with respect to y and then multiply by $\dfrac{dy}{dx}$. Terms such as xy are treated in accordance with the product rule

$$\frac{d}{dx}(xy) = x\cdot\frac{d}{dx}(y) + y\cdot\frac{d}{dx}(x) = x\cdot\frac{dy}{dx} + y$$

Example   103

Find $\dfrac{dy}{dx}$ for the curve $y^2 - 2xy + x^2 - y = 6$. Hence find the gradient at the points where $x = 6$.

First differentiate each term in the manner illustrated above. This gives

$$2y\cdot\frac{dy}{dx} - 2\left(x\cdot\frac{dy}{dx} + y\right) + 2x - \frac{dy}{dx} = 0$$

Then collect together all the terms involving $\dfrac{dy}{dx}$

$$(2y - 2x - 1)\frac{dy}{dx} = 2y - 2x \tag{1}$$

$$\Rightarrow \qquad \frac{dy}{dx} = \frac{2y - 2x}{2y - 2x - 1}$$

Notice that in order to find the gradient at a particular point on the curve both the x and y coordinates are required. In order to find the y coordinate when $x = 6$ we substitute $x = 6$ into the original equation, obtaining

$$y^2 - 12y + 36 - y = 6$$
$$y^2 - 13y + 30 \quad = 0$$
$$(y - 3)(y - 10) \quad = 0$$
$$y = 3 \qquad \text{or} \quad y = 10$$

There are 2 points on this curve with x coordinate 6,

at (6, 3) the gradient is $\dfrac{2y-2x}{2y-2x-1} = \dfrac{6-12}{6-12-1} = \dfrac{6}{7}$

at (6, 10) the gradient is $\dfrac{2y-2x}{2y-2x-1} = \dfrac{20-12}{20-12-1} = \dfrac{8}{7}$

Note: This method of differentiation may also be used for relatively simple functions such as $y^2 = 9x$ which could be differentiated by conventional methods, i.e.

$$y^2 = 9x \Rightarrow y = 3x^{-\frac{1}{2}} \Rightarrow \frac{dy}{dx} = \frac{3}{2}x^{-\frac{1}{2}}$$

By the implicit method we obtain

$$2y \cdot \frac{dy}{dx} = 9 \Rightarrow \frac{dy}{dx} = \frac{9}{2y}$$

This result gives the gradient in terms of the y coordinate. It is simpler to use than the first result given.

Exercise 16(b)

1. Differentiate each of the following terms with respect to x:

$3y^2,\ 6y,\ y^3,\ \dfrac{1}{y^2},\ \tan y,\ 2xy,\ x^2y,\ \dfrac{x}{y}$

2. Find $\dfrac{dy}{dx}$ for each of the following:
   (i) $y^2 = 4x^2 + 1$
   (ii) $2y^2 - x^2 = 3y + 3$
   (iii) $y^2 + 2x^2 - 3xy = 3$
   (iv) $\dfrac{1}{x} + \dfrac{1}{y} = 5$
   (v) $x^2y + y^2 = x$
   (vi) $2\cos x + 3\sin y = 1$

3. Find the gradients of the following curves at the points specified:
   (i) $y^2 = 2x^3 - 7$ at the point (4, 11)
   (ii) $3xy^2 = 5 + x - y$ at the intersection with the y-axis
   (iii) $x^2 + y^2 + 2xy - x = 7$ at the points where $x = 2$

4. Find the intersections of the curve $2y^2 + x^2 + xy - x = 6$ with the x-axis. Find also the equations of the tangents to the curve at these points.

5. Find the intersections of the line $y = 2x + 1$ with the curve $y^2 + 3x^2 - 3y - xy = 0$ and obtain the gradient of the curve at these points.

6. (i) If $\sin y = x$ prove that $\dfrac{dy}{dx} = \dfrac{1}{\sqrt{1-x^2}}$

   (ii) If $\tan y = x^2$ prove that $\dfrac{dy}{dx} = \dfrac{2x}{1+x^4}$

16.3 Further implicit differentiation (second derivative)

Example   104

Find $\dfrac{d^2y}{dx^2}$ for the curve $3y^2 - x^2 + y = 5$

Differentiating the first time gives

$$6y \cdot \frac{dy}{dx} - 2x + \frac{dy}{dx} = 0$$

i.e. $(6y + 1)\dfrac{dy}{dx} = 2x$ (1)

Do not solve for $\dfrac{dy}{dx}$ but proceed with the second differentiation, treating the left-hand side as a product, i.e.

$$(6y + 1) \cdot \frac{d}{dx}\left(\frac{dy}{dx}\right) + \frac{dy}{dx} \cdot \frac{d}{dx}(6y + 1) = \frac{d}{dx}(2x)$$

$$\Rightarrow \quad (6y + 1) \cdot \frac{d^2y}{dx^2} + \frac{dy}{dx} \cdot \left(6 \cdot \frac{dy}{dx}\right) = 2 \tag{2}$$

The working is completed by substituting the result for $\dfrac{dy}{dx}$ which is given by(1)

$$(6y + 1)\frac{d^2y}{dx^2} = 2 - 6\left(\frac{dy}{dx}\right)^2 = 2 - \frac{24x^2}{(6y + 1)^2}$$

$$\Rightarrow \quad \frac{d^2y}{dx^2} = \frac{2}{(6y + 1)} - \frac{24x^2}{(6y + 1)^3}$$

Problems on maxima and minima

When the second derivative is needed only for the investigation of turning points we may obtain a simpler result since at turning points we have $\dfrac{dy}{dx} = 0$. Thus in the above example line (2) reduces to

$$\frac{d^2y}{dx^2} = \frac{2}{6y + 1}$$

It is important to remember that this simplified result will only be valid at points where $\dfrac{dy}{dx} = 0$.

Example   105

Find any maximum and minimum points on the curve of Example 103 $(y^2 - 2xy + x^2 - y = 6)$.

For this curve we obtained $\dfrac{dy}{dx} = \dfrac{2y - 2x}{2y - 2x - 1}$

If $\dfrac{dy}{dx} = 0$ then $2y - 2x = 0 \Rightarrow y = x$.

So any turning points will lie on the line $y = x$ (i.e. will have equal coordinates). To find these points substitute $y = x$ into the equation of the curve

$$x^2 - 2x^2 + x^2 - x = 6 \Rightarrow x = -6$$

There is only 1 turning point: $(-6, -6)$.

To obtain the second derivative we proceed from line (1) of Example 103, i.e.

$$(2y - 2x - 1)\dfrac{dy}{dx} = 2y - 2x$$

$$\Rightarrow (2y - 2x - 1)\dfrac{d^2y}{dx^2} + \dfrac{dy}{dx} \cdot \dfrac{d}{dx}(2y - 2x - 1) = 2\dfrac{dy}{dx} - 2$$

At turning points the second derivative reduces to

$$\dfrac{d^2y}{dx^2} = \dfrac{-2}{2y - 2x - 1} \qquad\qquad \left(\dfrac{dy}{dx} = 0\right)$$

This is positive at the point $(-6, -6)$ which must therefore be a minimum point.

Exercise 16(c)

1. Find expressions for $\dfrac{d^2y}{dx^2}$ for Exercise 16(b), question 2, parts (i) and (ii).

2. Find the value of $\dfrac{dy}{dx}$ and of $\dfrac{d^2y}{dx^2}$ for

    (i) $y^2 + xy + x^2 = 3$ at the point $(1, -2)$
    (ii) $y^2 - x^2 - y + 2x = 2$ at the intersections with the y-axis.

3. Find the maximum and minimum points on each of the following curves:
    (i) $3y^2 = x^2 + 12$ (ii) $x^2 + 2y^2 - 6x - 3y = 0$
    (iii) $x^2y + y - 2x = 0$ (iv) $y^2 - x^2 - xy + y = 3$

16.4 Further rates of change

We now see how implicit differentiation and also the chain rule may be applied to problems involving rates of change.

Example 106

Air is blown into a balloon at a rate of $160\ \text{cm}^3/\text{sec}$. If the balloon is assumed spherical, find how quickly the radius is increasing at the instants when the radius is (i) 5 cm   (ii) 8 cm.

Method 1 (Chain Rule)

We are given the rate of increase of volume $\dfrac{dV}{dt} = +160$

We require the rate of increase of radius, i.e. $\dfrac{dr}{dt}$

By the chain rule $\quad \dfrac{dr}{dt} = \dfrac{dr}{dV} \cdot \dfrac{dV}{dt}$　　　　　　　(1)

also $V = \dfrac{4}{3}\pi r^3 \Rightarrow \dfrac{dV}{dr} = 4\pi r^2 \quad$ or $\quad \dfrac{dr}{dV} = \dfrac{1}{4\pi r^2}$

hence, from (1) $\quad \dfrac{dr}{dt} = \dfrac{1}{4\pi r^2} \cdot 160 = \dfrac{40}{\pi r^2}$　　　　　(2)

when $r = 5$ $\quad \dfrac{dr}{dt} = \dfrac{40}{25\pi} \approx \underline{0.51 \text{ cm/sec}}$

when $r = 8$ $\quad \dfrac{dr}{dt} = \dfrac{40}{64\pi} \approx \underline{0.20 \text{ cm/sec}}$

Method 2 (Implicit Differentiation)

Start from the formula for the volume of a sphere and differentiate both sides with respect to time t, i.e.

$$V = \frac{4}{3}\pi r^3 \Rightarrow \frac{dV}{dt} = \frac{d}{dt}\left(\frac{4}{3}\pi r^3\right) = \frac{d}{dr}\left(\frac{4}{3}\pi r^3\right)\frac{dr}{dt}$$

$$\frac{dV}{dt} = 4\pi r^2 \cdot \frac{dr}{dt} \tag{3}$$

Substituting $\dfrac{dV}{dt} = 160$ and rearranging gives line (2) of Method 1, from which the results are found as before.

Notes: In general the second method is neater. Line (3) may be written down directly. Care is necessary with the signs of all rates of change; remember that a quantity is decreasing if its rate of change is negative.

Example　107

Water drains from a conical funnel of semi-vertical angle $30°$ at a rate of $20 \text{ cm}^3/\text{sec}$. How rapidly is the level of water falling when the depth is 9 cm?

Here the volume of water in the funnel is a function of 2 variables (r and h) but we use the relation $r = h \tan 30 = \dfrac{h}{\sqrt{3}}$ (Fig. 1) to eliminate r, i.e.

$$V = \frac{1}{3}\pi r^2 h = \frac{1}{3}\pi\left(\frac{h^2}{3}\right)h = \frac{1}{9}\pi h^3$$

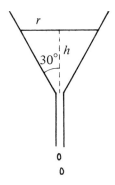

Fig. 1

Hence, differentiating with respect to time t

$$\frac{dV}{dt} = \frac{d}{dh}\left(\frac{1}{9}\pi h^3\right) \cdot \frac{dh}{dt} = \frac{1}{3}\pi h^2 \cdot \frac{dh}{dt}$$

$$\Rightarrow \frac{dh}{dt} = \frac{3}{\pi h^2} \cdot \frac{dV}{dt} = \frac{3}{\pi h^2} \cdot (-20) = \frac{-60}{\pi h^2}$$

when $h = 9$ $\frac{dh}{dt} = \frac{-60}{81\pi} \approx -0.24$

(i.e. the level is falling at approximately 0.24 cm/sec.)

Example 108

Two concentric circles have radii R and r $(R > r)$. If R increases steadily at 2 units/sec. and the area between the circles remains constant at 20 sq. units, find the rate at which r is increasing when $R = 5$.

We have $\qquad\qquad \pi R^2 - \pi r^2 = 20 \qquad\qquad$ (1)

If each term is differentiated (implicitly) with respect to time t we obtain

$$2\pi R \cdot \frac{dR}{dt} - 2\pi r \cdot \frac{dr}{dt} = 0$$

$$\Rightarrow \frac{dr}{dt} = \frac{2\pi R}{2\pi r} \cdot \frac{dR}{dt} = \frac{R}{r} \cdot \frac{dR}{dt} = \frac{2R}{r} \qquad \text{since} \qquad \frac{dR}{dt} = +2$$

To complete the question we must find the value of r when $R = 5$. From (1) we have

$$R^2 - r^2 = \frac{20}{\pi}$$

hence $\qquad\qquad r^2 = 25 - \frac{20}{\pi} \Rightarrow r \approx 4.317$

so, when $R = 5$ $\quad \dfrac{dR}{dt} = \dfrac{2R}{r} \approx \dfrac{10}{4.317}$ or 2.32

i.e. r is increasing at approximately 2.32 units/sec.

Exercise 16(d)

1. The radius of a circle is increasing by $\frac{1}{2}$ cm each second. Find how rapidly the area is increasing at the instant when the radius is (i) 5 cm (ii) 10 cm
2. The radius of a sphere is increasing by 0.6 cm each second. Find the rate at which (i) the surface area (ii) the volume is increasing at the instant when the radius is 12 cm.
3. A rectangle has dimensions x cm and y cm. Both x and y are changing but in such a way that the area of the rectangle remains constant at 40 cm^2. Show that

$$\frac{dy}{dt} = -\frac{40}{x^2} \cdot \frac{dx}{dt}$$

   If x increases at 0.2 cm/sec. find the rate at which y is changing when $x = 8$.
4. The volume of a cylinder is constant at 50 cm^3 but both the height h and the radius r are changing. Prove that

$$\frac{dh}{dt} = -\frac{100}{\pi r^3} \cdot \frac{dr}{dt}$$

   At the instant when the radius is 5 cm the height is decreasing by 3 cm/sec. What is the rate of change of radius at this instant?
5. The volume of a sphere is decreasing at 60 cm^3/sec. Find the rate at which the radius is decreasing when (i) the radius is 10 cm (ii) the volume is 800 cm^3
6. The volume of water required to fill a hemispherical bowl of radius r to a depth h is $\pi r h^2 - \frac{1}{3}\pi h^3$. Water runs into a bowl of radius 8 cm at a steady rate of 13 cm^3/sec. Find the rate at which the level of water is rising when the depth is (i) 3 cm (ii) 5 cm
7. The height of a conical funnel is 6 cm and the diameter of the circular rim is 8 cm. Find an expression for the volume of liquid in the funnel when the depth is h cm. If liquid drains from the funnel at 16 cm^3/sec, find the rate at which the level is falling when (i) $h = 6$ (ii) $h = 3$.
8. A trough 2 m in length has a triangular cross-section ABC in which $AB = AC = 40$ cm, angle $A = 90°$ and BC is horizontal. Find the capacity of the trough in litres. Water is poured into the trough at 5 litres per second. How fast is the level of water rising (i) when the depth is 10 cm? (ii) when the trough is half full?
9. The area of a circle is increasing by 50 cm^2/sec. Find the rate at which the circumference is increasing when the radius is 8 cm.
10. The volume of a cylinder is increasing by 30 cm^3/sec and the height is always twice the base radius. Find the rate at which the total surface area is increasing at the instant when the volume is 250π cm^3.
11. A rod AB is attached by rings at A and B to two perpendicular straight wires OA and OB. The end B moves away from O at 2 cm/sec. Find the

speed with which A is moving (i) when $OA = 2OB$ (ii) when $OA = OB$ (iii) when $OA = \frac{1}{2}OB$.

12. If, in question 11, the wires are such that angle $AOB = 120°$ and if $OA = x$, $OB = y$ prove that

$$\frac{dx}{dt} = -\frac{(2y + x)}{(2x + y)} \cdot \frac{dy}{dt}$$

Hence repeat question 11 for this situation.

13. The radius r and the height h of a solid cylinder change in such a way that the total surface area remains constant. Prove that

$$\frac{dh}{dt} = -\frac{(2r + h)}{r} \cdot \frac{dr}{dt}$$

and deduce that the height is always changing at least twice as rapidly as the radius.

14. In this question consider a balloon to be a spherical shell of outer radius R and inner radius r. As the balloon is inflated the volume of material in the shell remains constant. At a certain instant $R = 100$ mm, $r = 99$ mm and r is increasing at 5 mm/sec. Find the rates at which (i) R is increasing (ii) the thickness of the shell is decreasing at this instant.

15. The object distance u, image distance v and focal length f of a lens are related by the formula

$$\frac{1}{u} + \frac{1}{v} = \frac{1}{f}$$

If the focal length of a certain lens is 40 cm, find the image distance when the object is (i) 90 cm (ii) 60 cm from the lens. If the object is moved towards the lens at 10 cm/sec, find how rapidly the image is moving at the instants that the object passes through the positions (i) and (ii).

16. A triangle ABC has sides b and c fixed in length, but side a is increasing. Prove that angle A is increasing at a rate given by

$$\frac{dA}{dt} = \frac{a}{bc \sin A} \cdot \frac{da}{dt}$$

If $b = 8$ cm, $c = 5$ cm and a increases at $\frac{1}{2}$ cm/sec, find the rate of increase of angle A (in rads/sec) at the instant when $a = 7$ cm.

16.5 The quotient rule

In this section we obtain a method for differentiating functions such as

$$\frac{x^2 - x}{(x + 1)^2} \quad \text{and} \quad \frac{\cos x}{x - \sin x}$$

Functions like these, which are in the form of fractions, are usually called **quotients**.

Let the function concerned be $y = \dfrac{u}{v}$ where u and v are functions of x. If we regard this as the product $u \cdot \dfrac{1}{v}$ and differentiate implicitly (with respect to x) we obtain

$$\frac{dy}{dx} = \frac{du}{dx} \cdot \frac{1}{v} + u \cdot \frac{d}{dx}\left(\frac{1}{v}\right)$$

$$= \frac{1}{v} \cdot \frac{du}{dx} + u \cdot \left(-\frac{1}{v^2} \cdot \frac{dv}{dx}\right)$$

$$= \frac{1}{v^2}\left[v \cdot \frac{du}{dx} - u \cdot \frac{dv}{dx}\right]$$

i.e.

$$\frac{d}{dx}\left(\frac{u}{v}\right) = \frac{v \cdot \dfrac{du}{dx} - u \cdot \dfrac{dv}{dx}}{v^2}$$

Example   109

Differentiate (i) $y = \dfrac{x^2 - x}{(x+1)^2}$ (ii) $y = \dfrac{\cos x}{x - \sin x}$

(i) $y = \dfrac{x^2 - x}{(x+1)^2}$ or $\dfrac{u}{v}$

$$\frac{dy}{dx} = \frac{(x+1)^2 (2x-1) - (x^2-x)2(x+1)}{(x+1)^4}$$

The common factor $(x+1)$ should be cancelled before simplification is attempted. Hence

$$\frac{dy}{dx} = \frac{(x+1)(2x-1) - 2(x^2-x)}{(x+1)^3} = \frac{3x-1}{(x+1)^3}$$

(ii) $y = \dfrac{\cos x}{x - \sin x}$ or $\dfrac{u}{v}$

$$\frac{dy}{dx} = \frac{(x - \sin x)(-\sin x) - \cos x(1 - \cos x)}{(x - \sin x)^2}$$

$$= \frac{-x \sin x + \sin^2 x - \cos x + \cos^2 x}{(x - \sin x)^2}$$

$$= \frac{1 - x \sin x - \cos x}{(x - \sin x)^2}$$

Note: The quotient rule can lead to complicated expressions and it should therefore be avoided if other methods are available. In particular remember that certain 'quotients' are more easily handled as products and that functions of the form $1/f(x)$ are best treated by the 'function of a function' method, e.g.

$$y = \frac{\cos 3x}{x^2} \quad \text{or} \quad \frac{1}{x^2}\cos 3x \qquad \frac{dy}{dx} = \frac{-3}{x^2}\sin 3x - \frac{2}{x^3}\cos 3x$$

$$y = \frac{1}{(2x-1)^2} \quad \text{or} \quad (2x-1)^{-2} \qquad \frac{dy}{dx} = -2(2x-1)^{-3}\cdot 2 = \frac{-4}{(2x-1)^3}$$

Exercise 16(e)

1. Differentiate, using the quotient rule

   (i) $\dfrac{x}{x^2+1}$ (ii) $\dfrac{\sin x}{1+\sin x}$ (iii) $\dfrac{x^2+1}{3x-2}$

   (iv) $\dfrac{1+x}{\sin x}$ (v) $\dfrac{x}{(2x-1)^2}$ (vi) $\dfrac{1+\sin x}{1-\cos x}$

   (vii) $\dfrac{\cos 3x}{(1+x)^2}$ (viii) $\dfrac{x+\tan x}{x-\tan x}$ (ix) $\dfrac{x}{\sqrt{x^2+1}}$

2. Differentiate by whichever method is most suitable

   (i) $\dfrac{x+1}{x^2}$ (ii) $\dfrac{\tan x}{x}$ (iii) $\dfrac{1}{(3x+1)^2}$

   (iv) $\dfrac{x}{\sin x}$ (v) $\dfrac{x+1}{x^2-1}$ (vi) $\dfrac{\sin 2x}{\cos^2 x}$

   (vii) $\dfrac{1}{x+\cos x}$ (viii) $\left(\dfrac{x}{\cos x}\right)^2$ (ix) $\dfrac{\sin 3x}{x^2}$

   (x) $\dfrac{x^2-4}{x^2+2x}$ (xi) $\dfrac{\sin^2 x}{1-\sin^2 x}$ (xii) $\dfrac{x+2}{x(x-3)}$

3. This question involves the derivatives of trigonometric ratios. Once the derivatives of sin x and cos x have been established (as in Section 14.1) the derivatives of the other trigonometric ratios may be obtained as follows:

   $$\frac{d}{dx}(\tan x) \quad \text{by the quotient rule i.e.} \quad \frac{d}{dx}\left(\frac{\sin x}{\cos x}\right)$$

   $$\frac{d}{dx}(\sec x) \quad \text{by function of a function i.e.} \quad \frac{d}{dx}(\cos x)^{-1}$$

   Complete the above two examples and obtain also, by similar methods, the derivatives of cot x and cosec x.

4. Prove that (i) $\dfrac{d}{dx}(\sec^2 x) = 2\tan x \sec^2 x$

   (ii) $\dfrac{d}{dx}(\sec^3 x) = 3\tan x \sec^3 x$

   Suggest a result for $\dfrac{d}{dx}(\sec^n x)$

5. Prove that $\dfrac{d}{dx}\left(\dfrac{x-1}{x+1}\right)^2 = \dfrac{4(x-1)}{(x+1)^3}$ and obtain similar expressions for the second and third derivatives. Suggest results for the fourth derivative and the nth derivative.

6. Using only the results for $\sin x$, $\cos x$ and $\tan x$ obtain the first derivatives for

(i) $\tan x \sin x$ (ii) $\dfrac{\sec^2 x}{\csc^2 x}$ (iii) $\dfrac{\tan x}{\cos x}$ (iv) $\sec x \csc x$

7. Prove that the function $\dfrac{1+x}{1+3x}$ is always decreasing and find the equation of the tangent to the curve (i) at its intersection with the x axis (ii) at its intersection with the y axis.

8. Find the turning points on the following curves. Determine their nature by considering the sign of the gradient.

(i) $y = \dfrac{x^2}{1+x}$ (ii) $y = \dfrac{3-2x}{x^2-2}$

9. Differentiate

(i) $x \sin x \cos x$ (ii) $(x+1)^3 (x-1)^3$

(iii) $\dfrac{x \sin x}{1+x}$ (iv) $\dfrac{x\sqrt{1+x^2}}{1+x}$

10. For the curve $y = \dfrac{x^3}{x^2-3}$

(i)   state the equations of the vertical asymptotes.
(ii) state the equation of the asymptote for $x \to \pm \infty$.
(iii) investigate the nature of any turning points.
Sketch the curve.

17

Coordinate Geometry

17.1 Loci

In this section we consider the loci of points moving in two dimensions in accordance with some stated rule.

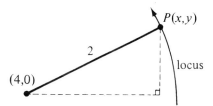

Fig. 1

The simplest example is the circle; suppose a point $P(x, y)$ moves in such a way that its distance from the point $(4, 0)$ is always 2 units. Then from Fig. 1 we have

$$(x - 4)^2 + (y - 0)^2 = 2^2 \qquad \text{(Pythagoras)}$$
$$\Rightarrow x^2 - 8x + 16 + y^2 = 4$$
$$x^2 - 8x + y^2 + 12 = 0$$

This must be true for all points on the locus; it is therefore the equation of the locus, i.e. a circle of radius 2 units with centre $(4, 0)$.

The equation of a circle is considered in more detail in Section 17.2 Some examples of different loci are first investigated.

Example 110

Find the equations of the following loci:

(i) A point which is always equidistant from the line $x = -5$ and the point $(5, 0)$

(ii) A point whose distance from the origin is always twice its distance from the point $(3, 0)$.

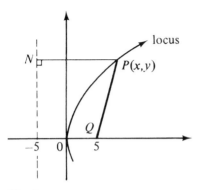

Fig. 2a

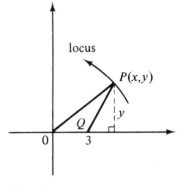

Fig. 2b

(i) In Fig. 2a the moving point is $P(x, y)$ and we require $PN = PQ$ or $PN^2 = PQ^2$

But $PN = x + 5$ and $PQ^2 = (x - 5)^2 + y^2$ (Pythagoras)

Thus $(x + 5)^2 = (x - 5)^2 + y^2$

$\Rightarrow$ $20x = y^2$

The equation of the locus is $y^2 = 20x$. This is a **parabola.** The line $x = -5$ is the **directrix** and the point $(5, 0)$ is the **focus.** (See Section 19.2.)

(ii) In Fig. 2b the moving point is again $P(x, y)$ and we require $PO = 2PQ$ or $PO^2 = 4PQ^2$. Hence, by Pythagoras, we have

$$x^2 + y^2 = 4[(x - 3)^2 + y^2]$$
$$x^2 + y^2 = 4x^2 - 24x + 36 + 4y^2$$
$$0 = 3x^2 - 24x + 36 + 3y^2$$

The equation of the locus is $x^2 - 8x + y^2 + 12 = 0$ (after division by 3). This locus is in fact a circle. (We notice that it has the same equation as the circle considered at the start of this section.)

Exercise 17(a)

Find the locus of the point $P(x, y)$ which moves in such a way that:

1. its distance from the origin is always 3 units.
2. the product of its distances from each of the two coordinate axes is constant and equal to 4.
3. it is always equidistant from the origin and the line $x = -4$.
4. it is always equidistant from the fixed points $A(3, -2)$ and $B(1, 1)$.
5. its distances from the points $A(3, -2)$ and $B(1, 1)$ are in the ratio 3:1.
6. its distance from the point $(-2, 5)$ is always 6 units.
7. its distance from the y-axis is always twice its distance from the line $y = 2$.
8. its distance from the x-axis is always twice its distance from the point $(1, 3)$.
9. PQ is always perpendicular to PR where Q and R are the fixed points $(1, 2)$ and $(5, 4)$ respectively.

10. it is always equidistant from the line $x = -a$ and the point $(a, 0)$.
11. the tangents from P to a circle of radius 2 units with centre at the origin are always 3 units in length.
12. the area of the triangle OAP, where A is the fixed point $(4, 3)$, is constant and equal to 6 sq. units.
13. its distance from the y-axis is always equal to its shortest distance from a circle of radius 2 units with centre at $(4, 0)$.
*14. the sum of the distances from P to $(-1, 0)$ and from P to $(1, 0)$ is constant and equal to 3 units.

17.2 The circle

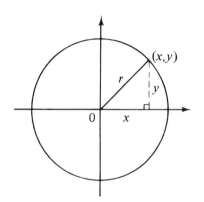

Fig. 3a

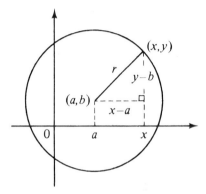

Fig. 3b

If (x, y) is any point on a circle of radius r with centre at the origin then by Pythagoras'

$$x^2 + y^2 = r^2 \qquad \text{(Fig. 3a)}$$

In the same way, a circle with radius r and centre (a, b) has equation

$$\boxed{(x - a)^2 + (y - b)^2 = r^2} \qquad \text{(Fig. 3b)}$$

This is the general equation for the circle. For example, the circle with centre $(2, -3)$ and radius 5 has equation

$$(x - 2)^2 + (y + 3)^2 = 5^2$$

This may be multiplied out to obtain the alternative form

$$x^2 - 4x + y^2 + 6y - 12 = 0$$

Any equation of this type should be recognised as a circle. The important points to notice are
(i) equal coefficients for the terms in x^2 and y^2.
(ii) terms in x and y but no term involving xy.

Example 111

Show that the equation $2x^2 + 12x + 2y^2 - 2y - 1 = 0$ represents a circle and find its centre and radius.

Essentially the method is to complete the square on the x terms and on the y terms. In order to do this we first reduce the coefficients of the squared terms to 1

$$
\begin{aligned}
2x^2 + 12x + 2y^2 - 2y - 1 &= 0 \\
\Rightarrow x^2 + 6x + y^2 - y &= \tfrac{1}{2} \\
(x+3)^2 - 9 + (y - \tfrac{1}{2})^2 - \tfrac{1}{4} &= \tfrac{1}{2} \\
(x+3)^2 + (y - \tfrac{1}{2})^2 = 9\tfrac{3}{4} &= \tfrac{39}{4}
\end{aligned}
$$

Comparing this with the general equation of a circle above, we see that the equation represents a circle with centre $(-3, \tfrac{1}{2})$ and radius $r = \tfrac{1}{2}\sqrt{39}$.

Example 112

Find the lengths of the tangents from the point $(1, 2)$ to the circle $2x^2 + 12x + 2y^2 - 2y - 1 = 0$.

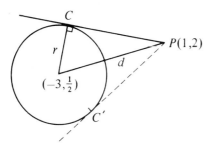

Fig. 4

The 'length' of the tangent is the distance from the point $P(1, 2)$ to the point of contact C (or C') in Fig. 4. Since the tangent is perpendicular to the radius this may be found by Pythagoras' Theorem.

First we find the centre $(-3, \tfrac{1}{2})$ and the radius $r = \tfrac{1}{2}\sqrt{39}$ of the circle (as in the previous example).

Then $d^2 = 4^2 + (1\tfrac{1}{2})^2 = 18\tfrac{1}{4}$

and $PC^2 = d^2 - r^2 = \dfrac{73}{4} - \dfrac{39}{4} = \dfrac{34}{4}$

So the lengths of the tangents are $\frac{1}{2}\sqrt{34} \approx 2.92$ units. Notice that it is not necessary to find the coordinates of the point of contact C.

Exercise 17(b)

1. Write down the equations of the following circles:
   (i) centre $(0, 0)$ radius 7 (ii) centre $(3, 1)$ radius 4
   (iii) centre $(4, -1)$ radius 2 (iv) centre (a, a) radius $2a$
2. Write down the equation of the circle centre $(-3, 5)$ which touches the x-axis. Find the intersections of the circle with the y-axis.
3. Find the equation of the circle centre $(4, 3)$ which passes through the origin and write down the other intersections of this circle with the coordinate axes.
4. Find the centres and radii of the following circles:
   (i) $x^2 + y^2 = 16$ (ii) $x^2 - 4x + y^2 - 2y = 4$
   (iii) $x^2 + y^2 + 8x - 10y + 5 = 0$ (iv) $x^2 + 12x + y^2 = 13$
   (v) $2x^2 + 2y^2 + 6x + 2y + 1 = 0$ (vi) $3x^2 + 3y^2 + 6x - 8y = 0$
5. Find the equations of the two circles of radius 5 which intersect the x-axis at $(-3, 0)$ and $(5, 0)$.
6. Prove that the circle $x^2 + y^2 - 9x + 2y + 15 = 0$ has no intersections with the y-axis. Find the point on the y-axis which is closest to the circle and state the magnitude of this closest distance.
7. Find the coordinates of the intersections of the line $y = 2x$ with the circle $x^2 + y^2 - 3x + 4y = 10$. Hence find the point on $y = 2x$ which is closest to the centre of the circle.
8. Find the lengths of the tangents from
   (i) the origin to the circle $x^2 + y^2 - 10x + 6y + 16 = 0$.
   (ii) the point $(4, 4)$ to the circle $x^2 + 2x + y^2 - 4y = 8$.
9. Find the equations of the circles centre $(8, 0)$ which touch the circle $x^2 + y^2 + 8x - 10y - 8 = 0$ (i) externally (ii) internally.
10. Find the points on the circle $x^2 + y^2 - 8x - 4y + 15 = 0$ which are nearest and farthest from the origin.
11. Prove that the circles $x^2 + y^2 - 8x - 6y = 0$ and $x^2 + y^2 + 4x - 2y = 10$ intersect at right angles.
12. Find the equation of the diameter of the circle $x^2 + y^2 - 6y = 16$ which passes through the point $(-4, 6)$ on the circle. Find also the coordinates of the other end point of the diameter.
13. Find the equations of the two circles which pass through $(1, 2)$ and $(1, 4\frac{1}{2})$ and which touch the x-axis.
14. A circle intersects the x-axis at $(1, 0)$ and $(5, 0)$. One of its intersections with the y-axis is $(0, 2)$. Find the centre of the circle and the second intersection with the y-axis.

17.3 The distance from a point to a line

The perpendicular distance of the point (h, k) from the line $ax + by + c = 0$ is given by

$$\boxed{\dfrac{ah + bk + c}{\sqrt{a^2 + b^2}}}$$

i.e. substitute the coordinates of the point into $ax + by + c$ and divide by $\sqrt{a^2 + b^2}$.

Example 113

Find the distances of the points (i) $(4, 1)$ (ii) $(-5, 2)$ from the line $3x + 2y = 1$.

(i) distance $= \dfrac{3(4) + 2(1) - 1}{\sqrt{3^2 + 2^2}} = \dfrac{13}{\sqrt{13}} = \sqrt{13}$ units

(ii) distance $= \dfrac{3(-5) + 2(2) - 1}{\sqrt{3^2 + 2^2}} = \dfrac{-12}{\sqrt{13}}$ units

The sign of the answer is determined by which side of the line the point is on. In this example we can deduce that the two points are on opposite sides of the line.

Proof of result

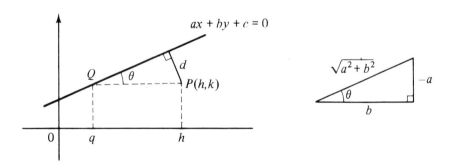

Fig. 5a   Fig. 5b

In Fig. 5a, P is the point (h, k) and the required distance is $d = PQ \sin\theta$

but $\tan\theta = -\dfrac{a}{b}$ (the gradient of the line)

so $\sin\theta = \dfrac{-a}{\sqrt{a^2 + b^2}}$ (by Pythagoras: Fig. 5b)

To find PQ we need the x coordinate of Q; let this be q. Now Q lies on the line $ax + by + c = 0$ and its y coordinate is k, the same as P. Hence

$$aq + bk + c = 0$$

$$q = \frac{-(bk+c)}{a}$$

$$PQ = h - q = h + \frac{(bk+c)}{a} = \frac{ah + bk + c}{a}$$

So if we ignore the sign of $\sin\theta$ we obtain

$$d = \frac{ah + bk + c}{a} \cdot \frac{a}{\sqrt{a^2+b^2}} = \frac{ah + bk + c}{\sqrt{a^2+b^2}}$$

Example 114

Find the length of the chord cut off from the circle $x^2 + y^2 - 10x + 2y = 10$ by the line $y = 2x - 1$.

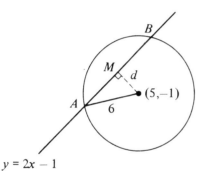

$y = 2x - 1$

Fig. 6

The equation of the circle may be written as

$$(x-5)^2 - 25 + (y+1)^2 - 1 = 10$$

$$(x-5)^2 + (y+1)^2 = 36$$

So the circle has centre $(5, -1)$ and radius 6 units (Fig. 6). The distance of the centre $(5, -1)$ from the line $y = 2x - 1$ or $y - 2x + 1 = 0$ is

$$d = \frac{-1 - 10 + 1}{\sqrt{1^2 + 2^2}} = \frac{-10}{\sqrt{5}} = -2\sqrt{5}$$

Hence by Pythagoras (ignoring the sign of d)

$$AM^2 = 6^2 - d^2 = 36 - 20 = 16$$

So $AM = 4$ and the length of the chord is 8 units.

Exercise 17(c)

1. In each case find the distance of the given point from the given line. Leave answers in surd form.
   (i) $(3, 2)$ from $3x + 4y - 2 = 0$
   (ii) $(-4, 2)$ from $y = 3x + 4$
   (iii) $(5, -3)$ from $y = x$
   (iv) $(0, 0)$ from $2y + 3x = 1$
   (v) $(-2, -1)$ from $2y - 3x = 4$
   (vi) $(7, 5)$ from $\frac{1}{2}x + \frac{1}{4}y = 1$

2. Which two of the following three points are on the same side of the line $2y = 5x + 1$?
   $A(4, 3)$ $B(1, 5)$ and $C(-2, -3)$.

3. Prove that the line $y = 3x + 3$ touches the circle $x^2 + y^2 - 8x + 10y + 1 = 0$.

4. Prove that the line $4y - 3x = 1$ does not intersect the circle $x^2 + y^2 + 6x - y + 7 = 0$. What is the least distance between the line and the circle?

5. Find the equations of the following circles:
   (i) centre $(1, 3)$, touching the line $y = x - 4$
   (ii) centre $(0, \frac{1}{2})$, touching the line $8y = 6x - 1$

6. Find the length of the chord cut off from the circle $x^2 + y^2 - 4x + 10y = 20$ by the line $2y + 3x = 9$.

7. Prove that the line $4y = 2x - 3$ is a tangent to the circle $2x^2 + 2y^2 + 2x - 6y - 5 = 0$. Find the equation of the diameter through the point of contact and hence obtain the coordinates of the point of contact.

8. If the point $P(x, y)$ is 1 unit in distance from the line $5y - 12x = 7$ write down two possible expressions involving the coordinates of P. Hence obtain the equations of the two lines parallel to and 1 unit away from $5y - 12x = 7$.

17.4 Further problems on circles

Gradient at a point

There are two methods available: (i) implicit differentiation   (ii) using the fact that the tangent is perpendicular to the radius.

Example 115

Find the equation of the tangent to the circle $x^2 + 4x + y^2 - 2y - 32 = 0$ at the point $(4, 2)$

Method (i) Differentiating implicitly we have

$$2x + 4 + 2y \cdot \frac{dy}{dx} - 2\frac{dy}{dx} = 0$$

$$\frac{dy}{dx} = -\frac{(2x + 4)}{(2y - 2)} = -\frac{(x + 2)}{y - 1}$$

Hence the gradient at $(4, 2)$ is -6 and the equation of the tangent is therefore

$$\frac{y-2}{x-4} = -6 \implies y + 6x = 26$$

Method (ii)   The equation of the circle may be written

$$(x+2)^2 + (y-1)^2 = 37$$

so the centre is $(-2, 1)$ and the gradient of the radius to the point $(4, 2)$ is

$$\frac{2-1}{4-(-2)} = \frac{1}{6}$$

As the tangent is perpendicular to this radius, its gradient is -6. The equation of the tangent follows as above.

Circle through three given points

In general the most suitable method is that used in the next example. In some situations, however, quicker methods may be found, e.g. Exercise 17(d) question 6.

Example   116

Find the equation of the circle through the points $(1, 2)$, $(2, 0)$ and $(-3, 1)$.

Let the equation be $x^2 + y^2 + ax + by + c = 0$ where a, b and c are constants to be found. Substituting

$$\begin{array}{lll} (1, 2) & \implies & 1+4+\ a+2b+c = 0 \\ (2, 0) & & 4\quad\ +2a\quad\ \ +c = 0 \\ (-3, 1) & & 9+1-3a+\ b+c = 0 \end{array}$$

We obtain simultaneous equations in 3 unknowns, i.e.

$$\begin{array}{ll} a+2b+c = -5 & \text{(1)} \\ 2a\quad\ +c = -4 & \text{(2)} \\ -3a+\ b+c = -10 & \text{(3)} \end{array}$$

Subtracting $(2)-(1)$ and $(2)-(3)$ we have $a - 2b = 1$ and $5a - b = 6$. From these $a = \frac{11}{9}$, $b = \frac{1}{9}$ and hence, from (2), $c = -\frac{58}{9}$. The equation of the circle is therefore

$$x^2 + y^2 + \frac{11}{9}x + \frac{1}{9}y - \frac{58}{9} = 0$$

or $9x^2 + 9y^2 + 11x + y - 58 = 0$

Circle on a given diameter

If the endpoints of a diameter are given, then the equation of the circle can be found using the result which follows.

Let the endpoints of the diameter be $A(x_1, y_1)$ and $B(x_2, y_2)$. Then if $P(x, y)$ is any other point on the circle the lines PA and PB must be perpendicular, i.e.

$$\text{gradient } PA = \frac{-1}{\text{gradient } PB}$$

$$\frac{(y - y_1)}{(x - x_1)} = -\frac{(x - x_2)}{(y - y_2)}$$

After cross-multiplication this leads to the equation

$$\boxed{(x - x_1)(x - x_2) + (y - y_1)(y - y_2) = 0}$$

For example the circle on $(5, 1)$ and $(2, -3)$ as diameter has the following equation:

$$(x - 5)(x - 2) + (y - 1)(y + 3) = 0$$
$$\Rightarrow \qquad x^2 - 7x + y^2 + 2y + 7 = 0$$

Equation of the common chord of two intersecting circles

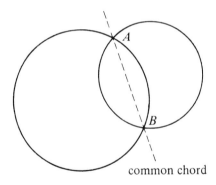

common chord

Fig. 7

The equations $\qquad x^2 + y^2 + 4x - 2y = 10$ $\qquad\qquad$ (1)
and $\qquad\qquad\;\; x^2 + y^2 - 8x - 6y = 0$ $\qquad\qquad$ (2)

represent two circles which intersect. The coordinates of the points of intersection (A and B in Fig. 7) must satisfy both (1) and (2) and hence they must also satisfy the equation obtained by subtracting (1) $-$ (2), i.e.

$$12x + 4y = 10 \qquad \text{or} \qquad 6x + 2y = 5$$

But this equation is a straight line. It follows that it is the line through A and B, i.e. the common chord.

So the common chord of two intersecting circles is found by subtracting their equations. (The coefficients of the squared terms must first be made equal.)

Exercise 17(d)

1. Find the two points on the circle $x^2 + y^2 - 3x - 7y = 18$ with y coordinate 2. Find the gradient of the circle at each of these points.

2. Find the equations of the tangents to the following circles at the points specified:
   (i) $x^2 + y^2 - 8y + 6 = 0$ at the point $(3, 5)$
   (ii) $2x^2 + 2y^2 + x - 5y = 6$ at the intersection of the circle with the positive x-axis.

3. Find the equation of
   (i) the tangent
   (ii) the normal to the circle $x^2 + y^2 - 6x + 5y + 9 = 0$ at the point $(1, -4)$.

4. Find the equation of the normal to the circle $3x^2 + 3y^2 + 8x = 9$ which meets the line $3y + 2x = 19$ at right angles. Hence find the coordinates of the point on $3y + 2x = 19$ which is closest to the circle.

5. Use the method of Example 116 to find the equation of the circle through the 3 points given.
   (i) $(0, 3)$, $(2, 1)$ and $(-3, 2)$ (ii) $(3, 2)$, $(-1, 0)$ and $(2, -1)$

6. Find the equation of the circle through the 3 points given. Try to find a quicker method than that used in Example 116.
   (i) $(1, 4)$, $(1, 6)$ and $(4, 1)$ (ii) $(-1, 1)$, $(-1, 5)$ and $(3, 3)$

7. The equation $x^2 + y^2 + ax + by + c = 0$ represents a circle. What is the geometric effect on the circle of changing the sign of (i) a? (ii) b? (iii) both a and b?

8. The equation $x^2 + y^2 + ax + by + c = 0$ represents a circle.
   (i) Prove that in all cases $a^2 + b^2 > 4c$.
   (ii) What is the condition for the circle to touch the x-axis?

9. Prove that the equation of the circle on AB as diameter, where A and B have coordinates (a_1, a_2) and (b_1, b_2) respectively, is

$$(x - a_1)(x - b_1) + (y - a_2)(y - b_2) = 0$$

   Find the equation of the circle on $(-2, 4)$ and $(5, 3)$ as diameter.

10. Find the locus of the point P which moves such that angle $APB = 90°$ where A and B have coordinates $(-1, -3)$ and $(6, 2)$. Hence find two points R and S on the y-axis such that angle $ARB =$ angle $ASB = 90°$.

11. Find the equation of the circle which passes through the centre of the circle $x^2 + y^2 - 3x + 5y = 16$ and which touches this circle internally at the point $(-2, 1)$.

12. Prove that the circles $x^2 + y^2 + 2x - 4y + 1 = 0$ and $x^2 + y^2 - 4x + 4y - 8 = 0$ intersect and find the equation of their common chord.

*13. Find a quadratic equation whose solutions give the x coordinates of the intersections of the line $y = mx$ with the circle $x^2 + y^2 - 8x - 6y + 20 = 0$. If $y = mx$ touches the circle, find the two possible values of m. Hence find the two tangents to the circle which pass through the origin.

14. Find the two values of m for which the line $y = mx + 7$ touches the circle $x^2 + y^2 + 2x = 9$. Hence find the two tangents from $(0, 7)$ to this circle.

18

Logarithmic and Exponential Functions

18.1 The graph of a logarithmic function

In this chapter we shall be concerned firstly with the differentiation of $\log x$ and how this is affected by the choice of base number. Secondly we shall consider an important class of associated functions: the exponential or power functions.

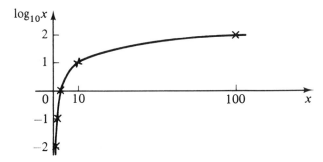

Fig. 1

Fig. 1 is a sketch of the function $x \to \log_{10} x$ (or $y = \log_{10} x$). It has been obtained by considering the values $x = 10^2, 10^1, 10^0, 10^{-1}$ and 10^{-2} for which the logarithms to base 10 are respectively 2, 1, 0, -1 and -2.

All logarithmic functions have the same general shape as this sketch. (As a further example the student should sketch the graph of $x \to \log_2 x$.) We notice two points of particular importance about this type of function:

(i) The function is not defined for negative values of x, since logarithms of negative numbers do not exist.

(ii) The gradient of the function (which is always positive) decreases as x increases.

18.2 Differentiation of log x

To begin with we shall not specify the base to which the logarithms are taken.

Let
$$y = \log x$$
$$y + \delta y = \log(x + \delta x)$$

then
$$\delta y = \log(x + \delta x) - \log x$$
$$= \log \frac{(x + \delta x)}{x} = \log\left(1 + \frac{\delta x}{x}\right)$$
$$\frac{\delta y}{\delta x} = \frac{1}{\delta x} \log\left(1 + \frac{\delta x}{x}\right)$$

To proceed further we take the unusual step of substituting $\delta x = tx$. (For any given value of x we may then let $\delta x \to 0$ by taking values of t which are sufficiently small.) We obtain

$$\frac{\delta y}{\delta x} = \frac{1}{tx} \log(1 + t) = \frac{1}{x} \log(1 + t)^{\frac{1}{t}}$$

The derived function is now obtained by letting $\delta x \to 0$ (i.e. $t \to 0$). Thus

$$\frac{dy}{dx} = \frac{1}{x} \log L \tag{1}$$

where L is a constant number given by

$$L = \lim_{t \to 0} (1 + t)^{\frac{1}{t}}$$

Before proceeding we notice (i) that the working so far is valid for logarithms to any base, and (ii) that since $\log L$ will be a constant, the gradient of the function is proportional to $1/x$, i.e. the gradient will decrease as x increases.

We shall now investigate the value taken by the limit L. At first sight the student might expect this limit to be 1, since as $t \to 0$ it is clear that $(1 + t) \to 1$ and since 1 raised to any power remains as 1. The following particular cases should be sufficient, however, to suggest that this is not the case.

With $t = 0.5$ $(1 + t)^{\frac{1}{t}}$ $= (1.5)^2$ $= 2.25$

        $= 0.25$ $= (1.25)^4$ $= 2.441$

        $= 0.2$ $= (1.2)^5$ $= 2.488$

The following short exercise should now be worked. The differentiation will be completed in the next section.

Exercise 18(a)

1. Use a calculator to find the values of $(1 + t)^{\frac{1}{t}}$ when $t = \frac{1}{5}, \frac{1}{8}, \frac{1}{10}, \frac{1}{20}$.
2. When $t = \frac{1}{10}$ we may obtain a value for $(1 + t)^{\frac{1}{t}}$ by using the Binomial Expansion, i.e.

$$\left(1 + \frac{1}{10}\right)^{10} = 1 + 10\left(\frac{1}{10}\right) + \frac{10 \cdot 9}{2!}\left(\frac{1}{10}\right)^2 + \frac{10 \cdot 9 \cdot 8}{3!}\left(\frac{1}{10}\right)^3 + \ldots$$

Find, to 2 decimal places, the value of this expansion.

*3. Write down, *but do not evaluate*, the first four terms of the binomial expansion for $(1 + t)^{\frac{1}{t}}$ when (i) $t = \frac{1}{100}$ (ii) $t = \frac{1}{1000}$. By studying these expansions suggest a series which the expansion of $(1 + t)^{\frac{1}{t}}$ will approach as $t \to 0$. Sum the first eight terms of this series to obtain an estimate for the limit L, correct to three decimal places.

Note: Answers to Exercise 18(a) are not supplied.

18.3 The number e

The binomial expansions of question 3 above suggest that as $t \to 0$ the value of $(1 + t)^{\frac{1}{t}}$ approaches

$$1 + 1 + \frac{1}{2!} + \frac{1}{3!} + \frac{1}{4!} + \cdots$$

This series is easily summed, each term being obtained from the previous one by a further division. Thus, working to six places of decimals we obtain

	1.000000
	1.000000
$\div 2$	0.500000
$\div 3$	0.166667
$\div 4$	0.041667
$\div 5$	0.008333
$\div 6$	0.001389
$\div 7$	0.000198
$\div 8$	0.000025
$\div 9$	0.000003
	2.718282

The value of the limit L encountered in the previous section is thus 2.7183 (to four decimal places). This turns out to be a number of such importance that it is given its own symbol: e

i.e. $\lim_{t \to 0} (1 + t)^{\frac{1}{t}} = e \approx 2.7183$

We may now return to the differentiation of the function $y = \log x$. From line (1) of Section 18.2 we obtain

$$\frac{dy}{dx} = \frac{1}{x} \log e \quad \text{or} \quad \frac{1}{x} \log(2.7183)$$

We now see how the choice of base for the logarithms affects this result.

If $y = \log_{10} x$ then $\dfrac{dy}{dx} = \dfrac{1}{x} \log_{10}(2.718) = (0.4343)\dfrac{1}{x}$

$y = \log_2 x$ $\dfrac{dy}{dx} = \dfrac{1}{x} \log_2(2.718) = (1.443)\dfrac{1}{x}$

In all cases the gradient is proportional to $1/x$, the constant of proportionality being dependent upon the choice of base. Consider now the result if we choose to take logarithms to base e (i.e. base 2.7183).

If $y = \log_e x$ then $\dfrac{dy}{dx} = \dfrac{1}{x} \log_e e = \dfrac{1}{x}$

Thus logarithms to base e are of great importance. They are called 'Natural' or 'Napieran' logarithms. The notation $\ln x$ will be used to denote the logarithm of x to base e.

Summary

$$\frac{d}{dx}(\ln x) = \frac{1}{x}$$

$$\int \frac{1}{x}\,dx = \ln x + c$$

$$e = 1 + 1 + \frac{1}{2!} + \frac{1}{3!} + \frac{1}{4!} + \ldots \approx 2.7183$$

Example 117

Differentiate $\ln 3x$, $\ln x^2$, $\ln(\sin x)$

These may be differentiated by the chain rule, i.e.

$$\frac{d}{dx}\cdot \ln f(x) = \frac{1}{f(x)}\cdot f'(x)$$

thus

$$\frac{d}{dx}\cdot \ln(3x) = \frac{1}{3x}\cdot 3 = \frac{1}{x}$$

$$\frac{d}{dx}\cdot \ln(x^2) = \frac{1}{x^2}\cdot 2x = \frac{2}{x}$$

$$\frac{d}{dx}\cdot \ln(\sin x) = \frac{1}{\sin x}\cdot \cos x = \cot x$$

An alternative method for $\ln x^2$ is to remember that this is equivalent to $2\ln x$.

Exercise 18(b)

1. Differentiate with respect to x
   (i) $\ln 2x$ (ii) $\ln x^3$ (iii) $\ln(x-5)$
   (iv) $\ln\frac{1}{x}$ (v) $\ln(3x+1)$ (vi) $\ln(x^2-1)$
   (vii) $\ln(\cos x)$ (viii) $\ln(7-2x)$ (ix) $\ln(1+\sin x)$

2. Find the gradient of each of the following functions at the point specified
   (i) $y = \ln x$ at $x = 5$
   (ii) $y = \log_{10} x$ at $x = 2$
   (iii) $y = \ln(2x-1)$ at $x = 3$
   (iv) $y = \ln(\sin x)$ at $x = \frac{1}{6}\pi$

3. Find $\dfrac{dy}{dx}$ for each of the following functions
   (i) $y = \ln(\tan x)$ (ii) $y = \ln(3+x)^2$ (iii) $y = \ln(\sin^2 x)$
   (iv) $y = \ln(\sec x)$ (v) $y = \ln\sqrt{x+1}$ (vi) $y = \ln(x+\frac{1}{x})$

4. For which values of x is the function $\ln(x^2-3)$ defined? Find a value of x for which the gradient of this function is 1.
5. Find the first and second derivatives of
   (i) $y = x\ln x$ (ii) $y = x^2\ln x$
6. Use the results of question 5 to find
   (i) the gradient of $x\ln x$ at $x = e$

(ii) a value of x for which the gradient of $x^2 \ln x$ is zero $(x > 0)$
(iii) the coordinates of the turning point on $x \ln x$, stating whether it is a maximum or a minimum point $(x > 0)$.

7. (i) By writing $\ln(\tan x) = \ln(\sin x) - \ln(\cos x)$ show that the gradient of $\ln(\tan x)$ is given by $\cot x + \tan x$.
(ii) Obtain, by a similar method, the gradients of the functions

$$\ln \frac{1+x}{1-x}, \qquad \ln \frac{1-\cos x}{1+\cos x}, \qquad \ln \sqrt{\frac{1+x^2}{1-2x}}$$

8. By differentiating implicitly find an expression for $\dfrac{dy}{dx}$ in each of the following cases:
(i) $y^2 = \ln x$ (ii) $\ln(1+y^2) = x$ (iii) $y = \ln(xy)$

18.4 Integrals leading to logarithmic functions

A number of functions may be integrated directly as logarithmic functions. The logarithmic function will frequently need to be multiplied by a constant; the safest way to establish the correct constant is by reverse differentiation, as the following examples illustrate.

(i) $\displaystyle\int \frac{1}{2x-7}\,dx = \frac{1}{2}\ln(2x-7)+c$ since $\dfrac{d}{dx}\{\ln(2x-7)\} = \dfrac{2}{2x-7}$

(ii) $\displaystyle\int \frac{5x}{x^2-1}\,dx = \frac{5}{2}\ln(x^2-1)+c$ since $\dfrac{d}{dx}\{\ln(x^2-1)\} = \dfrac{2x}{x^2-1}$

(iii) $\displaystyle\int \frac{2\sin x}{3-\cos x}\,dx = 2\ln(3-\cos x)+c$ since $\dfrac{d}{dx}\{\ln(3-\cos x)\} = \dfrac{\sin x}{3-\cos x}$

(iv) $\displaystyle\int \cot x\,dx = \int \frac{\cos x}{\sin x}\,dx = \ln(\sin x)+c$

In general any integral of the form $\displaystyle\int \frac{f'(x)}{f(x)}\,dx$ may be found in this way (i.e. any integral in which the top is the differential of the bottom).

When evaluating integrals between limits, care must be taken not to introduce the logarithms of negative numbers. For example

$$\int_1^2 \frac{1}{2x-7}\,dx = \frac{1}{2}\Big[\ln(2x-7)\Big]_1^2$$

involves the logarithms of -3 and -5 when the limits are substituted. This difficulty may be avoided by multiplying top and bottom by -1 before integrating. Thus

$$\int_1^2 \frac{1}{2x-7}\,dx = \int_1^2 \frac{-1}{7-2x}\,dx \quad = \frac{1}{2}\Big[\ln(7-2x)\Big]_1^2$$

$$= \frac{1}{2}(\ln 3 - \ln 5) \qquad = \frac{1}{2}\ln 0.6$$

Exercise 18(c)

In questions 1–4 integrate the functions with respect to x.

1. (i) $\dfrac{5}{x}$ (ii) $\dfrac{1}{3x}$ (iii) $\dfrac{1}{2x^2}$ (iv) $\dfrac{1}{\sec x}$

(v) $\dfrac{x-2}{x}$ (vi) $\left(1+\dfrac{1}{x}\right)^2$

2. (i) $\dfrac{1}{x-3}$ (ii) $\dfrac{1}{(x-3)^2}$ (iii) $\dfrac{1}{2x+1}$ (iv) $\dfrac{1}{4-x}$

(v) $\dfrac{1}{1-5x}$ (vi) $\dfrac{3}{7x+1}$

3. (i) $\dfrac{2x}{x^2+1}$ (ii) $\dfrac{3x}{x^2+1}$ (iii) $\dfrac{6x}{4-x^2}$ (iv) $\dfrac{x}{3x^2-5}$

(v) $\dfrac{x+2}{x^2+4x+1}$ (vi) $\dfrac{x^3}{x^4-1}$

4. (i) $\dfrac{3\cos x}{2+\sin x}$ (ii) $\tan x$ (iii) $\dfrac{\sec^2 x}{1+\tan x}$

(iv) $\dfrac{\cos x-\sin x}{\cos x+\sin x}$ (v) $\dfrac{\sin 2x}{1+\sin^2 x}$ (vi) $\dfrac{1}{x\ln x}$

5. Evaluate the following definite integrals:

(i) $\displaystyle\int_2^6 \dfrac{4-x}{x}\,dx$ (ii) $\displaystyle\int_1^3 \dfrac{1}{3x-1}\,dx$

(iii) $\displaystyle\int_2^3 \dfrac{x^2}{1+x^3}\,dx$ (iv) $\displaystyle\int_1^4 \dfrac{dx}{1-2x}$

(v) $\displaystyle\int_0^{\frac{1}{6}\pi} \dfrac{\sin 2x}{1+\cos 2x}\,dx$ (vi) $\displaystyle\int_0^{\frac{1}{4}\pi} \dfrac{1+\tan^2 x}{1+\tan x}\,dx$

6. (i) Differentiate $\ln(1+\sqrt{x})$ and hence evaluate the integral
$$\int_1^4 \dfrac{1}{x+\sqrt{x}}\,dx$$

(ii) Multiply both numerator and denominator by $\sin x$ and hence evaluate the integral
$$\int_{\frac{1}{3}\pi}^{\frac{1}{2}\pi} \dfrac{dx}{\operatorname{cosec} x-\cot x}$$

18.5 Integration of rational functions

A method by which certain rational functions may be integrated is illustrated by the following examples. The basic idea is to introduce into the numerator a function which is exactly divisible by the denominator. The notes below the examples should help the student to understand what is being achieved at each step.

Example 118

(i) $\displaystyle\int \frac{x}{x+2}\,dx = \int \frac{(x+2)-2}{x+2}\,dx$

$\displaystyle = \int 1 - \frac{2}{x+2}\,dx = x - 2\ln(x+2) + c$

(ii) $\displaystyle\int \frac{x-3}{2x-1}\,dx = \frac{1}{2}\int \frac{2x-6}{2x-1}\,dx$

$\displaystyle = \frac{1}{2}\int \frac{(2x-1)-5}{2x-1}\,dx$

$\displaystyle = \frac{1}{2}\int 1 - \frac{5}{2x-1}\,dx = \frac{1}{2}\left[x - \frac{5}{2}\ln(2x-1) + c\right]$

(iii) $\displaystyle\int \frac{x^2}{x+2}\,dx = \int \frac{(x^2-4)+4}{x+2}\,dx$

$\displaystyle = \int x - 2 + \frac{4}{x+2}\,dx = \frac{1}{2}x^2 - 2x + 4\ln(x+2) + c$

(iv) $\displaystyle\int \frac{x^2+x}{x-3}\,dx = \int \frac{(x+4)(x-3)+12}{x-3}\,dx$

$\displaystyle = \int x + 4 + \frac{12}{x-3}\,dx = \frac{1}{2}x^2 + 4x + 12\ln(x-3) + c$

Notes:

(a) In Examples (i) and (ii) the numerator is modified so as to include the same function as the denominator. In Example (ii) this necessitates doubling the numerator – hence the compensating factor of $\frac{1}{2}$ preceding the integral.

(b) The student should compare Examples (i) and (iii) carefully. In Example (iii) it is convenient to introduce the appropriate **difference of two squares** which is divisible by the denominator.

(c) In Example (iv) the numerator x^2+x is modified so as to include a quadratic function divisible by the denominator $x-3$. The only such function is given by the product of the factors $(x+4)(x-3)$.

Exercise 18(d)

Solve the following integrals

1. $\displaystyle\int \frac{x}{x-3}\,dx$ 2. $\displaystyle\int \frac{x}{2x+1}\,dx$ 3. $\displaystyle\int \frac{x-1}{x+2}\,dx$

4. $\displaystyle\int \frac{x}{1-x}\,dx$ 5. $\displaystyle\int \frac{x-1}{3x-2}\,dx$ 6. $\displaystyle\int \frac{4-x}{2x-3}\,dx$

7. $\displaystyle\int \frac{x^2}{x-1}\,dx$ 8. $\displaystyle\int \frac{x^2-x}{x+2}\,dx$ 9. $\displaystyle\int \frac{x^2-3}{x+1}\,dx$

10. $\displaystyle\int_0^2 \frac{1+x}{1+2x}\,dx$ 11. $\displaystyle\int_1^3 \frac{x^2}{x+3}\,dx$ 12. $\displaystyle\int_0^4 \frac{2x^2-x}{x+2}\,dx$

18.6 Exponential functions

A function whose variable is an index (or exponent) is called an exponential function, e.g.

$y = 2^x$
$y = 10^x$
$y = e^x$ i.e. $(2.7183)^x$

The shapes exhibited by the graphs of these functions are all similar. Fig. 2 is a sketch of the function $x \to 2^x$. Functions such as this cannot take negative values. Negative values of the variable x give the function fractional values, e.g.

when $x = -1$, $2^x = \dfrac{1}{2}$

when $x = -2$, $2^x = \dfrac{1}{4}$ etc.

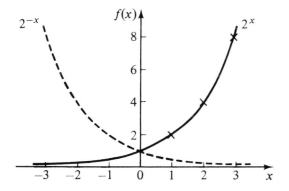

Fig. 2

Functions such as 2^{-x} and e^{-x} are, of course, also possible. These will take fractional values when the variable x is positive and positive powers will occur when x is negative. Thus their graphs are obtained by reflection in the vertical axis – as indicated by the broken line in Fig. 2.

In order to differentiate an exponential function, first take logarithms to base e and then differentiate implicitly. We shall demonstrate this procedure by considering the function 2^x.

Let $$y = 2^x$$

take logarithms to base e $$\ln y = x \ln 2$$

differentiate implicitly $$\frac{1}{y}\frac{dy}{dx} = \ln 2$$

$\Rightarrow$ $$\frac{dy}{dx} = y \ln 2 \quad \text{or} \quad \underline{2^x \ln 2}$$

Since $\ln 2$ is a constant (approximately 0.69) it follows that the gradient of the function is everywhere proportional to the value taken by the function, i.e. when the value of the function is doubled then the gradient is doubled also. It is clear that this is consistent with the shape of the graph in Fig. 2.

Exercise 18(e)

1. Plot an accurate graph of the function e^x for $-2 \leqslant x \leqslant 2$. Use your graph to find
   (i) the gradient of e^x at $x = 1$, $x = 0$ and $x = -1$
   (ii) solutions to the equation $e^x = x + 2$.
2. Use tables or a calculator to find values of x such that
   (i) $e^x = 3.5$ (ii) $e^{3x} = 6$ (iii) $e^{x^2} = 16$
   (iv) $e^x = 120e^{-x}$ (v) $e^{2x} - 3e^x + 2 = 0$ (vi) $3e^x - 4e^{-x} = 1$
   (Note: If $e^x = k$ then $x = \ln k$.)
3. Use the method of the above section to obtain the gradients of the following functions
   (i) $y = 10^x$ (ii) $y = 2^{-x}$ (iii) $y = e^x$
   (iv) $y = e^{-x}$ (v) $y = e^{x^2}$ * (vi) $y = x^x$

18.7 The function e^x

This function is of particular importance because of the unusual result we obtain for its gradient.

Let $$y = e^x$$

take logarithms to base e $$\ln y = x$$

differentiate implicitly $$\frac{1}{y}\frac{dy}{dx} = 1$$

$\Rightarrow$ $$\frac{dy}{dx} = y \quad \text{or} \quad e^x$$

In fact this function has the unique property that differentiation gives us the same function again. Graphically this means that the gradient is everywhere equal to the value of the function itself. The function will be similarly unchanged by integration, i.e.

$$\frac{d}{dx}(e^x) = e^x$$

$$\int e^x \, dx = e^x + c$$

Using this result we may deal with variations on e^x using the chain rule, i.e.

$$\frac{d}{dx} \cdot e^{f(x)} = e^{f(x)} \cdot f'(x)$$

thus $\quad \dfrac{d}{dx} \cdot e^{-x} \quad = e^{-x} \cdot (-1) = -e^{-x}$

$\qquad \dfrac{d}{dx} \cdot e^{3x} \quad = e^{3x} \cdot (3) \quad = 3e^{3x}$

$\qquad \dfrac{d}{dx} \cdot e^{x^2} \quad = e^{x^2} \cdot (2x) \quad = 2x \cdot e^{x^2}$

Integrations may be performed with similar ease, e.g.

$$\int e^{3x} \, dx = \frac{1}{3}e^{3x} + c \qquad \text{since} \quad \frac{d}{dx}(e^{3x}) = 3e^{3x}$$

$$\int e^{-x} \, dx = -e^{-x} + c \qquad \text{since} \quad \frac{d}{dx}(e^{-x}) = -e^{-x}$$

Exercise 18(f)

1. Differentiate the following functions

   (i) $\quad 3e^x$ (ii) $\quad e^{4x}$ (iii) $\dfrac{1}{e^x}$

   (iv) $e^x + e^{-x}$ (v) $\quad e^{-\frac{1}{2}x}$ (vi) $4e^{-3x}$

   (vii) $e^x(1 + e^{-x})$ (viii) $\sqrt{e^x}$ (ix) $(e^x - e^{-x})^2$

2. Find the gradient of $y = e^x$ at the following points
   (i) $x = 0$ (ii) $y = 3$ (iii) $x = \ln 2$

3. Integrate the following

   (i) $\displaystyle \int e^{2x} \, dx$ (ii) $\displaystyle \int e^{-4x} \, dx$ (iii) $\displaystyle \int_0^{\frac{1}{3}} e^{3x} \, dx$

   (iv) $\displaystyle \int_0^4 e^{\frac{1}{2}x} \, dx$ (v) $\displaystyle \int \frac{e^x - 1}{e^x}$ (vi) $\int (e^x + e^{-x})^2 \, dx$

4. Sketch on the same axes the graphs of

   (i) e^x (ii) e^{-x} (iii) $\dfrac{e^x + e^{-x}}{2}$ (iv) $e^x - e^{-x}$

   Prove that function (iv) is always increasing.

5. Find the 1st, 2nd and 3rd derivatives of $x\,e^x$. Suggest a result for the nth derivative.

6. Determine the values of x for which the function $x^2 e^{-x}$ has stationary values and in each case state whether it is a maximum or minimum point.

*7. Integrate the following functions

(i) $\dfrac{1+e^x}{e^x}$ (ii) $\dfrac{e^x}{1+e^x}$ (iii) $\dfrac{e^x - e^{-x}}{e^x + e^{-x}}$

8. Differentiate the functions of question 7.

9. Find the coordinates of the intersection of $y = e^x$ and $y = 2e^{-x} + 1$. Hence find the area of the region bounded by these two curves and the y-axis.

10. Sketch the curve $y = 1 - e^{-x}$ and find the volume of the solid of revolution formed when this curve is rotated about the x-axis from $x = 0$ to $x = \ln 3$.

18.8 Power series for e^x and ln $(1 + x)$

Series for e^x

Assume that for all values of x the function e^x is given by the series

$$e^x = a_0 + a_1 x + a_2 x^2 + a_3 x^3 + a_4 x^4 + \ldots \tag{1}$$

where a_0, a_1, a_2, etc. are constants. Putting $x = 0$ we obtain

$$e^0 = a_0 \qquad \Rightarrow a_0 = 1$$

We now make use of the fact that differentiating e^x gives e^x again. Hence by successive differentiations of (1) we have

$$e^x = a_1 + 2a_2 x + \quad 3\,a_3 x^2 + \quad 4\,a_4 x^3 + \ldots \tag{2}$$
$$e^x = \qquad 2a_2 + 3 \cdot 2 \cdot a_3 x + \quad 4 \cdot 3 \cdot a_4 x^2 + \ldots \tag{3}$$
$$e^x = \qquad\qquad 3 \cdot 2 \cdot a_3 + 4 \cdot 3 \cdot 2 \cdot a_4 x + \ldots \tag{4}$$
$$e^x = \qquad\qquad\qquad 4 \cdot 3 \cdot 2 \cdot a_4 + \ldots \tag{5}$$

Substituting $x = 0$ into (2) $\Rightarrow 1 = a_1$

$\qquad\qquad\qquad\qquad$ (3) $\quad 1 = 2a_2$

$\qquad\qquad\qquad\qquad$ (4) $\quad 1 = 3 \cdot 2 \cdot a_3$

$\qquad\qquad\qquad\qquad$ (5) $\quad 1 = 4 \cdot 3 \cdot 2 \cdot a_4$

Hence $\quad a_1 = 1 \quad a_2 = \dfrac{1}{2!} \quad a_3 = \dfrac{1}{3!} \quad a_4 = \dfrac{1}{4!}$ etc.

Returning these values to equation (1) the following series is obtained. The series for e^{-x} is found simply by replacing x by $-x$.

$$e^x = 1 + x + \frac{x^2}{2!} + \frac{x^3}{3!} + \frac{x^4}{4!} + \frac{x^5}{5!} + \ldots$$

$$e^{-x} = 1 - x + \frac{x^2}{2!} - \frac{x^3}{3!} + \frac{x^4}{4!} - \frac{x^5}{5!} + \ldots$$

Note: Substituting $x = 1$ we have

$$e^1 = e = 1 + 1 + \frac{1}{2!} + \frac{1}{3!} + \frac{1}{4!} + \ldots$$

$\hspace{9cm}$ (as in Section 18.3)

Example 119

Find power series for (i) e^{2x} (ii) $(1 - x^2)e^{-x}$

(i) Replace x by $2x$ in the series for e^x

$$e^{2x} = 1 + (2x) + \frac{(2x)^2}{2!} + \frac{(2x)^3}{3!} + \frac{(2x)^4}{4!} + \ldots$$

$$\Rightarrow e^{2x} = 1 + 2x + 2x^2 + \frac{4x^3}{3} + \frac{2x^4}{3} + \ldots$$

(ii)

$$1 \cdot e^{-x} = 1 - x + \frac{x^2}{2} - \frac{x^3}{6} + \frac{x^4}{24} - \frac{x^5}{120} + \ldots$$

$$-x^2 e^{-x} = -x^2 + x^3 - \frac{x^4}{2} + \frac{x^5}{6} - \ldots$$

$$\Rightarrow (1 - x^2)e^{-x} = 1 - x - \frac{x^2}{2} + \frac{5x^3}{6} - \frac{11x^4}{24} + \frac{19x^5}{120} + \ldots$$

Example 120

Find $\sqrt[3]{e}$ correct to 4 decimal places.

We first obtain a series for $\sqrt[3]{e}$ or $e^{\frac{1}{3}}$ by substituting $x = \frac{1}{3}$ into the series for e^x.

$$e^{\frac{1}{3}} = 1 + (\tfrac{1}{3}) + \frac{1}{2!}(\tfrac{1}{3})^2 + \frac{1}{3!}(\tfrac{1}{3})^3 + \frac{1}{4!}(\tfrac{1}{3})^4 + \ldots$$

The value of each term is obtained from that of the previous term by a further division by 3 and by the new number appearing in the factorial.

$$\begin{aligned}
&1.333\,33 \\
&0.055\,56 \\
&0.006\,17 \\
\text{Hence} \quad \sqrt[3]{e} \approx 1.3956 \quad &0.000\,51 \\
&0.000\,03 \\
\hline
&1.395\,60
\end{aligned}$$

Series for $\ln(1 + x)$

The method used is essentially the same as that used for e^x.

Assume

$$\ln(1 + x) = a_0 + a_1 x + a_2 x^2 + a_3 x^3 + a_4 x^4 + \ldots \quad (1)$$

differentiate repeatedly

$$\frac{1}{(1 + x)} = a_1 + 2a_2 x + 3a_3 x^2 + 4a_4 x^3 + \ldots \quad (2)$$

$$\frac{-1}{(1 + x)^2} = 2a_2 + 3.2a_3 x + 4.3a_4 x^2 + \ldots \quad (3)$$

$$\frac{2}{(1+x)^3} = \qquad\qquad 3.2a_3 \quad + 4.3.2.a_4 x + \ldots \qquad\qquad (4)$$

$$\frac{-3.2}{(1+x)^4} = \qquad\qquad 4.3.2.a_4 \ + \ldots \qquad\qquad (5)$$

Substitute $x = 0$ into

(1)	$\ln(1) =$	a_0	$\Rightarrow a_0 =$	0
(2)	$1 =$	a_1	$a_1 =$	1
(3)	$-1 =$	$2a_2$	$a_2 =$	$-\frac{1}{2}$
(4)	$2 =$	$3.2a_3$	$a_3 =$	$\frac{1}{3}$
(5)	$-3.2 = 4.3.2a_4$		$a_4 =$	$-\frac{1}{4}$

Substitute these values back into equation (1)

$$\ln(1+x) = x - \frac{x^2}{2} + \frac{x^3}{3} - \frac{x^4}{4} + \frac{x^5}{5} - \ldots$$

Note: It is not possible to derive a series for $\ln x$. If, for example, we assume $\ln x = a_0 + a_1 x + a_2 x^2 + a_3 x^3 + \ldots$ we immediately run into difficulty when substituting $x = 0$ for $\ln 0 = -\infty$.

Permissible values of x

The series for e^x is valid for all values of x. The series for $\ln(1 + x)$ is valid only for $-1 < x \leqslant 1$.
(The proof of these statements is beyond the scope of this book.)

Exercise 18(g)

1. Write down the first 5 terms in the series expansions of
   (i) e^{3x} (ii) e^{-2x} (iii) $e^{\frac{1}{2}x}$ (iv) e^{x^2} (v) $(e^x)^2$ (vi) $e^{-\frac{1}{x}}$
2. By adding successive terms of the appropriate series find, correct to 4 decimal places, the values of

   (i) $\sqrt{e}$ (ii) $\dfrac{1}{e}$ (iii) $\dfrac{1}{\sqrt[3]{e}}$

3. Find the first 5 terms in the series for

   (i) $\dfrac{e^x - 1}{e^x}$ (ii) $(1 + x)e^{-x}$ (iii) $\frac{1}{2}(e^x + e^{-x})$

   (iv) $(2 - x^2)e^x$ (v) $\dfrac{(1 + x)^2}{e^x}$ (vi) $(e^x - 1)(e^{-x} + 1)$

4. Show that if x is small enough for x^4 and higher powers to be neglected then $(e^x - e^{-x})^2 \approx 4x^2$.
5. Write down the Binomial series for $(1 + x)^{-1}$. Hence show that, if x is so small that powers of x above x^3 can be neglected, then

   (i) $\dfrac{1}{1+x} + e^x \approx 2 + \dfrac{3}{2}x^2 - \dfrac{5}{6}x^3$ (ii) $\dfrac{e^x}{1+x} \approx 1 + \dfrac{x^2}{2} - \dfrac{x^3}{3}$

6. Write down series for
   (i) $\ln(1-x)$ (ii) $\ln(1+2x)$ (iii) $\ln\sqrt{1+x}$ (iv) $\ln(1+x^2)$
7. Use the series for $\ln(1+x)$ and $\ln(1-x)$ to show that

$$\ln\left(\frac{1+x}{1-x}\right) = 2\left[x + \frac{x^3}{3} + \frac{x^5}{5} + \cdots\right]$$

Hence find $\ln 11$ correct to 4 decimal places given only $\ln 3 = 1.09861$.
8. Find the first 4 terms in the series expansions of

(i) $\ln\left(\frac{1+x^2}{1-x}\right)$ (ii) $(1-x)\ln(1-x)$ (iii) $e^{-x}\ln(1+x)$

9. Show that $\ln\left(\frac{n+x}{n}\right) = \left(\frac{x}{n}\right) - \frac{1}{2}\left(\frac{x}{n}\right)^2 + \frac{1}{3}\left(\frac{x}{n}\right)^3 - \frac{1}{4}\left(\frac{x}{n}\right)^4 + \cdots$

Hence find $\ln 103$ and $\ln 105$ correct to 4 decimal places given only $\ln 100 = 4.60517$.

10. Prove that $\ln\sqrt{\frac{n+1}{n-1}} = \left(\frac{1}{n}\right) + \frac{1}{3}\left(\frac{1}{n}\right)^3 + \frac{1}{5}\left(\frac{1}{n}\right)^5 + \cdots$

Given $\ln 7 = 1.945910$, find $\ln 51$ correct to 5 decimal places.

19

Further Coordinate Geometry

19.1 Parametric equations

The equation of a curve is said to be given **parametrically** if both the x and y coordinates are given as functions of some other variable. For example the equations $x = t^2 - 2$, $y = t^3 - 5t$ will define a curve. Here both x and y are given as functions of the **parameter** t. Each value of t corresponds to a particular point on the curve, e.g. $t = 1$ gives $x = -1$, $y = -4$, i.e. the point $(-1, -4)$, whereas $t = 2$ gives the point $(2, -2)$. We may plot the curve by working out a table of values as follows

parameter t	-3	-2	-1	0	1	2	3
x	7	2	-1	-2	-1	2	7
y	-12	2	4	0	-4	-2	12

The curve is shown in Fig. 1. This diagram shows the value of the parameter t corresponding to each of the points plotted. Notice that as t is increased from -3 to $+3$ we move around the curve in the direction indicated

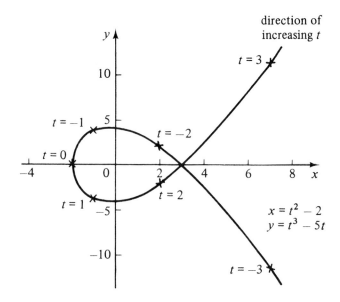

Fig. 1

Cartesian equation

The Cartesian equation for a curve given in terms of a parameter t is obtained by eliminating t from the two equations. An example is given below.

Gradient of a curve given parametrically

If x and y are both functions of a parameter t then we may obtain expressions for $\dfrac{dx}{dt}$ and $\dfrac{dy}{dt}$. The gradient $\dfrac{dy}{dx}$ is found by dividing these results, i.e.

$$\frac{dy}{dx} = \frac{dy}{dt} \cdot \frac{dt}{dx} \quad \text{or} \quad \frac{dy}{dt} \div \frac{dx}{dt}$$

Example 121

For the curve $x = t^2 - 2$, $y = t^3 - 5t$ find
(i) the Cartesian equation
(ii) the equation of the tangent at the point $t = 1$.

(i) We must eliminate the parameter t

$$x = t^2 - 2 \Rightarrow t^2 = x + 2$$
$$\text{hence} \qquad y = t^3 - 5t = t(t^2 - 5)$$
$$\Rightarrow y = \sqrt{x+2}\,(x - 3)$$

The equation is most conveniently written as

$$y^2 = (x + 2)(x - 3)^2$$

(ii) We have $\dfrac{dx}{dt} = 2t$ and $\dfrac{dy}{dt} = 3t^2 - 5$

hence $\dfrac{dy}{dx} = \dfrac{dy}{dt} \cdot \dfrac{dt}{dx} = \dfrac{3t^2 - 5}{2t}$

At the point $t = 1$ the gradient is $\dfrac{3-5}{2} = -1$ and the coordinates are $x = -1$, $y = -4$.

The equation of the tangent is therefore

$$\frac{y+4}{x+1} = -1 \Rightarrow y = -x - 5$$

Parameter θ

In some situations an angle θ may be used as a parameter. The simplest example is the circle. Fig. 2 shows a circle of radius 3 units with centre $(2, 1)$. The coordinates (x, y) of any point on the circle may be written $x = 2 + 3\cos\theta$, $y = 1 + 3\sin\theta$ where θ is the angle shown. As with all parametric equations we see that different points on the circle correspond to different values of the parameter θ. Thus $\theta = \frac{1}{2}\pi$ gives the highest point $(2, 4)$, $\theta = \pi$ gives the extreme left-hand point $(-1, 1)$ and so on.

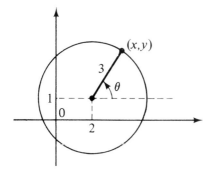

Fig. 2

When eliminating the parameter θ to obtain the Cartesian equation use can frequently be made of the identity $\sin^2\theta + \cos^2\theta = 1$. In the example considered we have

$$3\cos\theta = x - 2, \qquad 3\sin\theta = y - 1$$
$$\Rightarrow (x-2)^2 + (y-1)^2 = 9\cos^2\theta + 9\sin^2\theta$$
$$\text{i.e. } (x-2)^2 + (y-1)^2 = 9$$

the Cartesian equation for a circle with centre $(2, 1)$ and radius 3.

Exercise 19(a)

1. Plot the curve $x = t^2 - 4$, $y = t + 2$ for $-4 \leqslant t \leqslant 4$ and find the Cartesian equation of the curve. Find the gradient of the curve at the points of intersection with the y-axis.

2. Plot the curve $x = t - 2$, $y = t^3 - 2t^2$ for $-2 \leqslant t \leqslant 4$ and obtain the Cartesian equivalent. Find $\dfrac{dy}{dx}$ in terms of t and hence obtain the equation of the tangent at the point where $t = -1$.

3. Plot the curve $x = t + \dfrac{1}{t}$, $y = t - \dfrac{1}{t}$ for $t = \pm 3$, ± 2, ± 1 and also $\pm\frac{1}{2}$, $\pm\frac{1}{3}$. Prove that $\dfrac{dy}{dx} = \dfrac{t^2+1}{t^2-1} = \dfrac{x}{y}$. Verify this result by first obtaining the Cartesian equivalent and then differentiating implicitly.

4. Plot the curve $x = t^2 - 3$, $y = t^3 - 4t$ for $-3 \leqslant t \leqslant 3$. Obtain the Cartesian equivalent and hence establish the intersections of the curve with the y-axis. Find $\dfrac{dy}{dx}$ in terms of t and hence find the x coordinates of the two points where the tangent is parallel to the x-axis.

*5. Find in terms of t an expression for $\dfrac{d^2y}{dx^2}$ for the curve of (i) question 1 (ii) question 3.

6. Sketch the circles with the following parametric equations and write down their Cartesian equations

    (i) $x = 4 \cos$, $y = 4 \sin \theta$
    (ii) $x = 1 + \cos \theta$, $y = \sin \theta$
    (iii) $x = 2 \cos \theta + 3$, $y = 2 \sin \theta - 1$.

*7. (i) If the y coordinate of each point on the circle of question 6 part (i) is reduced by a factor $\frac{3}{4}$ we obtain the parametric equations $x = 4 \cos \theta$, $y = 3 \sin \theta$. This is an ellipse. Sketch the ellipse, showing clearly the intersections with both axes, and obtain its Cartesian equation.

    (ii) Find the Cartesian equation of the general ellipse $x = a \cos \theta$, $y = b \sin \theta$.

8. Find the coordinates of the points on the curve $x = \sin \theta$, $y = \sin 2\theta$ which correspond to $\theta = \frac{1}{6}\pi$ and $\theta = \frac{1}{2}\pi$. Find the length of the chord joining these points. Prove that the Cartesian equation is

$$y^2 = 4x^2(1 - x^2).$$

9. Show that the gradient of the curve $x = \cos 2\theta$, $y = \cos \theta$ is given by $1/4y$
    (i) by differentiating the parametric equations
    (ii) by obtaining the Cartesian equation and differentiating implicitly.

*10. Prove that the equation of the tangent to the curve $x = t^2$, $y = 2t$ at the point with parameter t is $ty = x + t^2$. Hence write down the equations of the tangents at the points $(9, 6)$ and $4, -4)$.

11 Find the equation of the tangent to the curve $x = t$, $y = 1/t$ at the point with parameter t. Hence show that there are two tangents which pass through the point $(-3, 1)$ and find their equations.

19.2 The parabola (standard form)

Locus definition

    The parabola is defined as the locus of a point which is always equidistant from a fixed point (the **focus**) and a fixed line (the **directrix**).

Standard form

    A parabola with vertex at the origin and symmetrical about the positive x-axis has equation $y^2 = 4ax$ where a is the distance of the focus and the directrix from the origin (Fig. 3).

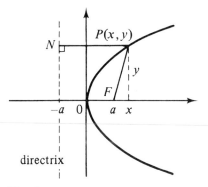

Fig. 3

To establish this result, consider Fig. 3 where the focus F is the point $(a, 0)$, and the directrix passes through the point $(-a, 0)$. If $P(x, y)$ is any point on the parabola then by definition we require $PN = PF$, or equivalently, $PN^2 = PF^2$

Hence $(x + a)^2 = y^2 + (x - a)^2$
$$x^2 + 2ax + a^2 = y^2 + x^2 - 2ax + a^2$$
$$\Rightarrow \quad y^2 = 4ax$$

A parabola with equation of the form $x^2 = 4ay$ is symmetrical about the y-axis (see Example 122 part (iii) below).

Example   122

Sketch the curves (i) $y^2 = 12x$ (ii) $y^2 = -12x$ (iii) $x^2 = 10y$

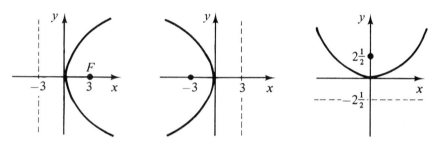

Fig. 4a   Fig. 4b   Fig. 4c

Equation (i) is of the form $y^2 = 4ax$ with $a = 3$ so that the focus is at $(3, 0)$ – Fig. 4a. Equation (ii) can be interpreted as $y^2 = 4ax$ with $a = -3$ so that the focus is $(-3, 0)$ – Fig. 4b. (Alternatively, since y^2 is always positive, notice that x can take only positive values if $y^2 = 12x$ and only negative values if $y^2 = -12x$.)

Equation (iii) is of the form $x^2 = 4ay$, i.e. symmetrical about the y-axis. The value of a is $2\frac{1}{2}$ so the focus is $(0, 2\frac{1}{2})$.

Example   123

Interpret the equation $y^2 - 8y = 8x$.

Completing the square on the y terms we have

$$(y - 4)^2 - 16 = 8x$$
$$\Rightarrow \quad (y - 4)^2 = 8(x + 2)$$
i.e. $$Y^2 = 8X$$

where $Y = y - 4$ and $X = x + 2$. This is a parabola with vertex at $y = 4$, $x = -2$. (Compare this with writing down the centre of a circle such as $(y - 4)^2 + (x + 2)^2 = 9$.) The value of a is 2 so that the focus is $(0, 4)$ and the directrix is $x = -4$ (Fig. 5).

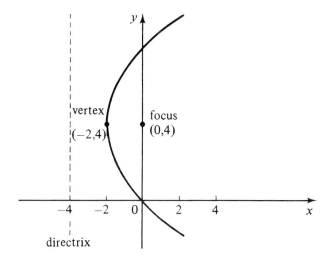

Fig. 5

Latus rectum

This term is not used much nowadays. The latus rectum of a parabola is the length of the chord through the focus which is perpendicular to the axis of symmetry. For the parabola of Fig. 5 this is the line joining the origin to the point (0, 8) so for this parabola the latus rectum is 8 units and the semi-latus rectum is 4 units.

Exercise 19(b)

1. Sketch the following parabolas, showing the focus and directrix of each.

   (i) $y^2 = 16x$ (ii) $y^2 = 2x$ (iii) $x^2 = 4y$
   (iv) $y^2 = -8x$ (v) $x^2 + 6y = 0$ (vi) $y^2 + x = 0$

2. Sketch the following parabolas. In each case state the coordinates of the vertex and the focus, also the equations of the axis of symmetry and the directrix.

   (i) $(y - 2)^2 = 4x$ (ii) $(y + 1)^2 = 20(x - 2)$
   (iii) $y^2 - 6y = 12x + 3$ (iv) $x^2 = 8y - 4$

3. Write down the equations of the following parabolas:
   (i) focus $(2\tfrac{1}{2}, 0)$,   directrix $x = -2\tfrac{1}{2}$
   (ii) focus $(-3, 0)$,   directrix $x = 3$
   (iii) focus $(0, 6)$,   directrix $y = -6$
   (iv) focus $(4, 3)$,   directrix $x = -4$
   (v) focus $(2, 2)$,   directrix $x = 0$

4. (i) Find the equation of the parabola with vertex $(0, 0)$ which passes through $(2, 6)$ and $(2, -6)$.

(ii) Find the equations of two parabolas with vertex $(0, 0)$ which pass through $(12, 8)$.

5. Find the gradient of
   (i) $y^2 = 16x$ at the point $(1, 4)$
   (ii) $y^2 = -3x$ at the point $(-12, 6)$
   (iii) $(y - 2)^2 = 5x$ at the point $(20, -8)$

6. Find the intersections of the line $y = 2x - 3$ with the parabola $y^2 = 8x$ and obtain the equations of the tangents at these points.

7. (i) A **focal chord** is a chord of a parabola which passes through the focus. Find the equation of the focal chord through the point $A(4, 4)$ on the parabola $y^2 = 4x$. Find also the coordinates of the other endpoint, B, of this chord.

   (ii) Prove that the tangents to $y^2 = 4x$ at the points A and B are perpendicular and that they intersect on the directrix.

8. For the parabola $y^2 = 4ax$ find the coordinates of the endpoints, A and B, of the latus rectum. Show that the semi-latus rectum is $2a$. Find the equations of the tangents to the parabola at A and B and show that they cross on the directrix.

9. Find the equation of the tangent to the parabola $y^2 = 6x$ which is parallel to the line $3y - x = 5$.

*10. Find the equation of the chord of the parabola $y^2 = 10x$ which is bisected at the point $(3, 2)$.

19.3 The parabola (parametric form)

The parametric equations for the parabola $y^2 = 4ax$ are $x = at^2$, $y = 2at$. It is easily verified that these satisfy the equation $y^2 = 4ax$ for any value of the parameter t, i.e.

$$y^2 = (2at)^2 = 4a(at^2) = 4ax$$

As an example consider the parabola $y^2 = 8x$ for which $a = 2$. Here the parametric equations are $x = 2t^2$, $y = 4t$. An alternative way of writing these is as coordinates, i.e. $(2t^2, 4t)$. This is the 'general point' on the parabola $y^2 = 8x$. Each point on the parabola is of this form and corresponds to a particular value of the parameter t, e.g.

value of t	-1	0	1	2	3
point $(2t^2, 4t)$	$(2, -4)$	$(0, 0)$	$(2, 4)$	$(8, 8)$	$(18, 12)$

Example 124

Describe the curves with the following parametric coordinates and state their Cartesian equations:

(i) $(3t^2, 6t)$ (ii) $(4t, 2t^2)$ (iii) $(10t, -5t^2)$

All of these curves are parabolas. We need to consider carefully how the basic parametric form $(at^2, 2at)$ is modified in parts (ii) and (iii).

(i) Basic form $(at^2, 2at)$ with $a = 3$.

Equation $y^2 = 4ax$ i.e. $y^2 = 12x$
Symmetrical about positive x-axis, focus $(3, 0)$ directrix $x = -3$

(ii) Here the parametric coordinates are reversed
i.e. $(2at, at^2)$ with $a = 2$.
Equation $x^2 = 4ay$,   i.e. $x^2 = 8y$
Symmetrical about positive y-axis, focus $(0, 2)$, directrix $y = -2$

(iii) This is of the form $(2at, -at^2)$ with $a = 5$. Notice that the y coordinate is always negative so this parabola is symmetrical about the negative y-axis and has focus $(0, -5)$, directrix $y = 5$.
Equation $x^2 = -4ay$,   i.e. $x^2 = -20y$

Example 125

Find the intersections of the line $y = 3x - 4$ with the parabola $(4t^2, 8t)$.

Substituting the parametric coordinates into the equation of the line we have

$$8t = 12t^2 - 4$$
$$\Rightarrow 0 = 3t^2 - 2t - 1$$
$$0 = (3t + 1)(t - 1) \qquad \Rightarrow t = -\tfrac{1}{3} \quad \text{or} \quad t = 1$$

These are the values of t at the intersection points on the parabola. Substituting these values into $(4t^2, 8t)$ we obtain the coordinates, i.e. $(\tfrac{4}{9}, -\tfrac{8}{3})$ and $(4, 8)$.

Questions 1–8 of Exercise 19(c) may now be tackled.

General equation of tangent to a parabola

Our object here is to find the equation of the tangent to the parabola $y^2 = 4ax$ at the general point $(at^2, 2at)$. First we require the gradient at this point

$$x = at^2, \qquad y = 2at \qquad \Rightarrow \frac{dx}{dt} = 2at, \qquad \frac{dy}{dt} = 2a$$

Hence $\qquad \dfrac{dy}{dx} = \dfrac{dy}{dt} \cdot \dfrac{dt}{dx} = \dfrac{2a}{2at} = \dfrac{1}{t}$

(i.e. the gradient at any point is given by $1/t$ where t is the value of the parameter at that point.) The required tangent therefore passes through the point $(at^2, 2at)$ with gradient $1/t$. Its equation is

$$\frac{y - 2at}{x - at^2} = \frac{1}{t}$$
$$\Rightarrow ty - 2at^2 = x - at^2 \qquad \text{or} \qquad ty = x + at^2 \qquad (1)$$

This equation applies to any tangent for any parabola of the form $y^2 = 4ax$, e.g. for the parabola $y^2 = 8x$ we have $a = 2$ so that the parametric coordinates are $(2t^2, 4t)$ and the general tangent is $ty = x + 2t^2$. Thus at the point $t = 3$, i.e. $(18, 12)$, the tangent is $3y = x + 18$ and at the point $t = -1$, i.e. $(2, -4)$ the tangent is $-y = x + 2$ etc.

Example   126

Find the equations of the tangents from the point $(2, 6)$ to the parabola $y^2 = 10x$.

For the parabola $y^2 = 10x$ we have $a = 2\frac{1}{2}$ so the general tangent, using (1) above is

$$ty = x + 2\tfrac{1}{2}t^2 \tag{2}$$

If this tangent passes through the point $(2, 6)$ then

$$6t = 2 + 2\tfrac{1}{2}t^2$$
$$\Rightarrow \quad 0 = 5t^2 - 12t + 4$$
$$0 = (t - 2)(5t - 2)$$
$$\Rightarrow \quad t = 2 \quad \text{or} \quad t = \tfrac{2}{5}$$

These are the values of the parameter t for the points of contact of the two tangents on the parabola. The equations of the tangents are found by substituting these values back into (2), i.e.

$$t = 2 \qquad \Rightarrow 2y = x + 10$$
$$t = \tfrac{2}{5} \qquad \Rightarrow 2y = 5x + 2 \qquad \text{(after multiplying by 5)}$$

Exercise 19(c)

1. Find the parametric coordinates for each of the parabolas in Exercise 19(b), question 1.
2. Sketch the following parabolas and state their Cartesian equations:
   (i) $(4t^2, 8t)$ (ii) $(t^2, 2t)$ (iii) $(2t, t^2)$
   (iv) $(6t^2, 12t)$ (v) $(-6t^2, 12t)$ (vi) $(6t, -3t^2)$.
3. Find the semi-latus rectum of the parabola $(8t^2, 16t)$.
4. Find the gradient of
   (i)   the parabola $(5t^2, 10t)$ at the point $t = 2$.
   (ii) the parabola $(-4t^2, 8t)$ at the point $t = 1\frac{1}{2}$.
   (iii) the parabola $(4t, 2t^2)$ at the point $t = -\frac{1}{2}$.
5. Find the intersections of the line $y = 3x - 10$ with the parabola $(2t^2, 4t)$.
6. Prove that the line $y = 3x + 1$ is a tangent to the parabola $(3t^2, 6t)$ and find the coordinates of the point of contact.
7. Find the equation of the focal chord of the parabola $(2t^2, 4t)$ which passes through the point $t = 3$ on the parabola. Find also the value of t at the other endpoint of the focal chord.
8. Find the equation of
   (i)   the tangent to $(5t^2, 10t)$ at the point $t = \frac{1}{2}$.
   (ii) the normal to $(6t, 3t^2)$ at the point $t = 3$.
   (iii) the tangent to $(t^2, 2t)$ at the point with parameter t.
9. Prove that the equation of the tangent to the parabola $(8t^2, 16t)$ at the point with parameter t is $ty = x + 8t^2$. Hence find the equations of the two tangents to the parabola from the point $(-6, 8)$.
10. Two tangents are drawn from the point $(3, 5)$ to the parabola $y^2 = 8x$. Find the equation of the chord joining their points of contact.

11. Prove that the tangent to the parabola $y^2 = 4ax$ with gradient m has equation $y = mx + (a/m)$. Find also the coordinates of the point of contact in terms of a and m. If the line $y = px + (5/p)$ touches a certain parabola for all values of p, find the equation of the parabola.

12. (i) Prove that the equation of the normal to the parabola $(at^2, 2at)$ at the point with parameter t is $y + tx = at^3 + 2at$.
    (ii) If the tangent and the normal at the point $(at^2, 2at)$ intersect the x-axis at R and S, prove that the midpoint of RS is always the focus of the parabola. (See Fig. 6.)

19.4 Geometric properties of the parabola

Some of the more important properties are given in the form of an exercise.

Exercise 19(d)

The questions refer to Fig. 6 in which P is the general point $(at^2, 2at)$ on the parabola $y^2 = 4ax$.

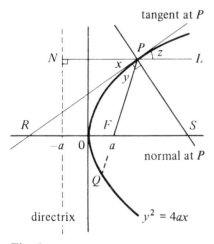

Fig. 6

1. *The reflective property*
   (i) Find the equation of the tangent at P and deduce the coordinates of R.
   (ii) Show that $RF = NP$ and hence prove that the figure $RFPN$ is a rhombus.
   (iii) Prove that the angles x, y and z are equal (NPL is a straight line).
   (iv) Explain why any ray of light from the focus is reflected from the parabola in a direction parallel to the x-axis.

   It follows that light from a source at the focus is reflected as a parallel beam.

2. *The tangents at the endpoints of a focal chord are perpendicular.*
   (i) What is the gradient of the parabola at the point $(at^2, 2at)$?

(ii) If the other end of the focal chord PF is $Q(aT^2, 2aT)$ explain why

$$\frac{2at}{at^2 - a} = \frac{-2aT}{a - aT^2}$$

Hence prove that $tT = -1$, or alternatively, $T = -1/t$.

(iii)   Deduce that the tangents at P and Q are perpendicular.

As a consequence of part (ii) notice that focal chords join points such as $t = 2$ and $t = -\frac{1}{2}$, $t = 3$ and $t = -\frac{1}{3}$ etc.

3. *The tangents from a focal chord intersect on the directrix.*
    (i)   Obtain the equations of the tangents at $P(at^2, 2at)$ and $Q(aT^2, 2aT)$.
    (ii)   Use the result of question 2 part (ii) to prove that they intersect on the directrix $x = -a$.

4. Prove in Fig. 6 that the perpendicular from the focus F to any tangent PR of the parabola $y^2 = 4ax$ meets the tangent on the y-axis. *This property is the basis for an interesting method of generating a parabola* –Draw two axes and choose a convenient focus F. Use a set square to draw numerous different lines from the y-axis as in Fig. 7. A parabola will appear as the 'envelope' of these lines.

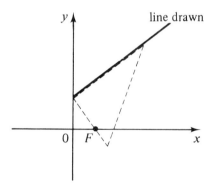

Fig. 7

19.5 Further loci

Example   127

In Fig. 6, as the point $P(at^2, 2at)$ moves around the parabola $y^2 = 4ax$, find the locus of
(i)   the midpoint of PF
(ii)   the midpoint of the focal chord PQ.

(i)   The midpoint of $P(at^2, 2at)$ and $F(a, 0)$ is

$$\left(\frac{at^2 + a}{2}, \frac{2at + 0}{2}\right) \quad \text{or} \quad \left(\frac{1}{2}at^2 + \frac{1}{2}a, \ at\right)$$

As in Section 19.1 the locus of this point is found by eliminating the parameter t from the equations $x = \frac{1}{2}at^2 + \frac{1}{2}a$, $y = at$.

We have $2x = \dfrac{(at)^2}{a} + a = \dfrac{y^2}{a} + a$

$\Rightarrow y^2 = 2ax - a^2$

(ii) If the value of the parameter at the point Q is T, then, by the result of Exercise 19(d), question 2 we have $T = -1/t$. The endpoints of the focal chord are therefore $P(at^2, 2at)$ and $Q\left(\dfrac{a}{t^2}, -\dfrac{2a}{t}\right)$

The midpoint of PQ has coordinates

$$x = \frac{a}{2}\left(t^2 + \frac{1}{t^2}\right) \qquad y = a\left(t - \frac{1}{t}\right)$$

thus $y^2 = a^2\left(t^2 - 2 + \dfrac{1}{t^2}\right) = a^2\left(t^2 + \dfrac{1}{t^2}\right) - 2a^2$

$\Rightarrow y^2 = 2ax - 2a^2$

Exercise 19(e)

Questions 1–6 refer to Fig. 6 in which P is the general point $(at^2, 2at)$ on the parabola $y^2 = 4ax$.

1. Find the locus of the midpoint of the perpendicular from P to (i) the x-axis (ii) the y-axis.
2. Find the coordinates of R and show that the locus of the midpoint of PR is the line $x = 0$.
3. Find the coordinates of S and deduce the locus of the midpoint of PS.
4. Find the locus of the point W on FP produced which is such that $FW = 2FP$.
5. Find the locus of the midpoint of PV where V is the intersection of the tangent PR with the y-axis.
6. If Z is the point $(aT^2, 2aT)$ on the parabola and is such that angle $POZ = 90°$, prove that $T = -4/t$ and hence prove that the midpoint of PZ has locus $y^2 = 2ax - 8a^2$.
7. The general point on the curve $xy = 1$ may be written $(t, 1/t)$. Prove that the locus of the midpoint of the line joining this point to the point $(1, 1)$ has equation $(2x - 1)(2y - 1) = 1$.
8. The point $P(2 + \cos\theta, \sin\theta)$ is the general point on the circle of radius 1 unit with centre $(2, 0)$. Find the equations of the following loci:
   (i) the midpoint of OP
   (ii) the midpoint of the perpendicular from P to the y-axis.
9. If the line $y = mx + c$ intersects the parabola $y^2 = 4ax$ at (x_1, y_1) and (x_2, y_2) prove that $y_1 + y_2 = 4a/m$. Hence show that when a series of parallel chords is drawn for the parabola $y^2 = 4ax$ the locus of the midpoint of these chords is a line parallel to the x-axis.
10. The tangents to the parabola $y^2 = 4ax$ at the points $P(ap^2, 2ap)$ and $Q(aq^2, 2aq)$ meet at the point R. Show that the coordinates of R are $[apq, a(p + q)]$.
    (i) If PQ is a focal chord prove that the locus of R is the directrix of the parabola.
    (ii) Find the locus of R if the midpoint of PQ always lies on the line $x = 2a$.

20

Complex Numbers

20.1 Introduction

Numbers are so much a part of our everyday lives that we tend to take them for granted. It is easy to forget that numbers had to be invented by man, just like all the other products of civilised life, and that our present system of numbers is something which has evolved quite slowly from very rudimentary beginnings.

It is probable that the very first number system consisted of just three numbers: one, two and many. Then, as man found it necessary to keep a check on his possessions a fuller range of 'counting numbers' was developed. Later, to facilitate the division or sharing of property, whole numbers had to be split into parts and the fractions (or 'rational numbers') were introduced. Later still the remarkable discovery was made that some numbers could not be written as fractions, e.g. $\sqrt{2}$ and π. Numbers such as these are now called 'irrational numbers'.

Another aspect entirely is the way in which the writing of numbers has been developed. Early mathematicians were handicapped greatly by the clumsy number systems of their day, the best known example, of course, being the Roman numerals. In view of the immense difficulty in performing calculations with the early systems of numbers the achievements of some of these mathematicians in estimating, for example, the radius of the earth or the distance to the sun were quite staggering. Our present way of writing fractions and the introduction of the decimal system, coupled with the idea of place value (in which the same figure is used in different positions to represent different numbers, i.e. hundreds, tens, units, tenths etc.) have been enormous steps forward.

The number system, therefore, undergoes a slow but definite process of modification and improvement. With the study of Mathematics came the need for another type of number; in order to solve equations such as $2x + 6 = 0$ negative numbers were introduced. A similar but more recent innovation are the **imaginary numbers**. These enable us to 'solve' equations such as $x^2 = -4$ which have no solutions if we restrict our attention to the normal range of 'real' numbers. If the square root of -1 is denoted i then the square roots of all negative numbers can be written in terms of i, e.g.

$$\sqrt{-4} = \sqrt{4 \times (-1)} = \pm 2\sqrt{-1} = \pm 2i$$

Using these imaginary numbers we can obtain solutions for equations which were previously insoluble, e.g.

if $5x^2 - 6x + 5 = 0$

then $x = \dfrac{6 \pm \sqrt{-64}}{10} = \dfrac{6 \pm 8i}{10}$

$x = \dfrac{3}{5} \pm \dfrac{4}{5}i$

These solutions are examples of *complex numbers*, i.e. numbers which are the sum of a real part (i.e. $\frac{3}{5}$) and an imaginary part (i.e. $\pm \frac{4}{5}i$).

The justification for the introduction of any new type of number can only be the uses which can be found for them. The usefulness of negative numbers is now universally accepted but it is worthwhile to realise that at the time of their introduction they probably seemed unnecessary and rather bewildering to many people. Complex numbers may seem even more strange and pointless but they too have proved to be worthwhile. Their usefulness depends largely on their two dimensional nature (i.e. the real and imaginary parts) which means that they can be used to store two pieces of information and that operations involving complex numbers can be used to process data on two different physical quantities simultaneously. In this sense they are rather similar to vectors but their two parts behave rather differently under manipulation to those of vectors so that complex numbers are applied to rather different physical situations.

Exercise 20(a)

1. Write in terms of i
   (i) $\sqrt{-9}$ (ii) $\sqrt{-100}$ (iii) $\sqrt{-7}$ (iv) $\sqrt{-\frac{1}{4}}$
2. Write down the solutions of the following equations:
   (i) $x^2 = -25$ (ii) $x^2 + 16 = 0$
   (iii) $4x^2 + 9 = 0$ (iv) $x^3 + 4x = 0$
3. Simplify
   (i) i^2 (ii) $4i^2$ (iii) $(4i)^2$ (iv) i^4

   (v) $\dfrac{1}{i^2}$ (vi) i^3 (vii) $(2i)^3$ (viii) $\dfrac{1}{i}$

   (ix) $\left(\dfrac{2}{i}\right)^3$ (x) $i^3 + i$ (xi) $i^3 \div i$ (xii) $4i \div 2i^2$

4. (i) If $x^4 = 16$ write down two possible values for x^2 and hence four possible values for x.
   (ii) Find four possible fourth-roots of the number 81.

20.2 Types of number

The set of **real** numbers (usually denoted $\mathbb{R}$) has the following important subsets:

(i) Integers — whole numbers
(ii) Rational numbers — numbers which can be written as fractions (or ratios) i.e. of the form p/q where p and q are integers

(iii) Irrational numbers   – numbers which cannot be written as fractions, i.e. non-recurring decimal numbers such as π and $\sqrt{2}$.

The set of **imaginary** numbers (denoted $\mathbb{I}$) consists of multiples ki where $i = \sqrt{-1}$ and k is real (i.e. $k \in \mathbb{R}$) e.g. $2i$, $-\frac{5}{7}i$, $\sqrt{2}i$. There is a one-to-one correspondence between $\mathbb{R}$ and $\mathbb{I}$; for every real number k there is a corresponding imaginary number ki.

The set of **complex** numbers (denoted $\mathbb{C}$) consists of all numbers of the form $a + bi$ where a and b are real, e.g. $2 + 3i$, $5 - 4i$. a is said to be the **real part** and bi the **imaginary part** of the complex number.

Notation

The symbol z is commonly used to denote a complex number. $\text{Re}(z)$ and $\text{Im}(z)$ are the real and imaginary parts of z, i.e.

if $z = a + bi$

then $\text{Re}(z) = a$ $\text{Im}(z) = bi$

Conjugate complex numbers

Two complex numbers are said to be **conjugate** if they have the same real parts but opposite imaginary parts, e.g. $2 + 3i$ and $2 - 3i$.

The conjugate number to z is denoted $\bar{z}$. Thus if $z = a + bi$ then $\bar{z} = a - bi$. As we shall see in the next section, conjugate complex numbers occur frequently in the solution of equations.

20.3 Roots of equations

Quadratic equations

Equations which we previously regarded as insoluble are always found to have conjugate complex roots, e.g.

if $2x^2 - 2x + 3 = 0$

then $x = \dfrac{2 \pm \sqrt{-20}}{4} = \dfrac{2 \pm 2\sqrt{5}i}{4}$

$\Rightarrow x = \frac{1}{2} + \frac{1}{2}\sqrt{5}i$ or $\frac{1}{2} - \frac{1}{2}\sqrt{5}i$

(the two solutions are conjugate to one another). In general, with the equation $ax^2 + bx + c = 0$ we have three different possibilities. (See also Section 5.4.)

(i) $b^2 - 4ac > 0$ distinct real roots

(ii) $b^2 - 4ac = 0$ repeated real root

(iii) $b^2 - 4ac < 0$ conjugate complex roots.

Cubic equations

As we have seen in Section 5.6, the nature of the graphs of cubic functions is such that all cubic functions have at least one intersection with the x-axis. All cubic equations therefore have at least one real solution and can in theory be written as the product of a linear factor and a quadratic factor. It follows that cubic equations have either

(i) 3 real roots (one of which may be repeated)

or (ii) 1 real root and 2 conjugate complex roots

depending on whether the quadratic factor leads to real or complex solutions.

e.g. the equation $2x^3 + 2x^2 - x + 6 = 0$ may be shown to have a factor $(x + 2)$ by the Remainder Theorem.

$$\text{factorizing} \quad (x + 2)(2x^2 - 2x + 3) = 0$$
$$\Rightarrow x + 2 = 0 \quad \text{or} \quad 2x^2 - 2x + 3 = 0$$
$$\Rightarrow x = -2 \quad \text{or} \quad x = \tfrac{1}{2} \pm \tfrac{1}{2}\sqrt{5}\,i$$
$$\quad \text{(real)} \qquad \text{(conjugate complex)}$$

The quadratic equation here is the same as that considered above.

It is worth mentioning at this point an important theorem which states that complex roots of polynomial equations always occur in conjugate pairs, i.e. there will always be an even number of complex roots. Thus the following possibilities arise when solving equations of degree 4 (i.e. including powers of x up to x^4); (i) 4 real roots (ii) 2 real and 2 conjugate complex roots (iii) 4 complex roots, which occur as two conjugate pairs.

Exercise 20(b)

1. Classify the solutions of each of the following equations as rational, irrational, imaginary or complex:
   (i) $\quad 2x - 5 = 0$ (ii) $\quad 2x^2 - 5x = 0$
   (iii) $2x^2 - 5 = 0$ (iv) $\quad 2x^2 + 5 = 0$
   (v) $\quad 2x^2 - 5x + 4 = 0$ (vi) $\quad 2x^2 - 5x + 3 = 0$
   (vii) $x^3 - 3x = 0$ (viii) $x^3 + 3x = 0$

2. Write down the conjugates of
   (i) $3 + 5i$ (ii) $-2 - 7i$ (iii) $\sqrt{2} + \sqrt{3}i$ (iv) $3i - 1$
   (v) $2i$ (vi) $\cos\theta + i\sin\theta$

3. Solve the following quadratic equations:
   (i) $\quad x^2 + 9 = 0$ (ii) $x^2 + 8x + 25 = 0$
   (iii) $x^2 - x + 1 = 0$ (iv) $2x^2 - 3x + 2 = 0$

4. Solve the following cubic equations:
   (i) $\quad x^3 + 2x^2 - x - 14 = 0$ (ii) $3x^3 - x^2 - x - 1 = 0$
   (iii) $2x^3 - 3x^2 - 10x + 3 = 0$ (iv) $2x^3 - x^2 + 2x - 1 = 0$

*5. Show that $x^3 + 1 = (x + 1)(x^2 - x + 1)$ and hence find three cube roots of -1.

6. Obtain four solutions for each of the following equations:
   (i) $\quad x^4 - 5x^2 + 4 = 0$ (ii) $x^4 + 3x^2 - 4 = 0$
   (iii) $x^4 + x^3 - 2x = 0$ (iv) $x^4 + x^2 + 2x = 0$

20.4 Operations on complex numbers

We now consider how the four operations of addition, subtraction, multiplication and division may be performed with complex numbers. To illustrate the method we shall use the two numbers

$$z_1 = \quad 2 + 3i$$
$$z_2 = -5 + 4i$$

Addition and subtraction

Simply add (or subtract) the real parts and the imaginary parts

$$z_1 + z_2 = -3 + 7i$$
$$z_1 - z_2 = \quad 7 - i$$

Note: The notation $\overline{z_1 + z_2}$ means the conjugate of the sum $(z_1 + z_2)$. Hence $\overline{z_1 + z_2} = -3 \mp 7i$. Notice that this is equivalent to the sum of $\bar{z}_1$ and $\bar{z}_2$, though the truth of relationships such as this should not be assumed automatically.

Multiplication and division

Here we use the ordinary algebraic rules for brackets. Multiplication is straightforward

$$
\begin{aligned}
z_1 z_2 &= (2 + 3i)(-5 + 4i) \\
&= -10 + 12i^2 - 15i + 8i \\
&= -22 - 7i \quad \text{(since } 12i^2 = -12)
\end{aligned}
$$

For division it is necessary to multiply top and bottom by the number which is conjugate to the denominator,

e.g. $\dfrac{z_2}{z_1} = \dfrac{(-5 + 4i)}{(2 + 3i)} = \dfrac{(-5 + 4i)(2 - 3i)}{(2 + 3i)(2 - 3i)}$

$$= \dfrac{-10 - 12i^2 + 8i + 15i}{4 - 9i^2} = \dfrac{2 + 23i}{13}$$

i.e. $\dfrac{z_2}{z_1} = \dfrac{2}{13} + \dfrac{23}{13}i$

More about conjugate numbers

The reason why conjugate complex numbers are of such importance is that both their sum and their product are real. (The success of the method of division outlined above depends on this for it enables imaginary numbers to be cleared from the denominator.)

This result is easily established. Consider two conjugate numbers $a + bi$ and $a - bi$.

Their sum $\quad = (a + bi) + (a - bi) = 2a \quad$ (i.e. real)
Their product $= (a + bi)(a - bi) = a^2 - b^2 i^2 = a^2 + b^2 \quad$ (i.e. real)

The reader should notice how this result is also involved in Example 128 below. This will help to give some understanding of why complex roots of equations occur in conjugate pairs.

Example 128

Given that $3 + 2i$ is one solution of the equation $z^3 - 4z^2 + z + 26 = 0$ find the other solutions.

Since complex roots occur in conjugate pairs we know immediately that $3 - 2i$ is also a solution. The solutions $3 + 2i$ and $3 - 2i$ must be the roots of the quadratic factor of this equation. For this factor we have

sum of roots $= (3 + 2i) + (3 - 2i) = 6$

product of roots $= (3 + 2i)(3 - 2i) = 9 - 4i^2 = 13$

Hence the quadratic factor is $z^2 - 6z + 13$. We may now factorize the cubic function, i.e.

$$z^3 - 4z^2 + z + 26 = (z^2 - 6z + 13)(z + 2)$$

The third root is therefore $z = -2$ (real).

Answer: The solutions are $3 + 2i$, $3 - 2i$, -2.

Example 129

Express in the form $x + iy$ where $x, y \in \mathbb{R}$

(i) $(3 + 4i)^4$ (ii) $\sqrt{3 + 4i}$

(i) Here it is convenient to use the Binomial expansion, i.e.

$$(a + b)^4 = a^4 + 4a^3b + 6a^2b^2 + 4ab^3 + b^4$$
$$\Rightarrow (3 + 4i)^4 = 3^4 + 4(3)^3(4i) + 6(3)^2(4i)^2 + 4(3)(4i)^3 + (4i)^4$$
$$= 81 + 432i + 864i^2 + 768i^3 + 256i^4$$
$$= 81 + 432i - 864 - 768i + 256$$
$$= -527 - 336i$$

(ii) Let $\sqrt{3 + 4i} = x + iy$

then $3 + 4i = (x + iy)^2 = x^2 + i^2y^2 + 2xyi$

i.e. $3 + 4i = (x^2 - y^2) + 2xyi$

This can only be true if the real parts on both sides of the equation are equal and if the imaginary parts are also equal

$$\Rightarrow x^2 - y^2 = 3 \tag{1}$$

$$2xy = 4 \quad \text{or} \quad y = \frac{2}{x} \tag{2}$$

substituting (2) into (1)

$$x^2 - \frac{4}{x^2} = 3$$
$$\Rightarrow x^4 - 3x^2 - 4 = 0$$
$$(x^2 - 4)(x^2 + 1) = 0$$
$$x^2 = 4 \quad \text{or} \quad x^2 = -1$$
$$x = \pm 2 \quad \text{or} \quad x = \pm i$$

We reject the imaginary solutions for x since both x and y must be real numbers. Thus we obtain
$$x = 2, \quad y = 1 \quad \text{or} \quad x = -2, \quad y = -1$$
i.e. $\sqrt{3 + 4i} = \underline{2 + i} \quad \text{or} \quad \underline{-2 - i}$

Exercise 20(c)

1. If $z_1 = 3 + i$ and $z_2 = 4 - 5i$ find
   (i) $z_1 + z_2$ (ii) $z_2 - z_1$ (iii) $z_1 z_2$
   (iv) $\dfrac{z_2}{z_1}$ (v) $\dfrac{z_1}{z_2}$ (vi) $\dfrac{1}{z_1}$

2. Find the sums and products of
   (i) $3 + 2i$ and $7 - 4i$ (ii) $3i$ and $7 - i$
   (iii) $5 + 3i$ and $5 - 3i$ (iv) $1 + \sqrt{3}i$ and $2 + \sqrt{3}i$

3. For each part of question 2 divide the first number given by the second.

4. Express in the form $a + bi$
   (i) $(4 - 2i)^2$ (ii) $\dfrac{1}{(4 - 2i)^2}$ (iii) $(2 + 3i)^3$ (iv) $(1 - 2i)^4$

5. Simplify
   (i) $\dfrac{3 + i}{4 - 2i} - \dfrac{7 - 2i}{1 + i}$ (ii) $\dfrac{6 - i}{1 + 2i} \times \dfrac{-16 + 11i}{3 + 2i}$

6. Given one root of the following equations, find the remaining roots:
   (i) $z^3 - 2z^2 + z + 100 = 0$ root $3 + 4i$
   (ii) $z^3 - 3z^2 + 4z - 12 = 0$ root $2i$
   (iii) $z^3 - 23z + k = 0$ root $3 - 2i$ (Find also the value of k.)

7. Find x and y if
   (i) $x + iy = \dfrac{1}{2 - 5i}$ (ii) $\sqrt{x + iy} = 5 + 3i$

8. Find the square roots of (i) $8 - 6i$ (ii) $7 + 24i$

9. If $z = x_1 + iy_1$ and $z_2 = x_2 + iy_2$ find expressions for
   (i) $z_1 + z_2$ (ii) $z_1 z_2$ (iii) $\dfrac{z_1}{z_2}$

10. If $z_1 = 5 - 4i$ and $z_2 = -2 + i$ find
    (i) $z_1 + z_2$ (ii) $\overline{z_1 + z_2}$ (iii) $z_1 z_2$
    (iv) $\overline{z_1 \cdot z_2}$ (v) $\bar{z}_1 + \bar{z}_2$ (vi) $\bar{z}_1 \cdot \bar{z}_2$

11. Use the results of question 9 to prove that
    (i) $\overline{z_1 + z_2} = \bar{z}_1 + \bar{z}_2$ (ii) $\overline{z_1 z_2} = \bar{z}_1 \cdot \bar{z}_2$

12. Show that if $z = \cos\theta + i\sin\theta$ then
    (i) $z^2 = \cos 2\theta + i\sin 2\theta$ (ii) $\dfrac{1}{z} = \cos\theta - i\sin\theta$

13. If $z = x + iy$, express in the form $a + bi$
    (i) z^2 (ii) $z \cdot \bar{z}$ (iii) $\dfrac{1}{z}$ (iv) $z^2 - \bar{z}^2$

14. Use the results of question 9 to prove that if z_1 and z_2 are complex numbers whose sum and product are both real, then z_1 and z_2 must be conjugate.

20.5 The Argand diagram

(A basic knowledge of vectors is assumed in this section.)

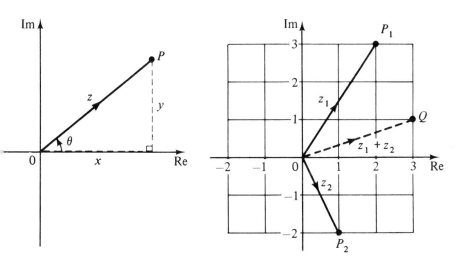

Fig. 1a   Fig. 1b

In the introduction to this chapter it was stated that complex numbers have a two dimensional nature. An obvious way of representing a complex number in two dimensions is to use horizontal and vertical axes to plot the real and imaginary parts. Thus a complex number $z = x + iy$ is represented in Fig. 1a either by the point P or, alternatively, by the **vector** OP.

Fig. 1b shows the representations of the following two numbers

$$z_1 = 2 + 3i \quad \text{(represented by the vector } OP_1)$$
$$z_2 = 1 - 2i \quad \text{(represented by the vector } OP_2)$$

A diagram such as this is called an **Argand diagram**.

Addition on the Argand diagram

If $z_1 = 2 + 3i$ and $z_2 = 1 - 2i$ as above then the sum of these numbers is $z_1 + z_2 = 3 + i$. This is represented by the vector OQ in Fig. 1b. The reader will notice that OQ may be obtained by the vector addition of OP_1 and OP_2 (using either the triangle or parallelogram methods). Thus the addition of two complex numbers z_1 and z_2 is equivalent to the vector addition of their representations on the Argand diagram.

This result is very much what one would expect. We shall see in the next section, however, that a far more surprising geometrical relation exists for the product of two numbers on the Argand diagram. It is first necessary to introduce two more terms.

Modulus and Argument

The **modulus** of a complex number is the magnitude of its vector representation on the Argand diagram and the **argument** is the angle θ, as shown in Fig. 1a. The notations $|z|$ and $\arg(z)$ are used for the modulus and argument respectively, i.e.

$$\text{modulus } |z| \qquad = \text{length } OP \quad \text{(Fig. 1a)}$$
$$\text{argument } \arg(z) \quad = \text{angle } \theta \qquad \text{(Fig. 1a)}$$

Thus giving the modulus and argument of a complex number z is equivalent to defining its position on the Argand diagram in polar coordinates (r, θ).

When stating the argument of a complex number it is usual to give the value of the angle θ in radians and in the range $-\pi \leqslant \theta \leqslant \pi$. This is called the **principal value** of the argument (clearly alternative values could be obtained by the addition or subtraction of multiples of 2π, i.e. 360°).

Example   130

(i) State the modulus and argument of z_1, z_2 and $z_1 + z_2$ where $z_1 = 2 + 3i$, $z_2 = 1 - 2i$.

(ii) If $|z| = 6$ and $\arg(z) = -\frac{5}{6}\pi$ find the complex number z in the form $x + iy$.

(i) The numbers z_1, z_2 and $z_1 + z_2$ are represented in Fig. 1b. We have

$$z_1 \qquad = 2 + 3i \qquad \Rightarrow |z_1| = \sqrt{4+9} = \sqrt{13}$$
$$z_2 \qquad = 1 - 2i \qquad |z_2| = \sqrt{1+4} = \sqrt{5}$$
$$z_1 + z_2 = 3 + i \qquad |z_1 + z_2| = \sqrt{9+1} = \sqrt{10}$$

The arguments are obtained by using tangents. Notice that arg (z_2) is negative, i.e. a negative angle of turn from the horizontal axis.

$$\arg(z_1) \qquad = \quad \arctan\left(\tfrac{3}{2}\right) = 0.98 \text{ rad} \quad (56.3°)$$
$$\arg(z_2) \qquad = \; -\arctan\left(\tfrac{2}{1}\right) = -1.11 \text{ rad} \quad (-63.4°)$$
$$\arg(z_1 + z_2) = \quad \arctan\left(\tfrac{1}{3}\right) = 0.32 \text{ rad} \quad (18.4°)$$

Note: In general, if $z = x + iy$ then, from Fig. 1a,

$$|z| = \sqrt{x^2 + y^2} \qquad \arg(z) = \arctan\left(\frac{y}{x}\right)$$

(ii) It is simpler to draw a rough diagram rather than use formulae. From Fig. 2 we have

$$\text{real part} \qquad x = -6\cos 30 = -3\sqrt{3}$$
$$\text{imaginary part} \quad y = -6\sin 30 = -3$$
$$\text{The number is} \qquad z = -3\sqrt{3} - 3i$$

University of London School Examinations Board
General Certificate of Education

	Candidate No.			
Centre No.		Level		
Subject Number & Title		Paper		
Surname & Initials		Section		
Signature	Date	Qu. No.		

AB31A

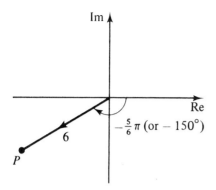

Fig. 2

Exercise 20(d)

1. (i) Plot on the Argand diagram $z_1 = 5 + i$, $z_2 = -2 + 4i$, $z_3 = 1 - 3i$. Find the modulus and argument of each number, giving the argument to the nearest 0.01 radian.

   (ii) Plot on the same diagram $\bar{z}_1$, $\bar{z}_2$ and $\bar{z}_3$. What relation exists on the Argand diagram between a complex number and its conjugate?

2. Plot the numbers $z_1 = 3 + 2i$, $z_2 = -1 + 3i$ and $z_3 = 1 - 4i$ on the Argand diagram. Find also the positions on the diagram which correspond to

   (i) $2z_1$ (ii) $z_1 + z_2$ (iii) $2z_1 + z_3$

   (iv) $\overline{z_1 + z_2}$ (v) $z_2 - z_1$ (vi) $\overline{z_2 - z_1}$

3. Find the modulus and argument of

   (i) $4 + 3i$ (ii) $4i$ (iii) $1 - i$

   (iv) $-1 + \sqrt{3}\,i$ (v) $-5 - 5i$ (vi) $6 - 2\sqrt{3}\,i$

4. Write the number z in the form $x + iy$

   (i) $|z| = 4$, $\arg(z) = \frac{3}{4}\pi$ (ii) $|z| = 10$, $\arg(z) = -\frac{1}{6}\pi$

   (iii) $|z| = 2$, $\arg(z) = -\frac{1}{2}\pi$ (iv) $|z| = 5$, $\arg(z) = \arctan 2$.

5. (i) Verify that the following inequalities are satisfied by the numbers $z_1 = 12 - 5i$, $z_2 = 4 + 3i$

$$|z_1 + z_2| \leqslant |z_1| + |z_2|$$

$$|z_1 - z_2| \leqslant |z_1| + |z_2|$$

   (ii) Justify the general truth of these inequalities with the help of the Argand diagram.

6. Given the numbers $z_1 = -3 + 3\sqrt{3}\,i$, $z_2 = \sqrt{3} + i$ find

   (i) $|z_1|, |z_2|, |z_1 z_2|$

   (ii) $\arg(z_1), \arg(z_2), \arg(z_1 z_2)$

   Repeat for the numbers $z_1 = 3i$, $z_2 = \sqrt{2} - \sqrt{2}\,i$.

   What do you notice?

7. Given the numbers $z_1 = -3 + 3\sqrt{3}\,i$, $z_2 = \sqrt{3} + i$ find $\dfrac{z_1}{z_2}$ and hence obtain $\left|\dfrac{z_1}{z_2}\right|$ and $\arg\left(\dfrac{z_1}{z_2}\right)$

Repeat for $z_1 = 3i$, $z_2 = \sqrt{2} - \sqrt{2}\,i$ as in question 6. What do you notice this time?

*8. (i) Show that $z^3 - 1 = (z-1)(z^2 + z + 1)$ and hence find the three cube roots of 1. Represent each root as a point on the Argand diagram and write down the arguments of the roots.

   (ii) Obtain the fourth roots of 1 and mark each of these on the Argand diagram.

   (iii) Without calculation, write down the arguments of the fifth roots of 1.

20.6 Multiplication and division on the Argand diagram

Question 6 of Exercise 20(d) suggests that when two complex numbers z_1 and z_2 are multiplied to form the product $z_1 z_2$ then the modulus of $z_1 z_2$ is the product of the individual moduli and the argument of $z_1 z_2$ is the sum of the individual arguments, i.e.

$$|z_1 z_2| = |z_1| \cdot |z_2|$$
$$\arg(z_1 z_2) = \arg(z_1) + \arg(z_2)$$

Question 7 suggests similar results for division, i.e. that the modulus of z_1/z_2 is obtained by dividing the individual moduli and the argument by subtracting the individual moduli

$$|z_1/z_2| = |z_1| \div |z_2|$$
$$\arg\left(\frac{z_1}{z_2}\right) = \arg(z_1) - \arg(z_2)$$

These results give a useful geometric interpretation of multiplication and division. Consider, for example, numbers z_1 and z_2 (Fig. 3a) which are such that

$$|z_1| = 3 \quad \arg(z_1) = 60°$$
$$|z_2| = 2 \quad \arg(z_2) = 45°$$

(For convenience the arguments are given in degrees here.) We can immediately mark in the positions of $z_1 z_2$ and z_1/z_2 on the Argand diagram (Fig. 3b) since according to these results

(i) $z_1 z_2$ has modulus $3 \times 2 = 6$, argument $60° + 45° = 105°$

(ii) $\dfrac{z_1}{z_2}$ has modulus $3 \div 2 = 1\frac{1}{2}$, argument $60° - 45° = 15°$

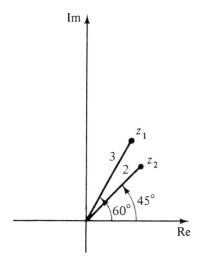

Fig. 3a

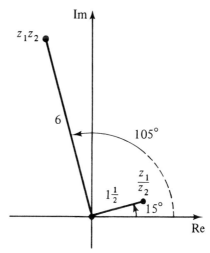

Fig. 3b

In the same way we can establish that

(iii) $\frac{z_2}{z_1}$ has modulus $2 \div 3 = \frac{2}{3}$, argument $45° - 60° = -15°$

(iv) $z_1{}^2$ has modulus $3 \times 3 = 9$, argument $60° + 60° = 120°$
    ($z_1{}^2$ is considered as $z_1 \times z_1$)

Furthermore we can deduce that $z_1{}^3$ will be a negative real number (since the argument will be $60° + 60° + 60° = 180°$) and hence that $z_1{}^3 = -27$ (since the modulus is $3 \times 3 \times 3 = 27$. Similarly $z_2{}^2$ is purely imaginary (argument $45° + 45° = 90°$) and hence $z_2{}^2 = 4i$ (modulus $2 \times 2 = 4$).

Proof of results

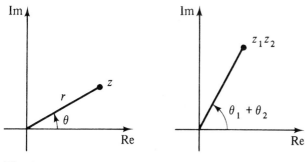

Fig. 4a

Fig. 4b

Suppose z_1 and z_2 have moduli r_1, r_2 and arguments θ_1, θ_2 respectively. Then we may write

$$z_1 = r_1 \cos \theta_1 + r_1 \sin \theta_1 \, i \qquad \text{(see Fig. 4a)}$$
$$z_2 = r_2 \cos \theta_2 + r_2 \sin \theta_2 \, i$$

Multiplying, we obtain the following (the second term is the term in i^2)

$$z_1 z_2 = (r_1 r_2 \cos \theta_1 \cos \theta_2 - r_1 r_2 \sin \theta_1 \sin \theta_2)$$
$$+ i(r_1 r_2 \sin \theta_1 \cos \theta_2 + r_1 r_2 \cos \theta_1 \sin \theta_2)$$
$$= r_1 r_2 \cos (\theta_1 + \theta_2) + r_1 r_2 \sin (\theta_1 + \theta_2) i$$

from which it follows (see Fig. 4b) that

$$|z_1 z_2| = r_1 r_2 = |z_1|.|z_2|$$
$$\arg (z_1 z_2) = \theta_1 + \theta_2 = \arg (z_1) + \arg (z_2)$$

The results for z_1/z_2 follow by a similar method. This is left as an exercise for the student.

Exercise 20(e)

Give arguments in degrees for questions 1 and 2. Use radians for the remaining questions.

1. z_1 and z_2 have moduli 6 and $1\frac{1}{2}$ and arguments $120°$ and $45°$ respectively.
   (i)   State the modulus and argument of $z_1 z_2$ and z_1/z_2.
   (ii) Explain why $z_2{}^2$ is purely imaginary. Hence find $z_2{}^2$.
   (iii) What can be said about $z_1{}^3$? Find $z_1{}^3$.

   (No calculation is needed in parts (ii) and (iii).)

- 2. z_1 and z_2 have moduli 10 and 2 and arguments $75°$ and $-15°$ respectively.
   (i)   State the modulus and argument of $z_1 z_2$, z_1^2, z_1/z_2 and z_2/z_1.
   (ii) Deduce the values of z_1/z_2 and z_2/z_1.

- 3. Find the modulus and argument of $z_1 = -1 + \sqrt{3}i$ and $z_2 = 2 - 2i$.
   Hence write down the values of
   (i) $|z_1 z_2|$, $\arg (z_1 z_2)$ (ii) $|z_1/z_2|$, $\arg (z_1/z_2)$
   (iii) $|z_2^2|$, $\arg (z_2^2)$. (Give arguments in radians.)

4. (i)   If $z = 1 + i$ write down $|z|$ and $\arg (z)$.
   (ii) Use the modulus and argument results to find z^2, z^3 and z^4 in the form $x + iy$. Plot these points on the Argand diagram.
   (iii) What is the least integer n such that z^n is a positive real number ($n > 0$). Find the value of z^n in this case.

- *5. Mark the point 4i on the Argand diagram. If $z = \sqrt{4i}$ state the value of $|z|$. Show that there are two possible positions for z on the Argand diagram and state the argument of each. Hence find the two square roots of 4i in the form $x + iy$.

- 6. Use the method of question 5 to find the two square roots of the number $-2 - 2\sqrt{3}i$.

- *7. What are the modulus and argument of the number $z = \cos \theta + i \sin \theta$? By considering the representations of z^2 and z^3 on the Argand diagram show that
   (i) $(\cos \theta + i \sin \theta)^2 = \cos 2\theta + i \sin 2\theta$
   (ii) $(\cos \theta + i \sin \theta)^3 = \cos 3\theta + i \sin 3\theta$

These are particular cases of a more general result known as de Moivre's theorem, i.e.

$$(\cos \theta + i \sin \theta)^n = \cos (n\theta) + i \sin (n\theta)$$

*8. Expand the left-hand side of 7(i) and, by equating real and imaginary parts verify the standard formulae for $\cos 2\theta$ and $\sin 2\theta$.

9. Expand the left-hand side of 7 (ii) and, by equating real and imaginary parts, prove the formulae

$$\cos 3\theta = 4\cos^3\theta - 3\cos\theta$$
$$\sin 3\theta = 3\sin\theta - 4\sin^3\theta.$$

20.7 Loci on the Argand diagram

The work in this section is given in the form of exercises.

Exercise 20(f)

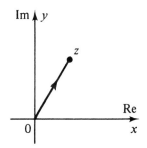

Fig. 5a   Fig. 5b

1. The complex number z (Fig. 5a) moves in the Argand diagram in such a way that
   (i) $|z| = 2$ (ii) $z = \bar{z}$ (iii) $\arg(z) = \tfrac{1}{4}\pi$
   In each case describe the locus of z and write down its equation when referred to Cartesian axes.

*2. In Fig. 5b the complex number z_0 remains constant but the number z moves in the Argand diagram in such a way that $|z - z_0| = \text{constant}$. Interpret $z - z_0$ in Fig. 5b and hence describe the locus of the point z. Use your result to interpret the following loci:
   (i) $|z - 2i| = 3$ (ii) $|z - (3 + 2i)| = 4$

   Obtain the Cartesian equation of these loci.

3. An alternative method which may be used to obtain the Cartesian equation for question 2(i) is as follows:

   let $z = x + yi$ then $z - 2i = x + (y - 2)i$

   hence $|z - 2i| = \sqrt{x^2 + (y - 2)^2}$

   So if $|z - 2i| = 3$ we must have $x^2 + (y - 2)^2 = 9$ (i.e. a circle centre $(0, 2)$ with radius 3 units). Use this method to verify the Cartesian equations obtained for questions 1 (i) and 2 (ii).

4. Describe the following loci on the Argand diagram and obtain their Cartesian equations:

(i) $|z| = 5$ (ii) $|z-3| = 5$ (iii) $|z-3+i| = 5$

*5. The point z on the Argand diagram moves in such a way that $|z-4i| = |z+3|$. Use the method of question 3 to obtain expressions for $|z-4i|$ and $|z+3|$. Hence show that the Cartesian equation of the locus is $6x + 8y = 7$. Interpret this locus on the Argand diagram.

6. Sketch the following loci on the Argand diagram and obtain their Cartesian equations:

(i) $|z| = |z+2|$ (ii) $|z-i| = |z-2|$

Find the complex number which lies on both loci.

21

Methods of Integration

21.1 Integration by parts

For the differentiation of a product we obtained

$$\frac{d}{dx}(uv) = u \cdot \frac{dv}{dx} + v \cdot \frac{du}{dx}$$

Rearranging

$$u \cdot \frac{dv}{dx} = \frac{d}{dx}(uv) - v \cdot \frac{du}{dx}$$

Integrating each term gives the following result. (The second term, being the derivative of uv, gives uv again when integrated.)

$$\int \left(u \cdot \frac{dv}{dx} \right) \cdot dx = uv - \int \left(v \cdot \frac{du}{dx} \right) dx$$

This result is best remembered in words, i.e.

$$\text{integral} \left(u \cdot \frac{dv}{dx} \right) = uv - \text{integral} \left(v \cdot \frac{du}{dx} \right)$$

It enables us to integrate certain products if we regard one of the individual functions involved in the product as u and the other as $\dfrac{dv}{dx}$. This is best illustrated by examples.

Example 131

Integrate the functions (i) $x \cos 2x$ (ii) $x^3 \ln x$

(i) We regard x as the function u and $\cos 2x$ as the function $\dfrac{dv}{dx}$, (so that $v = \frac{1}{2} \sin 2x$).

$$\int x \cos 2x \, dx = x \left(\frac{1}{2} \sin 2x \right) - \int \left(\frac{1}{2} \sin 2x \right) \cdot 1 \, dx$$

$$\underset{u \cdot \frac{dv}{dx}}{} \qquad \underset{u \quad \cdot v}{} \qquad \underset{v \quad \cdot \frac{du}{dx}}{}$$

Notice that the integral which remains may now be found directly. We obtain

$$\int x \cos 2x \, dx = \frac{1}{2}x \sin 2x + \frac{1}{4}\cos 2x + c$$

(ii) $\int x^3 \cdot \ln x \, dx = \frac{1}{4}x^4 \cdot \ln x - \int \frac{1}{4}x^4 \cdot \frac{1}{x} dx$

$$\underset{\substack{\uparrow\ \ \uparrow \\ \frac{dv}{dx}\cdot u}}{} \quad \underset{\substack{\uparrow\ \ \uparrow \\ v\ \cdot\ u}}{} \quad \underset{\substack{\uparrow\ \ \uparrow \\ v\cdot\frac{du}{dx}}}{}$$

i.e. $\int x^3 \cdot \ln x \, dx = \frac{1}{4}x^4 \cdot \ln x - \int \frac{1}{4}x^3 \, dx$

$$= \frac{1}{4}x^4 \cdot \ln x - \frac{1}{16}x^4 + c$$

Note: The student should investigate the effect of reversing the roles of u and $\frac{dv}{dx}$ in this example, i.e. taking $\cos 2x$ as u and x as $\frac{dv}{dx}$ in part (i). He will find that the new integral obtained is more complicated than the original. Clearly u and $\frac{dv}{dx}$ should be chosen with a view to obtaining a *simpler* integral than the original.

Example 132

Solve the integral $\int e^{2x} \cdot \sin x \, dx$

In this example the nature of the function $\sin x$ is such that after integrating by parts twice we return to the same integral as the original. A rather neat device then enables the solution to be completed.

Let $\quad u = e^{2x}, \quad \frac{dv}{dx} = \sin x \quad (v = -\cos x)$

then $\quad \int e^{2x} \sin x \, dx = e^{2x}(-\cos x) - \int(-\cos x) \cdot 2e^{2x} \, dx$

$$= -e^{2x}\cos x + 2\int e^{2x}\cos x \, dx$$

Continuing with a second integration by parts, in which

$u = e^{2x}, \quad \frac{dv}{dx} = \cos x \quad (v = \sin x)$, we obtain

$$\int e^{2x}\sin x \, dx = -e^{2x}\cos x + 2e^{2x}\sin x - 2\int 2e^{2x}\sin x \, dx$$

i.e. $\quad I = -e^{2x}\cos x + 2e^{2x}\sin x - 4I$

where I is the required integral. Thus

$$5I = -e^{2x}\cos x + 2e^{2x}\sin x$$

$$\Rightarrow I = \frac{1}{5}e^{2x}(2\sin x - \cos x) + c$$

Exercise 21(a)

1. Solve the following integrals:

(i) $\int x\cos x\,dx$ (ii) $\int x\sin 3x\,dx$ (iii) $\int x^2\ln x\,dx$

(iv) $\int x\,e^x\,dx$ (v) $\int\frac{1}{x^2}\ln x\,dx$ (vi) $\int x\cos\frac{1}{2}x\,dx$

2. Evaluate

(i) $\int_0^\pi x\sin x\,dx$ (ii) $\int_0^2 x\,e^{-x}\,dx$ (iii) $\int_1^2 x\ln x\,dx$

*3. Find $\int\ln x\,dx$ by considering it as $\int 1\cdot\ln x\,dx$ with $u = \ln x$ and $\dfrac{dv}{dx} = 1$.

4. Find the following integrals:

(i) $\int x\sin x\cos x\,dx$ (ii) $\int x^2 e^x\,dx$ (iii) $\int x\sec^2 x\,dx$

(iv) $\int x^2\cos x\,dx$ (v) $\int x\cos^2 x\,dx$ (vi) $\int\frac{1}{x}\ln x\,dx$

5. Evaluate

(i) $\int_0^{\frac{1}{2}} x^2\cdot e^{2x}\,dx$ (ii) $\int_0^{\frac{1}{4}\pi} x\sin^2\frac{1}{2}x\,dx$ (iii) $\int_0^1 (x+e^x)^2\,dx$

6. Use the method of Example 132 to find the following integrals:

(i) $\int e^x\cos x\,dx$ (ii) $\int e^{-x}\sin x\,dx$ (iii) $\int e^{3x}\cos 2x\,dx$

21.2 Integration by substitution

Many integrals can be simplified by a change of variable. To illustrate the kind of problems involved in this method we consider the definite integral $\int_3^5 (2x+1)^4\,dx$. In fact this integral may be evaluated directly, i.e.

$$\int_3^5 (2x+1)^4\,dx = \left[\frac{1}{10}(2x+1)^5\right]_3^5$$

but here we investigate the **substitution** $u = 2x+1$, the intention being to replace $(2x+1)^4$ by the rather simpler u^4. Two difficulties arise.

Change of limits

The values of the function $(2x+1)^4$ over the range $x = 3$ to $x = 5$ are identical to those of u^4 for $u = 7$ to $u = 11$ (since $u = 2x+1$). Thus the corresponding integration in terms of u must be between the limits 7 and 11, i.e.

$$\int_3^5 dx \qquad \text{becomes} \qquad \int_7^{11} du$$

It is *not* correct, however, simply to change $\displaystyle\int_3^5 (2x+1)^4 \, dx$ to $\displaystyle\int_7^{11} u^4 \, du$.

Change of scale

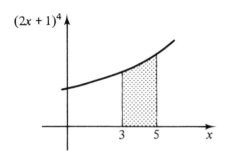

Fig. 1a

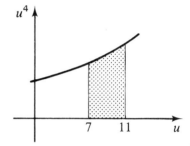

Fig. 1b

$\displaystyle\int_3^5 (2x+1)^4 \, dx$ is equivalent to the area shown in Fig. 1a. Fig. 1b shows that if the same unit of distance is used for the horizontal scale then the area represented by $\displaystyle\int_7^{11} u^4 \, du$ is twice as wide. We see that a change of variable involves a change of scale and it appears that the equivalent integral should be $\frac{1}{2}\displaystyle\int_7^{11} u^4 \, du$. In practice, the best method for obtaining this is as follows:

$$\int_3^5 (2x+1)^4 \, dx$$

$$\int_7^{11} u^4 \cdot \frac{dx}{du} \cdot du$$

$$\int_7^{11} u^4 \cdot \frac{1}{2} \, du \qquad \text{since} \quad \frac{du}{dx} = 2 \;\Rightarrow\; \frac{dx}{du} = \frac{1}{2} \qquad (u = 2x-1)$$

The integral is now completed in the usual way, i.e.

$$\left[\frac{1}{10} u^5\right]_7^{11} = \frac{1}{10}(11^5 - 7^5)$$

Note: With a linear substitution, such as $u = 2x + 1$, there is a simple relationship between the areas shown in Fig. 1, i.e. every element of area in Fig. 1b is twice the corresponding area in Fig. 1a (since it has the same height but double the width). With more complicated substitutions, as in the two examples which follow, the 'scale factor' relating the areas may change with the value of x.

Example   133

Evaluate the definite integral $\int_0^1 x \sqrt{3x+1}\, dx$

We make the substitution $u = \sqrt{3x+1}$

then $u^2 = 3x + 1$ $\Rightarrow x = \frac{1}{3}(u^2 - 1)$ and $\frac{dx}{du} = \frac{2}{3}u$

To find the new limits

x	$3x+1$	$u = \sqrt{3x+1}$
1	4	2
0	1	1

As x increases from 0 to 1, u increases from 1 to 2.

Thus $\int_0^1 x \cdot \sqrt{3x+1}\, dx$

$= \int_1^2 \frac{1}{3}(u^2 - 1).u \cdot \frac{dx}{du} \cdot du$ $= \int_1^2 \frac{1}{3}(u^2 - 1).u \cdot \frac{2}{3}u \cdot du$

$= \frac{2}{9}\int_1^2 u^4 - u^2\, du$ $= \frac{2}{9}\left[\frac{u^5}{5} - \frac{u^3}{3}\right]_1^2$

$= \frac{2}{9}\left(\frac{32}{5} - \frac{8}{3}\right) - \frac{2}{9}\left(\frac{1}{5} - \frac{1}{3}\right)$ $= \frac{2}{9}\left(\frac{31}{5} - \frac{7}{3}\right)$

$= \frac{2}{9} \cdot \frac{(93 - 35)}{15}$ $= \frac{116}{135}$

Indefinite integrals

The same general method is used but the answer should be expressed in terms of the original variable.

Example   134

Solve the integral $\int \frac{x}{(2x - 1)^3}\, dx$

Substitute $u = 2x - 1$ then $x = \frac{1}{2}(u + 1)$ and $\dfrac{dx}{du} = \frac{1}{2}$

$$\int \frac{x}{(2x-1)^3}\, dx = \int \frac{1}{2} \cdot \frac{(u+1)}{u^3} \cdot \frac{dx}{du}\, du$$

$$= \frac{1}{4}\int \frac{1}{u^2} + \frac{1}{u^3}\, du = \frac{1}{4}\left[\frac{-1}{u} - \frac{1}{2u^2}\right] + c$$

$$= -\frac{1}{4(2x-1)} - \frac{1}{8(2x-1)^2} + c$$

Exercise 21 (b)

Evaluate the following definite integrals by making the substitutions indicated.

1. $\displaystyle\int_3^6 \frac{x}{\sqrt{x-2}}\, dx$ $\qquad\qquad$ $(u = \sqrt{x-2})$

2. $\displaystyle\int_{\frac{1}{2}}^{2\frac{1}{2}} x\sqrt{2x-1}\, dx$ $\qquad\qquad$ $(u = \sqrt{2x-1})$

3. $\displaystyle\int_0^{\frac{1}{3}} \frac{x}{(3x+1)^4}\, dx$ $\qquad\qquad$ $(u = 3x+1)$

4. $\displaystyle\int_2^3 \frac{x^2}{(x-1)^2}\, dx$ $\qquad\qquad$ $(u = x-1)$

5. $\displaystyle\int_1^2 x^2\sqrt{x-1}\, dx$ $\qquad\qquad$ $(u = \sqrt{x-1})$

6. $\displaystyle\int_1^4 \frac{1}{1+\sqrt{x}}\, dx$ $\qquad\qquad$ $(u = \sqrt{x})$

*7. $\displaystyle\int_0^{\frac{1}{2}} \frac{1-2x^2}{\sqrt{1-x^2}}\, dx$ $\qquad\qquad$ $(x = \sin\theta)$

8. $\displaystyle\int_0^1 \frac{x^2}{1+x^2}\, dx$ $\qquad\qquad$ $(x = \tan\theta)$

Find the following integrals by using the substitutions given.

9. $\displaystyle\int \frac{x}{(2x-3)^2}\, dx$ $\qquad\qquad$ $(u = 2x-3)$

10. $\displaystyle\int \frac{x}{\sqrt{2x+1}}\, dx$ $\qquad\qquad$ $(u = \sqrt{2x+1})$

11. $\displaystyle\int \frac{1}{\sqrt{x}} \sin\sqrt{x}\, dx$ $\qquad\qquad$ $(u = \sqrt{x})$

12. $\displaystyle\int \frac{1}{x}\ln x\, dx$ $\qquad\qquad$ $(u = \ln x)$

13. $\int x \sqrt{x+1}\, dx$ $\qquad\qquad (u = \sqrt{x+1})$

14. $\int \dfrac{1}{x + \sqrt{x}}\, dx$ $\qquad\qquad (u = \sqrt{x})$

*15. $\int \dfrac{1}{x^2} \cdot \sqrt{1 - x^2}\, dx$ $\qquad\qquad (x = \cos\theta)$

16. $\int \dfrac{x^3}{\sqrt{1 - x^2}}\, dx$ $\qquad\qquad (x = \sin\theta)$

21.3 Two important substitutions

Integrals of the following two types occur quite frequently. They may be solved by using the substitutions shown. General results for these integrals are given after Example 135.

$$\int \dfrac{1}{\sqrt{a^2 - x^2}}\, dx \qquad \text{substitute} \quad x = a \sin\theta \qquad\qquad (1)$$

$$\int \dfrac{1}{a^2 + x^2}\, dx \qquad \text{substitute} \quad x = a \tan\theta \qquad\qquad (2)$$

The aim of the substitution in integral (1) is to simplify the square root by using the identity $1 - \sin^2\theta = \cos^2\theta$ (or $a^2 - a^2\sin^2\theta = a^2\cos^2\theta$). In integral (2) we make use of $1 + \tan^2\theta = \sec^2\theta$.

Example   135

Evaluate (i) $\displaystyle\int_1^{\sqrt{3}} \dfrac{1}{\sqrt{4 - x^2}}\, dx$ $\qquad$ (ii) $\displaystyle\int_0^4 \dfrac{1}{16 + x^2}\, dx$

(i) This integral is of type (1), above, with $a = 2$. Substitute $x = 2\sin\theta$ $\Rightarrow \sqrt{4 - x^2} = 2\cos\theta$ and $\dfrac{dx}{d\theta} = 2\cos\theta$. The new limits are the values of the angle θ (in radians) which correspond to the given limits on x.

x	$\sin\theta$	θ
$\sqrt{3}$	$\frac{1}{2}\sqrt{3}$	$\frac{1}{3}\pi$ (or $60°$)
1	$\frac{1}{2}$	$\frac{1}{6}\pi$ (or $30°$)

Thus $\displaystyle\int_1^{\sqrt{3}} \dfrac{1}{\sqrt{4 - x^2}}\, dx = \int_{\pi/6}^{\pi/3} \dfrac{1}{2\cos\theta} \cdot \dfrac{dx}{d\theta}\, d\theta$

$= \displaystyle\int_{\pi/6}^{\pi/3} \dfrac{1}{2\cos\theta} \cdot 2\cos\theta \cdot d\theta \qquad = \int_{\pi/6}^{\pi/3} 1 \cdot d\theta$

$= \Big[\theta\Big]_{\pi/6}^{\pi/3} \qquad\qquad\qquad = \dfrac{1}{3}\pi - \dfrac{1}{6}\pi = \dfrac{1}{6}\pi$

(ii) This is an integral of type (2), with $a = 4$. Substitute $x = 4 \tan \theta$

$\Rightarrow 16 + x^2 = 16 \sec^2 \theta$ and $\dfrac{dx}{d\theta} = 4 \sec^2 \theta$

New limits

x	$\tan \theta$	θ
4	1	$\frac{1}{4}\pi$
0	0	0

$$\int_0^4 \frac{1}{16 + x^2} \cdot dx \qquad = \int_0^{\frac{1}{4}\pi} \frac{1}{16 \sec^2 \theta} \cdot \frac{dx}{d\theta} \cdot d\theta$$

$$= \int_0^{\frac{1}{4}\pi} \frac{1}{16 \sec^2 \theta} \cdot 4 \sec^2 \theta \cdot d\theta \quad = \int_0^{\frac{1}{4}\pi} \frac{1}{4} \cdot d\theta$$

$$= \left[\frac{1}{4} \theta \right]_0^{\frac{1}{4}\pi} \qquad\qquad\qquad = \frac{1}{16}\pi - 0 = \frac{1}{16}\pi$$

General results

For the sake of completeness the following results are quoted. It is probably more important that the student should remember the general method of solution, as shown in Example 135.

$$\int \frac{1}{\sqrt{a^2 - x^2}} \, dx = \arcsin\left(\frac{x}{a}\right) + c$$

$$\int \frac{1}{a^2 + x^2} \, dx = \frac{1}{a} \cdot \arctan\left(\frac{x}{a}\right) + c$$

Exercise 21 (c)

Evaluate the following definite integrals:

1. $\displaystyle\int_0^3 \frac{1}{\sqrt{9 - x^2}} \, dx$ 2. $\displaystyle\int_1^{\sqrt{3}} \frac{1}{1 + x^2} \, dx$ 3. $\displaystyle\int_{-5}^5 \frac{1}{\sqrt{25 - x^2}} \, dx$

4. $\displaystyle\int_0^1 \frac{1}{3 + x^2} \, dx$ 5. $\displaystyle\int_{\frac{1}{4}}^{\frac{1}{2}} \frac{1}{\sqrt{1 - 4x^2}} \, dx$ *6. $\displaystyle\int_3^6 \frac{1}{x^2 - 6x + 18} \, dx$

7. $\displaystyle\int_0^1 \frac{x^2}{1 + x^6} \, dx$ (substitute $u = x^3$)

8. $\displaystyle\int_0^1 \frac{1}{e^x + e^{-x}} \, dx$ (substitute $u = e^x$)

21.4 Partial fractions

An expression such as $\dfrac{5x + 1}{2x^2 + 5x - 3}$ is said to be split into **partial fractions** when it is written as the sum of two or more simpler fractions. In fact it may be verified that

$$\frac{5x+1}{2x^2+5x-3} \equiv \frac{1}{(2x-1)} + \frac{2}{(x+3)}$$

Partial fractions can be particularly useful for integration. In the example given above the partial fractions enable the original expression to be integrated without difficulty, i.e.

$$\int \frac{5x+1}{2x^2+5x-3}\,dx = \int \frac{1}{2x-1} + \frac{2}{x+3}\,dx$$

$$= \frac{1}{2}\ln(2x+1) + 2\ln(x+3) + c$$

The following examples illustrate the basic procedure for obtaining partial fractions.

Example 136

Express $\dfrac{4x-13}{2x^2+x-6}$ in partial fractions and hence integrate this function.

The denominator may be factorized as $(2x-3)(x+2)$.

Let $$\frac{4x-13}{(2x-3)(x+2)} \equiv \frac{A}{2x-3} + \frac{B}{x+2}$$

Then, multiplying through by $(2x-3)(x+2)$ in order to remove the fractions, we must have

$$4x-13 \equiv A(x+2) + B(2x-3)$$

The expression on the righthand side must be identical to $4x-13$ if our partial fractions are to be correct.

Equating the x terms $\qquad A+2B = \quad 4$
Equating the constants $\qquad 2A-3B = -13$

From these equations we obtain $A = -2$, $B = 3$.

Thus $$\frac{4x-13}{2x^2+x-6} \equiv \frac{3}{x+2} - \frac{2}{2x-3}$$

$$\Rightarrow \int \frac{4x-13}{2x^2+x-6}\,dx = \int \frac{3}{x+2} - \frac{2}{2x-3}\,dx$$

$$= 3\ln(x+2) - \ln(2x-3) + c$$

$$= \ln\left[\frac{(x+2)^3}{(2x-3)}\right] + c$$

Note: The numerator must be one power of x lower than the denominator if this method is to be used. (Notice that the same is true of the partial fractions.) Where the numerator involves the *same* power of x, begin by taking out a constant multiple of the denominator, as in the next example.

298 Essentials of Pure Mathematics

Example 137

Write $\dfrac{3x^2 + x}{x^2 - 1}$ in partial fractions and hence integrate the expression.

$$\frac{3x^2 + x}{x^2 - 1} = \frac{3(x^2 - 1) + 3 + x}{x^2 - 1} = 3 + \frac{x + 3}{x^2 - 1}$$

We may now use the method of Example 136.

Let $\qquad \dfrac{x + 3}{x^2 - 1} \equiv \dfrac{A}{(x + 1)} + \dfrac{B}{(x - 1)}$

then $\qquad x + 3 \equiv A(x - 1) + B(x + 1)$ multiplying by $(x^2 - 1)$

$\Rightarrow \qquad A + B = 1 \qquad\qquad\qquad$ equating x terms

$\qquad\qquad -A + B = 3 \qquad\qquad\quad$ equating constants

From these equations $A = -1$ and $B = 2$ so that

$$\frac{3x^2 + x}{x^2 - 1} \equiv 3 - \frac{1}{x + 1} + \frac{2}{x - 1}$$

Integrating we obtain

$$\int \frac{3x^2 + x}{x^2 - 1}\, dx = 3x - \ln(x + 1) + 2\ln(x - 1) + c$$

$$= 3x + \ln\left[\frac{(x - 1)^2}{(x + 1)}\right] + c$$

Exercise 21 (d)

Express in partial fractions

1. $\dfrac{2x - 5}{(x + 2)(x - 1)}$ 2. $\dfrac{2x}{x^2 - 1}$ 3. $\dfrac{x + 4}{x(x + 2)}$

4. $\dfrac{x - 8}{2x^2 + 3x - 2}$ 5. $\dfrac{2x^2 - 5}{x^2 - x}$ 6. $\dfrac{7}{3x^2 + 5x - 2}$

7. $\dfrac{3x - 7}{3x^2 + x - 2}$ 8. $\dfrac{x^2 + 4x + 1}{x^2 + 3x + 2}$

Solve the following integrals, using partial fractions except where direct integration is possible.

9. $\displaystyle\int \frac{3x + 1}{x^2 + 2x - 3}\, dx$ 10. $\displaystyle\int \frac{4x - 1}{2x^2 - x - 3}\, dx$ 11. $\displaystyle\int \frac{1}{x^2 - 1}\, dx$

12. $\displaystyle\int \frac{5x}{x^2 - x - 6}\, dx$ 13. $\displaystyle\int_1^3 \frac{x + 2}{x^2 + 4x + 3}\, dx$ 14. $\displaystyle\int_3^4 \frac{2x^2 - 4}{x^2 - 4}\, dx$

15. $\displaystyle\int \frac{x^2 + x - 3}{x^2 - 3x + 2}\, dx$ 16. $\displaystyle\int \frac{x - 1}{x^2 - 3x}\, dx$

Solve the following integrals, using the substitutions given.

17. $\displaystyle\int \frac{1}{\sqrt{x}\,(x-1)}\,dx \quad (u=\sqrt{x})$

18. $\displaystyle\int \frac{1}{e^x+1}\,dx \quad (u=e^x)$

19. $\displaystyle\int_2^4 \frac{1}{x(x^3-1)}\,dx \quad (u=x^3-1)$

20. $\displaystyle\int_3^8 \frac{\sqrt{1+x}}{x}\,dx \quad (u=\sqrt{1+x})$

21.5 Further partial fractions

In the following example we consider two further types of function where the partial fractions obtained differ slightly from those of the previous section. Again we find that the partial fractions enable us to integrate the functions.

Example 138

Express in partial fractions (i) $\dfrac{x-5}{(x-2)^2}$ (ii) $\dfrac{x-1}{(x-2)(x^2+1)}$

(i) The denominator has a 'repeated' factor. To obtain two partial fractions with different denominators we must use $(x-2)^2$ as a denominator in one fraction.

$$\text{Let} \qquad \frac{x-5}{(x-2)^2} \equiv \frac{A}{(x-2)} + \frac{B}{(x-2)^2}$$

then $\qquad x-5 \equiv A(x-2)+B \qquad$ multiplying by $(x-2)^2$

$\Rightarrow \qquad A \quad = 1 \qquad\qquad$ equating x terms

$\qquad\qquad -2A+B = -5 \qquad\qquad$ equating constants

Hence $A=1$ and $B=-3$ so that

$$\frac{x-5}{(x-2)^2} \equiv \frac{1}{(x-2)} - \frac{3}{(x-2)^2}$$

(ii) The denominator has a quadratic factor. Notice that the partial fraction involving this quadratic factor should have a **linear** numerator (i.e. $Bx+C$). The general rule is that the numerator should be one power of x lower than the denominator.

$$\text{Let} \qquad \frac{x-1}{(x-2)(x^2+1)} \equiv \frac{A}{(x-2)} + \frac{Bx+C}{(x^2+1)}$$

then $\qquad x-1 \equiv A(x^2+1)+(Bx+C)(x-2)$

i.e. $\qquad x-1 \equiv (A+B)x^2+(C-2B)x+(A-2C)$

$\Rightarrow \qquad A+B \;= 0 \quad$ equating x^2 terms $\qquad$ (1)

$\qquad\qquad C-2B = 1 \quad$ equating x terms $\qquad$ (2)

$\qquad\qquad A-2C = -1 \quad$ equating constants $\qquad$ (3)

Substitute (1) into (2) $C + 2A = 1$

Multiply (3) by 2 $2A - 4C = -2$

$\left.\begin{array}{c}\end{array}\right\}$ $\Rightarrow 5C = 3$ $C = \dfrac{3}{5}$

Hence $A = \dfrac{1}{5}$, $B = -\dfrac{1}{5}$, $C = \dfrac{3}{5}$ and the answer is

$$\frac{x-1}{(x-2)(x^2+1)} \equiv \frac{1}{5(x-2)} + \frac{3-x}{5(x^2+1)}$$

Note: A neat alternative method for part (i) is as follows

$$\frac{x-5}{(x-2)^2} = \frac{(x-2)-3}{(x-2)^2} = \frac{1}{(x-2)} - \frac{3}{(x-2)^2}$$

Example 139

Integrate the functions (i) $\dfrac{x-5}{(x-2)^2}$ (ii) $\dfrac{x-1}{(x-2)(x^2+1)}$

First we express the functions in partial fractions as in the preceding example. Then

(i) $\displaystyle\int \frac{x-5}{(x-2)^2}\,dx = \int \frac{1}{(x-2)} - \frac{3}{(x-2)^2}\,dx$

$$= \ln(x-2) + \frac{3}{(x-2)} + c$$

(ii) $\displaystyle\int \frac{x-1}{(x-2)(x^2+1)}\,dx = \int \frac{1}{5(x-2)} + \frac{3}{5(x^2+1)} - \frac{x}{5(x^2+1)}\,dx$

The second partial fraction has itself been split into two terms. All terms may now be integrated: the last term integrates directly as a logarithm whilst the middle term may be integrated by using the substitution $x = \tan\theta$ as in section 21.3. The results obtained are

$$\frac{1}{5}\ln(x-2) + \frac{3}{5}\arctan x - \frac{1}{10}\ln(x^2+1) + c$$

i.e. $\dfrac{1}{10}\ln\left\{\dfrac{(x-2)^2}{x^2+1}\right\} + \dfrac{3}{5}\arctan x + c$

Exercise 21(e)

Express in partial fractions

1. $\dfrac{x+1}{(x+3)^2}$ 2. $\dfrac{x-4}{x(x^2+2)}$

3. $\dfrac{x-1}{(2x-3)^2}$ 4. $\dfrac{5+x}{(1-x)(5+x^2)}$

Use partial fractions to solve the following integrals:

5. $\displaystyle\int \frac{1}{x(x^2+1)}\,dx$

6. $\displaystyle\int \frac{x}{(1-x)^2}\,dx$

7. $\displaystyle\int \frac{2x+3}{(x-2)(x^2+3)}\,dx$

8. $\displaystyle\int \frac{x+2}{x(x^2+x+1)}\,dx$

9. $\displaystyle\int_1^2 \frac{2x-1}{(x+1)^2}\,dx$

10. $\displaystyle\int_0^1 \frac{2x}{(1+x)(1+x^2)}\,dx$

11. $\displaystyle\int \frac{x^2-3x+1}{x^2-4x+4}\,dx$

12. $\displaystyle\int \frac{6-x}{(1-x)(4+x^2)}\,dx$

*13. *Use of partial fractions for differentiation*
Partial fractions are of considerable help in the determination of higher derivatives. Although the first derivative of a rational function can be obtained by the quotient rule, this method frequently gets out of hand for second and higher derivatives.
Express the following functions in partial fractions and hence find their second and third derivatives:

(i) $\displaystyle\frac{1}{x^2+x}$

(ii) $\displaystyle\frac{x+4}{(x-2)(2x-1)}$

(iii) $\displaystyle\frac{3}{(x-2)(x^2-1)}$

14. Find an expression for the nth derivative of $\displaystyle\frac{x}{(1-x)^2}$.

*15. *Use of partial fractions in expansions*
Show that

$$\frac{x}{1+2x-3x^2} \equiv \frac{1}{4}\left[\frac{1}{(1-x)} - \frac{1}{(1+3x)}\right]$$

By writing out the binomial series for $(1-x)^{-1}$ and $(1+3x)^{-1}$ obtain the first four terms in the series expansion of $\displaystyle\frac{x}{1+2x-3x^2}$. For which values of x is the series valid?

16. Use the method of question 15 to obtain a series expansion for $\displaystyle\frac{1}{1+3x+2x^2}$ as far as the term in x^4.

17. Show that the function $\displaystyle\frac{1+x^2}{x-x^2}$ may be written as a series of the form
$\displaystyle\frac{a}{x}+b+cx+dx^2+ex^3+\ \dots$ and find the values of the constants a, b, c, d, e. State the values of x for which the series is valid.

21.6 Miscellaneous integrals

The following exercise is intended as a revision of the various methods of integration covered in this book. The student should watch out for functions which can be integrated directly (often as logarithms). For example

(i) $\int \dfrac{2x-3}{x^2-3x-4}\,dx$ should be integrated directly

as $\ln(x^2-3x-4)+c.$ (Partial fractions are not needed.)

(ii) $\int \dfrac{x}{\sqrt{1-x^2}}\,dx$ may be integrated directly

as $-\sqrt{1-x^2}+c.$ (A substitution is not necessary.)

Exercise 21 (f)

(Only a few of the following integrations require a substitution.)

1. $\displaystyle\int \dfrac{(2x+1)^2}{x}\,dx$ 2. $\displaystyle\int \sec^2 2\theta\,d\theta$ 3. $\displaystyle\int \cos^2\theta - \sin^2\theta\,d\theta$

4. $\displaystyle\int \dfrac{1}{(2x-3)^3}\,dx$ 5. $\displaystyle\int \dfrac{x}{1+2x}\,dx$ 6. $\displaystyle\int x\sqrt{x^2+1}\,dx$

7. $\displaystyle\int \cos^2 2\theta\,d\theta$ 8. $\displaystyle\int \sin 3\theta \cos 2\theta\,d\theta$ 9. $\displaystyle\int x\sin 2x\,dx$

10. $\displaystyle\int \dfrac{1-x}{\sqrt{x}}\,dx$ 11. $\displaystyle\int \sin\theta\cos^2\theta\,d\theta$ 12. $\displaystyle\int \sin^2 2\theta\cos\theta\,d\theta$

13. $\displaystyle\int \dfrac{x^2}{x-3}\,dx$ 14. $\displaystyle\int \dfrac{x^2}{(x-3)^2}\,dx$ 15. $\displaystyle\int x\sqrt{1+2x}\,dx$

16. $\displaystyle\int \dfrac{e^x}{(1+e^x)^2}\,dx$ 17. $\displaystyle\int \dfrac{\cos 2\theta}{1+\sin 2\theta}\,d\theta$ 18. $\displaystyle\int \dfrac{1}{1+\cos 2\theta}\,d\theta$

19. $\displaystyle\int \dfrac{x}{2x^2+x-1}\,dx$ 20. $\displaystyle\int \dfrac{x^2-1}{x^3-3x+1}\,dx$ 21. $\displaystyle\int \dfrac{1}{\sqrt{4-x^2}}\,dx$

22. $\displaystyle\int x^2 e^{-x}\,dx$ 23. $\displaystyle\int \sin\theta\sec^2\theta\,d\theta$ 24. $\displaystyle\int \sin^2\theta\cos^2\theta\,d\theta$

25. $\displaystyle\int \dfrac{1}{x}\sqrt{\ln x}\,dx$ 26. $\displaystyle\int \dfrac{x^2}{\sqrt{1+x}}\,dx$ 27. $\displaystyle\int \dfrac{x+1}{(x+2)(x+3)}\,dx$

28. $\displaystyle\int \dfrac{x+2}{(x+1)(x+3)}\,dx$ 29. $\displaystyle\int \dfrac{1}{x(x^4-1)}\,dx$ 30. $\displaystyle\int \dfrac{x}{x^4-1}\,dx$

22

Miscellaneous II

22.1 Arrangements

Six people are to be seated on a bench. In how many different ways can this be done? Imagine that we fill the six positions on the bench in turn, from left to right. We may choose one of six people for the first position. For each of these six choices we then have a choice of five people for the second position, four people for the third position, and so on. Finally we have only one choice for the sixth position, as only one person will remain at this stage, i.e.

number of arrangements = $6 \times 5 \times 4 \times 3 \times 2 \times 1 = 6!$

Suppose now that there is only room for three people on the bench. In how many different ways can we fill the bench with three of our six people? Considering the three positions on the bench in turn we have six choices, then five, and then four, i.e.

number of arrangements = $6 \times 5 \times 4 = \dfrac{6!}{3!}$

These are simple examples of questions on arrangements (sometimes called **permutations**). In general, such questions are best solved from first principles.

Example   140

The numbers 1, 2, 4, 7 and 9 are written on five pieces of card. Using these pieces of card how many different (i) five digit numbers (ii) three digit numbers (iii) even numbers, may be formed?

For parts (i) and (ii) the method is the same as that outlined above. We have five choices for the first digit, then four for the second digit and so on. Thus

(i)   Number of 5 digit numbers = $5 \times 4 \times 3 \times 2 \times 1 = \underline{5! \text{ or } 120}$

(ii)   Number of 3 digit numbers = $5 \times 4 \times 3 = \underline{60}$

For part (iii) the number of digits is not specified. It is best to consider *separately* numbers with one digit, with two digits, with three digits and so on. In each case it is convenient to consider the *last* digit first since this must either be 2 or 4 if the number is even.

Choices for

	last digit,	remaining digits		
1 digit numbers	2		=	2
2 digit numbers	2	× 4	=	8

3 digit numbers	2 ×	4 × 3	= 24
4 digit numbers	2 ×	4 × 3 × 2	= 48
5 digit numbers	2 ×	4 × 3 × 2 × 1	= 48

On addition we see that there must be 130 even numbers.

Example   141

Six people are to sit in adjacent seats in a cinema. In how many different ways can they take their places if two of the six must not sit together?

Let the two people who must sit apart be A and B. It is easier to find the number of arrangements in which they sit *together*. This is achieved by imagining them to be joined (perhaps glued) together inseparably: the problem is then equivalent to arranging five items in a row (four single bodies and one 'double'). But we must remember that for each such arrangement we can obtain another by interchanging the positions of A and B (see Fig. 1).

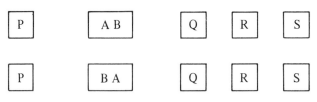

Fig. 1

So number of arrangements in which A and B are together $= 2 \times 5!$ or   240

But total number of seating arrangements with 6 people $=$ $6!$ or   720

Thus there are $720 - 240 = 480$ arrangements in which A and B are apart. (In terms of factorials we could work this as $6! - 2.5! = 6.5! - 2.5! = 4.5!$)

Note: This is the usual method of approach in problems of this type. It is not easy to find directly the number of arrangements in which A and B are apart since, if we first allocate A to one of the six seats, the number of seats open to B will vary according to whether A is at the end of the row or in one of the four 'central' seats.

Example   142

How many distinct arrangements can be made of the letters in the word REVERSE?

The difficulty here is because there are two R's and three E's. Imagine these to be labelled R_1, R_2 and E_1, E_2, E_3: there are then 7! arrangements of the seven letters. But

(i) for every arrangement in which R_1 appears before R_2 there will be a corresponding arrangement in which the positions are reversed (Fig. 2a) and these arrangements will be indistinguishable. We must therefore divide our number of arrangements by two.

- R_1 - - R_2 - -	- E_1E_2 - - - E_3	- E_2E_3 - - - E_1
- R_2 - - R_1 - -	- E_1E_3 - - - E_2	- E_3E_1 - - - E_2
	- E_2E_1 - - - E_3	- E_3E_2 - - - E_1

Fig. 2a   Fig. 2b

(ii) Similarly, we further divide our number of arrangements by six (or 3!) since the three E's may occur in six different orders, (Fig. 2b).
The number of distinct arrangements is therefore

$$\frac{7!}{2!\,3!} = 420$$

Exercise 22(a)

1. In how many different orders is it possible to lay down on a table
   (i) the Ace, King, Queen and Jack of Hearts?
   (ii) any four cards selected from the Heart suit?
2. Six sprinters compete in a race. In how many orders may
   (i) the six sprinters finish?
   (ii) the first three places be taken?
3. At a restaurant there are four different starters, six different main courses and three different sweets. How many selections are possible for a three-course meal? How many are possible for a five-course meal with two different starters and two different sweets?
4. The same restaurant has ten tables. If reservations are received for four tables, in how many ways may they be allocated?
5. In how many ways can the results of six football matches be forecast if each match can end as a home win, an away win or a draw?
6. Six colours are available to paint three doors. In how many ways can this be done if the doors are to be of different colours?
7. Five bottles of wine are to be stored on a rack with eight spaces. How many arrangements are possible if (i) the bottles are all different? (ii) two bottles are the same?
8. Five men and their wives are to be seated at a table in two facing rows of five. In how many ways can this be done if each man must sit opposite his wife?
9. (i) How many three figure odd numbers can be made from the digits 1, 3, 6, 7, 8, 9
   (ii) How many of these contain the figure 6?
10. A man has five shirts ready to wear. Two are blue and the remainder are all of different colours. In how many different orders may he wear the shirts if he is to avoid wearing the two blue shirts on consecutive days? (The blue shirts are not identical.)
11. Six pieces of card bear the numbers 2, 3, 5, 7, 7, and 8. How many distinct six digit numbers can be formed with these cards? In how many of these numbers are the two sevens together?

12. How many distinct arrangements can be made of the letters from each of the following words?
    (i) CIRCLE   (ii) PARABOLA   (iii) AVERAGE
    (iv) DIFFERENCE

13. How many distinct arrangements of four letters can be made from the word TRIANGLE? How many of these contain at least one vowel?

*14 How many arrangements of three letters can be made from the word DIVISION? (You should consider separately the arrangements containing no I's, one I, two I's etc.)

15. Three travellers enter a railway compartment in which there are eight seats in facing rows of four. In how many ways can they sit down if
    (i)   they all occupy corner seats?
    (ii) no two sit opposite one another?
    (iii) all three sit together?

*16. In how many ways can four boys and three girls be seated in a row if no two girls are to sit together?

22.2 Combinations

There are eight novels on my shelf and I wish to choose three to take away on holiday. How many different sets of three may be chosen?

This is called the number of **combinations of three items chosen from eight**. It is written

$$^{8}C_{3} \text{ or sometimes } \binom{8}{3}$$

Let us call the books A, B, C, D, E, F, G and H. It is important to realise that each choice of three books may be selected in many different orders. For example, books A, B and C may be chosen in the orders ABC, ACB, BAC ... etc. and books C, D and E in orders CDE, DEC, DCE ... etc. In fact the number of different orders corresponding to each choice of three books is $3 \times 2 \times 1$ or 3! But the *total* number of orders of selection possible when choosing three books from eight is $8 \times 7 \times 6$. It therefore follows that

$$\frac{\text{number of sets of}}{\text{three books}} = \frac{\text{total number of orders of selection}}{\text{orders corresponding to each set}}$$

i.e.
$$^{8}C_{3} = \frac{8 \times 7 \times 6}{3 \times 2 \times 1} \quad \text{or} \quad \frac{8!}{5!\,3!} = 56$$

Suppose now that we are selecting four books from eleven. Each choice of four books may be selected in $4 \times 3 \times 2 \times 1$ or 4! different orders. But the total number of orders of selection is $11 \times 10 \times 9 \times 8$. So the number of distinct sets of four which may be chosen is given by

$$^{11}C_{4} = \frac{11 \times 10 \times 9 \times 8}{4 \times 3 \times 2 \times 1} \quad \text{or} \quad \frac{11!}{7!\,4!} = 330$$

In the same way we may show that

number of combinations of 5 items chosen from 12, $^{12}C_{5} = \dfrac{12!}{7!5!}$

number of combinations of 6 items chosen from 9, $\quad {}^9C_6 = \dfrac{9!}{6!\,3!}$

$$\text{in general} \quad {}^nC_r = \dfrac{n!}{r!\,(n-r)!}$$

Notice that the two factorials on the bottom involve numbers which sum to the number involved on top. To compute the values of these 'combinations' cancel the *larger* factorial on the bottom into the factorial on top. Thus

$$^{12}C_5 \text{ (cancel 7! into 12!)} = \dfrac{12 \times 11 \times 10 \times 9 \times 8}{5 \times 4 \times 3 \times 2 \times 1} = 792$$

$$^{9}C_6 \text{ (cancel 6! into 9!)} = \dfrac{9 \times 8 \times 7}{3 \times 2 \times 1} = 84$$

Notice also that

$$^9C_6 = {}^9C_3 = \dfrac{9!}{6!\,3!}; \quad ^{12}C_5 = {}^{12}C_7 = \dfrac{12!}{7!\,5!}$$

This is because each time we select six items from nine we make a simultaneous selection of three (the items rejected).

Example 143

How many different bridge fours may be made up from a group of ten people in each of the following situations?
(i) Two of the ten do not wish to play.
(ii) One of the ten must always be included since he is providing the cards.
(iii) Two of the ten refuse to play at the same table.

(i) Here we must select four players from the eight people prepared to play. The number of different selections is

$$^8C_4 = \dfrac{8 \times 7 \times 6 \times 5}{4 \times 3 \times 2 \times 1} = 70$$

(ii) If one person is always included then three more players must be selected from the remaining nine people. The number of different selections is

$$^9C_3 = \dfrac{9 \times 8 \times 7}{3 \times 2 \times 1} = 84$$

(iii) The simplest method is to find the total number of selections of four players from ten people and then subtract those in which *both* of the two players concerned are included. If both these players are included then two more players must be chosen from eight. Thus

$$\text{total number of selections } {}^{10}C_4 = \dfrac{10 \times 9 \times 8 \times 7}{4 \times 3 \times 2 \times 1} = 210$$

$$\text{selections not permitted} \quad {}^8C_2 = \dfrac{8 \times 7}{2 \times 1} = 28$$

The number of possible bridge fours is therefore 182.

Example   144

At a certain cricket club ten batsmen and five bowlers are available for the next match. How many teams may be selected if at least three bowlers must be included?

We must consider three separate cases, depending on the number of bowlers selected. The working is conveniently set out as follows.

		Five bowlers	Ten batsmen	Number of choices
Select	(i)	3	8	$^5C_3 \times {}^{10}C_8 = 10 \times 45 = 450$
	(ii)	4	7	$^5C_4 \times {}^{10}C_7 = 5 \times 120 = 600$
	(iii)	5	6	$^5C_5 \times {}^{10}C_6 = 1 \times 210 = 210$

The total number of different teams is 1260. Notice that in each case the combinations are multiplied together since the various choices of batsmen may be repeated for each choice of bowlers.

Exercise   22(b)

1. Evaluate $^7C_3$, $^9C_4$, $^6C_4$, $^{10}C_5$, $^{12}C_3$, $^{14}C_9$.
2. Eight letters await posting but there are only five stamps. How many different sets of five letters may be posted?
3. My spice rack holds twelve small jars in two rows of six. If I have a different herb or spice in each jar, how many different sets of six jars may be placed on the top row?
4. A pools punter is to select eight draws from fifty-five football fixtures. How many different combinations are possible?
5. A party of sixteen people is to be transported in a twelve-seater minibus and a four-seater car. In how many ways can the party be split up?
6. If in question 5 there were only two drivers, how many ways could the party be split up?
7. In how many ways can four eggs be arranged in a box with six spaces if
   (i) the eggs are indistinguishable?
   (ii) the eggs are of different colours or sizes?
8. A man has ten shirts, five pairs of trousers and four jackets. For a short business trip he needs three shirts, two pairs of trousers and two jackets. How many different selections are possible?
9. If seven coins are tossed, in how many different ways may five or more heads be obtained?
10. A burglar is trying to open a safe with a five-digit combination lock. He knows that the correct number contains exactly three eights. How many possible numbers are there?
11. A committee of six is to be chosen from seven men and three women. How many different committees may be chosen if at least one woman must be included?
12. At a club dinner twelve people are to be seated at three separate tables of four. In how many ways can the party be split up if
    (i) there is no restriction?   (ii) the President's place is fixed?

13. Four places are available on a school outing. If six boys and eight girls wish to go, in how many ways can the four places be allocated in each of the following situations?
    (i)   Two boys and two girls must go.
    (ii) At least two boys must go.
    (iii) Two of the boys are twins and must not be separated (i.e. either both go or neither goes).
14. Five red and seven blue counters are placed in a row. How many different orders are possible? In how many of these are no two red counters together?
15. A tennis club is to choose a team of four mixed doubles pairs from six ladies and eight gentlemen. How many different teams may be chosen? Once a team has been chosen, in how many different ways can the four partnerships be selected?
16. A hand of thirteen cards is dealt from a standard pack of playing cards. Express, in terms of combinations, the number of hands containing
    (i) no aces   (ii) exactly one ace   (iii) exactly two aces   (iv) cards of one colour only   (v) a 'void' suit (i.e. cards in three suits only).
17. The back row of a cinema has twenty seats and four are vacant. How many different sets of four empty seats are possible? In how many of these is no pair of adjacent seats empty? (There is no central gangway dividing the row.)
18. How many different selections of five letters can be made from the word MISANTHROPE so as to include (i) no vowels?   (ii) one vowel?   (iii) two vowels? Hence obtain the number of distinct arrangements of five letters taken from this word if not more than two vowels are to be included.
19. How many different rectangles may be found on a chessboard? (i.e. by considering the squares to be grouped into rectangles of different shapes and sizes.) How many different squares may be found?

22.3 Combinations and the Binomial Theorem

We shall now see that the coefficients in a binomial expansion may be interpreted as combinations. Imagine that we are multiplying out $(1 + x)^6$. This may be written as

$$(1 + x)(1 + x)(1 + x)(1 + x)(1 + x)(1 + x)$$

A term in x^2 is obtained whenever we multiply x's from two of the brackets with 1's from the four remaining brackets. The number of x^2 terms obtained in the multiplication is therefore equal to the number of different selections of two x's from six, i.e.

coefficient of $x^2 = {}^6C_2$

In the same way a term in x^3 is obtained for each selection of three x's from six, i.e.

coefficient of $x^3 = {}^6C_3$

In fact it follows that the complete binomial expansion for $(1 + x)^6$ may be written as

$$(1 + x)^6 = 1 + {}^6C_1x + {}^6C_2x^2 + {}^6C_3x^3 + {}^6C_4x^4 + {}^6C_5x^5 + {}^6C_6x^6$$

and in general it is true that

$$(1 + x)^n = 1 + {}^nC_1x + {}^nC_2x^2 + {}^nC_3x^3 + \ldots$$

Pascal's triangle

It is now instructive to consider Pascal's triangle as a table of combinations, for we may then understand how the triangle works.

	coefficients						combinations				
$(1+x)^2$		1	2	1			1	${}^2C_1$	${}^2C_2$		
$(1+x)^3$		1	3	3	1		1	${}^3C_1$	${}^3C_2$	${}^3C_3$	
$(1+x)^4$	1	4	6	4	1		1	${}^4C_1$	${}^4C_2$	${}^4C_3$	${}^4C_4$
$(1+x)^5$	1	5	10	10	5	1	1	${}^5C_1$	${}^5C_2$	${}^5C_3$	${}^5C_4$ ${}^5C_5$

An example of the way in which Pascal's triangle operates is indicated above. We have

for the example shown ${}^5C_3 = {}^4C_2 + {}^4C_3$

or in general ${}^nC_r = {}^{n-1}C_{r-1} + {}^{n-1}C_r$

${}^nC_r$ is the number of selections of r items from n. These selections may be subdivided into

(i) those including a particular item X.

(ii) those not including the item X. .

A moment's thought should convince the reader that the number of selections in category (i) is ${}^{n-1}C_{r-1}$ and the number in category (ii) is ${}^{n-1}C_r$.

Exercise 22(c)

1. We have seen that

$$(1 + x)^6 = 1 + {}^6C_1x + {}^6C_2x^2 + {}^6C_3x^3 + {}^6C_4x^4 + \ldots \text{ etc.}$$

Write out, as far as the terms in x^4, similar expansions for $(1 + x)^9$, $(1 + x)^{12}$, $(1 + x)^{20}$ and hence find

(i)   the coefficient of x^3 in $(1 + x)^{12}$

(ii) the coefficient of x^4 in $(1 + x)^9$

(iii) the coefficient of x^2 in $(1 + x)^{20}$.

2. Draw Pascal's triangle as far as the coefficients for $(1 + x)^8$. Draw rings around the terms which correspond to the following combinations:

$${}^5C_2, {}^8C_3, {}^6C_4, {}^4C_1, {}^7C_5, {}^8C_6$$

*3. Use the expansion of $(1 + x)^6$ to prove that

$$^6C_1 + {}^6C_2 + {}^6C_3 + {}^6C_4 + {}^6C_5 + {}^6C_6 = 2^6 - 1$$

Find also (i) $\sum_{r=1}^{10} {}^{10}C_r$ (ii) $\sum_{r=1}^{n} {}^nC_r$

4. By differentiating the expansion of $(1 + x)^n$ prove that

$$1.{}^nC_1 + 2.{}^nC_2 + 3.{}^nC_3 + \ldots + n.{}^nC_n = n.2^{n-1}$$

22.4 Differential equations

The scope of this book permits only a brief treatment of first order differential equations in which the variables are separable. A more detailed chapter covering some of the applications of these equations will be found in *Essentials of Applied Mathematics*. This section is intended to give some further practice.

A differential equation is a relation involving a variable y and its derivatives $\dfrac{dy}{dx}, \dfrac{d^2y}{dx^2}$ etc.

e.g. $2y + (1 - x^2)\dfrac{dy}{dx} = 0$ (1)

$\dfrac{d^2y}{dx^2} - x \cdot \dfrac{dy}{dx} + y = 0$ (2)

Equation (1) involves only the first derivative $\dfrac{dy}{dx}$. It is said to be a **first order** differential equation. Equation (2), which involves the second derivative, is a **second order** equation. When solving these equations we attempt to find an expression for y in terms of x.

In the examples that follow the variables y and x are said to be **separable**. This means that terms in y can be collected on one side and terms in x on the other side. The solution then proceeds by integrating both sides of the equation.

Example 145

Obtain the general solution of the equation

$$2y + (1 - x^2)\dfrac{dy}{dx} = 0$$

We have $\dfrac{dy}{dx} = -\dfrac{2y}{1 - x^2} = \dfrac{2y}{x^2 - 1}$

When the variables are separated $\dfrac{dy}{dx}$ is replaced by the differentials dy and dx

and both sides of the equation are made into integrals, i.e.

$$\int \frac{dy}{y} = \int \frac{2}{x^2 - 1}\, dx$$

$$= \int \frac{1}{(x-1)} - \frac{1}{(x+1)}\, dx$$

$$\Rightarrow \ln y = \ln(x-1) - \ln(x+1) + C$$

C is a constant of integration. It is convenient in many questions of this type to regard this constant as being a logarithm also (i.e. $C = \ln A$ where A is another constant) for then we may write

$$\ln y = \ln \left[\frac{A(x-1)}{(x+1)} \right]$$

$$\Rightarrow y = \frac{A(x-1)}{(x+1)} \qquad (A \text{ constant})$$

Note: This solution will satisfy the differential equation for any value of the constant A. It is therefore called the **general solution**. A **particular solution** is one which corresponds to a particular value of the constant A, e.g.

$$y = \frac{3(x-1)}{(x+1)} \quad \text{or} \quad y = \frac{-5(x-1)}{(x+1)}$$

Example   146

Find the particular solution of the equation $1 + y^2 = y \cdot \dfrac{dy}{dx}$ for which $y = 2$ when $x = 0$.

The variables may be separated as follows:

$$\int \frac{y}{1+y^2}\, dy = \int dx$$

When finding a particular solution it is convenient to place the values $y = 2$ and $x = 0$ as lower limits on the y and x integrals respectively

i.e. $$\int_2^y \frac{y}{1+y^2}\, dy = \int_0^x dx$$

$$\Rightarrow \quad \left[\tfrac{1}{2}\ln(1+y^2) \right]_2^y = \left[x \right]_0^x$$

$$\tfrac{1}{2}\ln(1+y^2) - \tfrac{1}{2}\ln 5 = x - 0$$

i.e. $$\ln\left(\frac{1+y^2}{5} \right) = 2x$$

Hence $$\frac{1+y^2}{5} = e^{2x} \Rightarrow y^2 = 5e^{2x} - 1$$

Exercise 22(d)

Find the general solutions for

1. $\dfrac{dy}{dx} = 2xy$

2. $(1 + x^2)\dfrac{dy}{dx} = xy$

3. $2(x - 1)\dfrac{dy}{dx} = \dfrac{x}{y}$

4. $x \cdot \dfrac{dy}{dx} = (1 + 2x^2)y$

Find particular solutions of the following equations and in each case sketch the graph of y against x.

5. $\dfrac{dy}{dx} = xy^2$ given that $y = 2$ when $x = 0$

6. $(1 - x^2)\dfrac{dy}{dx} = -xy$ given that $y = 1$ when $x = 0$

7. $(y + 1)\dfrac{dy}{dx} + \dfrac{1}{x^2} = 0$ given that $y = 0$ when $x = 1$

8. $\dfrac{dy}{dx} = (1 - 2x)y^2$ given that $y = \frac{1}{4}$ when $x = 3$

9. A curve passing through the point $(1, 1)$ is such that the gradient at any point P is always three times the gradient of the straight line OP. Find the equation of the curve.

10. The rate at which electrical charge leaks from a capacitor is proportional to the charge remaining on the capacitor. Show that the charge on the capacitor at time t is $Q_0 e^{-kt}$ where Q_0 is the charge at time $t = 0$ and k is a constant.

11. A body moves away from a fixed origin O in such a way that its velocity at any instant is proportional to the square of its displacement S from O. If the initial displacement S_0 is doubled in the first five seconds find an expression for the displacement at time t seconds and show that after ten seconds its distance from O may be considered infinite.

12. Water leaks from a small hole in the base of a container. The rate at which the water escapes is proportional to the square root of the volume remaining in the container. If $\frac{7}{16}$ of the initial volume V_0 leaks away in the first hour, show that the container will be empty after four hours and find an expression for the volume of water in the container at time t hours $(0 \leqslant t \leqslant 4)$.

13. Show that the general solution of the equation $x \cdot \dfrac{dy}{dx} + 1 = y^2$ may be written in the form

$$y = \frac{1 + kx^2}{1 - kx^2} \qquad \text{where } k \text{ is a constant.}$$

14. Show that the general solution of the equation $\dfrac{dy}{dx} = y - y^2$ may be written in the form

$$y = \frac{1}{1 + Ae^{-x}} \qquad \text{where } A \text{ is a constant.}$$

*15. If $x + y = z$ express $\dfrac{dy}{dx}$ in terms of $\dfrac{dz}{dx}$.

Use the substitution $x + y = z$ to solve the following differential equations:

(i) $\dfrac{dy}{dx} = x + y$ given $y = 1$ when $x = 0$

(ii) $\dfrac{dy}{dx} = (x + y)^2$ given $y = 1$ when $x = 0$

*16. If $y = vx$ (where v is also a variable) write down $\dfrac{dy}{dx}$ in terms of $\dfrac{dv}{dx}$. Use the substitution $y = vx$ to solve the following differential equations:

(i) $xy \cdot \dfrac{dy}{dx} = y^2 + x^2$ given $y = 1$ when $x = 1$

(ii) $x^2 \cdot \dfrac{dy}{dx} = x^2 - xy + y^2$ given $y = 0$ when $x = 1$

22.5 Linear approximation

Given a function $f(x)$ we wish to find an expression for the change in the value of the function, δf, caused by a small increase δx in the value of x.

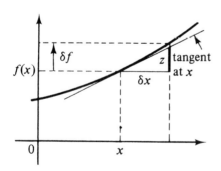

Fig. 3

An approximate value is obtained by using the tangent to the curve at the position x. The gradient of this tangent is given by $f'(x)$. From Fig. 3 we have

$$\delta f \approx z \quad \text{where} \quad \frac{z}{\delta x} = f'(x) \qquad \Rightarrow \qquad \boxed{\delta f \approx f'(x) . \delta x}$$

e.g. $\delta(\log x) \approx \dfrac{1}{x} \cdot \delta x$ $\delta(\sin x) \approx \cos x . \delta x$

i.e. a small change in $\log x$ is approximately $1/x$ times the change in x. A small change in $\sin x$ is approximately $\cos x$ times the change in x.

Example 147

Without using tables, find an approximate value for sin 31°.

The function considered is sin x. The value of this function at $x = 30°$ (or $\pi/6$ radians) is known to be 0.5 exactly. Now we increase x from 30° to 31°, i.e. $\delta x = 1° = \pi/180$ or 0.0175 radian. The increase in the value of sin x is

$$\delta(\sin x) \approx \cos x . \delta x$$

$$\approx \frac{\sqrt{3}}{2}(0.0175) \text{ or } 0.015$$

thus $\sin 31° \approx \sin 30° + 0.015 \approx \underline{0.515}$

Example 148

If $x \approx e^2$ show that $\ln x \approx 1 + \dfrac{x}{e^2}$

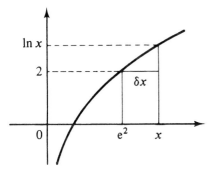

Fig. 4

The function considered is $\ln x$ and the value of this function at $x = e^2$ is 2 (Fig. 4). Now $\delta(\ln x) \approx (1/x).\delta x$ so taking an increase $\delta x = (x - e^2)$ we have

$$\delta(\ln x) \approx \frac{1}{e^2}.(x - e^2) \approx \frac{x}{e^2} - 1$$

Thus $\ln x \approx 2 + \left(\dfrac{x}{e^2} - 1\right) \approx \underline{1 + \dfrac{x}{e^2}}$

Exercise 22(e)

1. Write down expressions for
   (i) $\delta(\tan x)$ (ii) $\delta(e^x)$ (iii) $\delta(\cos 2x)$

   (iv) $\delta\left(\dfrac{1}{x}\right)$ (v) $\delta(\sin^2 x)$ (vi) $\delta(\ln . \sin x)$
2. The area of a circle is given by the formula $A = \pi r^2$. Write down an expression for δA and give a physical interpretation of the result. Find the

approximate increase in area when the radius of a circle is increased from 5 cm to 5.01 cm.

3. The formula $V = \frac{4}{3}\pi r^3$ gives the volume of a sphere. Write down an expression for δV and interpret the result physically. Find the approximate increase in volume when the radius of a sphere is increased from 6 cm to 6.05 cm.

4. Find, by linear approximation, estimates for
   (i) $\tan 46°$ (ii) $\ln 2.04$ (given $\ln 2 = 0.6931$)
   (iii) $\cos 60° \, 30'$ (iv) $e^{1.02}$ (given $e = 2.7183$)

5. Show that
   (i)   if $x \approx \frac{1}{4}\pi$ then $\tan x \quad \approx 1 - \frac{1}{2}\pi + 2x$
   (ii) if $x \approx 1$ then $e^{-x} \quad \approx (2-x)/e$
   (iii) if $x \approx 1$ then $\dfrac{1}{(1+x)} \approx \dfrac{3-x}{4}$
   (iv) if $x \approx 0$ then $\sin x \quad \approx x$
   (v)   if $x \approx 3$ then $\sqrt{1+x} \approx \frac{1}{4}(5+x)$
   (vi) if $x \approx \frac{1}{4}\pi$ then $\sin^2 x \quad \approx \frac{1}{2} - \frac{1}{4}\pi + x$

6. At extension x an elastic string stores energy E where $E = \frac{1}{2}kx^2$ (k constant). Show that the increase in energy caused by an increase δx is approximately $\dfrac{2E}{x}.\delta x$.

7. The maximum range of a projectile fired at speed V is $R = V^2/g$. If the maximum range is to be increased from R to $(R + \delta R)$ show that the velocity must be increased by approximately $(g/2V).\delta R$.

22.6 Approximate solution of equations (Newton's method)

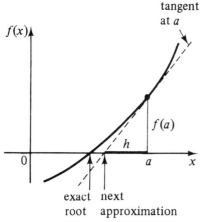

Fig. 5

Suppose we are trying to solve the equation $f(x) = 0$ and $x = a$ is known to be an approximate solution, i.e. $f(a) \approx 0$. In Fig. 5, which is exaggerated, it can be seen that a closer approximation to the exact root is $(a - h)$ where

$$\frac{f(a)}{h} = \text{gradient of tangent} = f'(a)$$

i.e. $\qquad h = \dfrac{f(a)}{f'(a)}$

Thus an improved approximation is given by

$$\boxed{a - \frac{f(a)}{f'(a)}}$$

The application of this result is illustrated by the next example. The method is not satisfactory when the gradient of the curve is close to zero for if $f'(a) \approx 0$ the correction $f(a)/f'(a)$ will be large and unreliable.

Example 149

Show graphically that the equation $\ln x = e^{-x}$ has a single root only and determine this root correct to two decimal places.

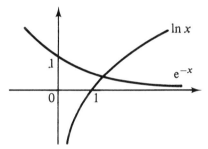

Fig. 6

Fig. 6 shows a sketch of the functions $\ln x$ and e^{-x}. It is clear that there is only one point of intersection so only one root is expected for this equation. This root is in the vicinity of $x = 1$ since $\ln 1 = 0$ and $e^{-1} \approx 0.3$. We could use $x = 1$ as a first approximation but work is often saved if the first approximation is as realistic as possible and we shall therefore choose a value slightly greater than 1; say 1.2.

It is necessary to write the equation in the form $f(x) = 0$. Thus

$$f(x) = \ln x - e^{-x}, \qquad f'(x) = \frac{1}{x} + e^{-x}.$$

With the first approximation $a_1 = 1.2$ we have

$$\frac{f(a_1)}{f'(a_1)} \approx \frac{0.1823 - 0.3012}{0.8333 + 0.3012} \approx -0.105$$

So a second approximation is $a_2 = 1.2 - (-0.105) = 1.305$
The process is now repeated

$$\frac{f(a_2)}{f'(a_2)} \approx \frac{0.2662 - 0.2712}{0.7663 + 0.2712} \approx -0.005$$

A third approximation is $a_3 = 1.305 - (-0.005) = 1.310$
The next correction will be smaller in magnitude than 0.005 so the root must already be correct to two decimal places, i.e.

$$x \approx 1.31$$

(This value should, of course, be checked by substitution in the equation.)

Exercise 22(f)

1. For each of the following quadratic equations, one approximate root is given. Determine these roots to a higher degree of accuracy by applying the method of this section twice. Check your results by using the quadratic formula,
   (i) $x^2 + x - 5 = 0$ approximate root   2
   (ii) $3x^2 - 4x - 1 = 0$ approximate root   1.5

2. An approximate solution is given for each of the following equations. Determine the correct value of each root to three places of decimals.
   (i) $x^3 + x - 5 = 0$ approximate root   1.5
   (ii) $\ln x = 4 - x$ approximate root   3
   (iii) $\ln x = \dfrac{1}{x}$ approximate root   2

3. Determine graphically the number of roots for each of the following equations. Determine the largest root of each equation correct to three decimal places.
   (i) $e^x = x + 2$ (ii) $x^3 = x^2 + 1$
   (iii) $x^2 + 2 = \dfrac{1}{x}$ (iv) $\ln x = x^2 - 3$.

Answers to Exercises

Exercise 1(a)

1. (i) 81   (ii) $\frac{1}{81}$ (iii) 32   (iv) $\frac{1}{32}$ (v) 1000
   (vi) $\frac{1}{1000}$ (vii) $\frac{1}{8}$ (viii) 8   (ix) 1   (x) 3
   (xi) $\frac{1}{3}$ (xii) 4   (xiii) $\frac{1}{4}$ (xiv) 4   (xv) $\frac{1}{4}$
2. (i) a^7 (ii) b^4 (iii) 1   (iv) d^{12} (v) $6a^5b^2$
   (vi) $4q^3$ (vii) $27t^6$ (viii) 4   (ix) $4a$ (x) 3
   (xi) $\frac{1}{4}r^4$ (xii) 8
3. (i) 7   (ii) $\frac{1}{27}$ (iii) 0.1   (iv) 9   (v) 64
   (vi) $\frac{16}{81}$ (vii) $\frac{1}{3}$ (viii) $\frac{1}{32}$ (ix) 0.4   (x) $1\frac{1}{3}$
   (xi) $1\frac{1}{2}$ (xii) 125
4. (i) 3   (ii) -2 (iii) 6   (iv) 625   (v) -1
   (vi) 243   (vii) 5   (viii) 0   (ix) $-\frac{1}{3}$

Exercise 1(b)

1. (i) $2\sqrt{3}$ (ii) $2\sqrt{7}$ (iii) $3\sqrt{5}$ (iv) $2\sqrt{2}$ (v) $4\sqrt{3}$
   (vi) $2\sqrt{10}$ (vii) $4\sqrt{5}$ (viii) $7\sqrt{2}$ (ix) $3\sqrt{13}$
2. (i) $\sqrt{27}$ (ii) $\sqrt{50}$ (iii) $\sqrt{24}$ (iv) $\sqrt{44}$
   (v) $\sqrt{90}$ (vi) $\sqrt{112}$
3. (i) $\sqrt{2}$ (ii) $\frac{2}{3}\sqrt{3}$ (iii) $\frac{1}{2}\sqrt{6}$ (iv) $\frac{1}{5}\sqrt{5}$
   (v) $\frac{1}{5}\sqrt{10}$ (vi) $\frac{1}{5}\sqrt{15}$
4. (i) $2\sqrt{13}$ (ii) $5\sqrt{7}$ (iii) $\frac{2}{3}\sqrt{2}$ (iv) $\frac{5}{4}\sqrt{2}$
5. (i) 6   (ii) $5\sqrt{2}$ (iii) $12\sqrt{6}$ (iv) 3
   (v) $2\sqrt{3}$ (vi) $5\sqrt{5}$ (vii) 24   (viii) $8\sqrt{2}$
   (ix) $30\sqrt{2}$ (x) $\frac{1}{3}\sqrt{6}$ (xi) $3\sqrt{3}$ (xii) $9\sqrt{5}$
   (xiii) $\sqrt{11}$ (xiv) $2\sqrt{2}$ (xv) $\frac{5}{6}\sqrt{3}$ (xvi) $\frac{3}{2}\sqrt{10}$

Exercise 1(c)

1. (i) $6x - 15$ (ii) $a^2 - 4a$ (iii) $2x^2 + 2xy$
   (iv) $8p^2 + 12pq$ (v) $6p^3 - 3p^2$ (vi) $a^2b^2 + abc$
2. (i) $2(3x + 2)$ (ii) $a(b - 4)$ (iii) $x(3x + 1)$
   (iv) $y(x - y)$ (v) $3r(2r + 3)$ (vi) $4p(q - 2p)$
3. (i) $x^2 + 5x + 6$ (ii) $x^2 + 4x - 12$ (iii) $a^2 - 9a + 14$
   (iv) $b^2 - b - 20$ (v) $2x^2 + x - 1$ (vi) $3y^2 + 11y + 6$

(vii) $4a^2 - 9a + 2$ (viii) $2p^2 - 7p - 15$ (ix) $6x^2 - 13x + 6$
(x) $x^2 + xy - 2y^2$

4. (i) $(x+2)(x+1)$ (ii) $(x+4)(x-2)$ (iii) $(p+5)(p-3)$
   (iv) $(a-4)(a-3)$ (v) $(y-6)(y+5)$ (vi) $(r-9)(r-1)$
  (vii) $(2x+3)(x+1)$ (viii) $(3a-1)(a-2)$ (ix) $(2y-3)(y+2)$
   (x) $(2x+1)(2x-9)$

5. (i) $x^2 + 2x + 1$ (ii) $x^2 + 14x + 49$ (iii) $a^2 - 8a + 16$
  (iv) $y^2 + y + \frac{1}{4}$ (v) $x^2 - \frac{3}{2}x + \frac{9}{16}$ (vi) $a^2 + \frac{4}{5}a + \frac{4}{25}$

6. (i)   4   (ii)   9   (iii)   25   (iv) $\frac{1}{4}$ (v) $6\frac{1}{4}$
  (vi) $\frac{4}{9}$ (vii) $\frac{1}{16}$ (viii) $20\frac{1}{4}$

7. (i) $p^2 - q^2$ (ii) $x^2 - 16$ (iii) $25 - y^2$ (iv) $4a^2 - 1$

8. (i) $(x+y)(x-y)$ (ii) $(p+1)(p-1)$ (iii) $(a+7)(a-7)$
  (iv) $(4+y)(4-y)$ (v) $(3x+1)(3x-1)$ (vi) $(2a+3b)(2a-3b)$

9. (i) $\dfrac{2b}{3a}$ (ii) $\dfrac{3}{5}$ (iii) $\dfrac{2y}{3x-1}$ (iv) $\dfrac{a-b}{3}$ (v) $\dfrac{a}{b}$

  (vi) $\dfrac{3}{x+2}$ (vii) $\dfrac{-a}{a+2}$ (viii) $\dfrac{y}{y-2}$

Exercise 1(d)

1. (i) 2, 3   (ii) 3, −4   (iii) −2, 9   (iv) −1, −1$\frac{1}{2}$
  (v) $\frac{1}{3}$, 1   (vi) 1$\frac{1}{2}$, 2   (vii) $\frac{1}{4}$, −2   (viii) −$\frac{1}{2}$, 1$\frac{1}{3}$

2. (i) $-2 \pm \sqrt{3}$ (ii) $5 \pm \sqrt{5}$ (iii) $1 \pm 2\sqrt{5}$
  (iv) $-4 \pm 3\sqrt{2}$ (v) $\frac{1}{2}(1 \pm \sqrt{5})$ (vi) $\frac{1}{2}(-3 \pm \sqrt{13})$

3. (i)   −2.62, −0.38   (ii)   −2.14, 5.14   (iii) −0.39, 3.89
  (iv) −1.82, 0.22   (v)   −1.77, −0.57   (vi) −0.29, 2.29
 (vii) 0.13, 1.87   (viii) −5.24, 1.24

4. (i) $3 \pm \sqrt{5}$ (ii) $\frac{1}{2}(-1 \pm \sqrt{3})$ (iii) $\frac{1}{3}(2 \pm \sqrt{13})$
  (iv) $\frac{3}{2}(1 \pm \sqrt{5})$

Exercise 1(e)

1. $\dfrac{a^2}{2b^2}$ 2. $\dfrac{r}{s}$ 3. $\dfrac{x+7y}{12}$ 4. $\dfrac{m}{2}$

5. $\dfrac{2b+3a}{ab}$ 6. $\dfrac{2x}{x^2-9}$ 7. $\dfrac{3a}{a+b}$ 8. $\dfrac{1}{m+n}$

9. $\dfrac{2q}{p+q}$ 10. $\dfrac{r+2}{r}$ 11. $\dfrac{y^2}{x^2-y^2}$ 12. $\dfrac{y^2+z^2}{yz(y+z)}$

Exercise 1(f)

1. (i) $\sqrt{17}$, $(3, 4\frac{1}{2})$ (ii) 13, $(4, 3\frac{1}{2})$ (iii) $3\sqrt{5}$, $(1, -1\frac{1}{2})$
  (iv) $7\sqrt{2}$, $(-4\frac{1}{2}, \frac{1}{2})$

2. 69 sq. units, $\sqrt{49\frac{1}{4}}$ or $\frac{1}{2}\sqrt{197}$
3. $\sqrt{65}$, $\sqrt{45}$ or $3\sqrt{5}$, $\sqrt{20}$ or $2\sqrt{5}$, area = 15 sq. units
4. 20 sq. units, 5, 8

Exercise 1(g)

1. $A, D, (-\frac{1}{3}, 0)$ 2. Q, R and $S, (-1, 0)$ and $(0, 0)$
3. $3\sqrt{10}$ units   4. 9 units
5. (i) $(-1, 1)$ and $(2, 4)$ (ii) $(-2, 7)$ and $(\frac{1}{2}, -\frac{1}{2})$
6. (i) $A(0, 5), B(2\frac{1}{2}, 0)$ (ii) $C(3, 0), D(0, -6)$
   (iii) $E(0, 10), F(-2, 0), G(5, 0)$ (iv) $H(0, 4) I(\frac{1}{2}, 0), J(4, 0)$
7. $A = 5, B = -3$ 8. $2 \pm \sqrt{2}, (2, 4)$

Exercise 2(a)

1. (i) 3   (ii) $-\frac{2}{3}$ (iii) $\frac{1}{2}$ (iv) $4\frac{1}{2}$
2. $\frac{3}{4}$, $\frac{3}{4}$, colinear
3. (i) $3a$ (ii) $a + b$ (iii) $a + 2b$
4. $-1, 5, -1, 5$, parallelogram
5. (i) $3, -7, 2\frac{1}{3}$ (ii) $3, 0, 0$ (iii) $-2, 5, 2\frac{1}{2}$
   (iv) $\frac{1}{2}, -3, 6$ (v) $1, 1, -1$ (vi) $\frac{1}{4}, -\frac{1}{2}, 2$
6. (i) $-3, 5$ (ii) $-\frac{2}{3}, 0$ (iii) $\frac{1}{2}, -\frac{1}{2}$ (iv) $-2, \frac{1}{3}$
   (v) $-\frac{1}{2}, \frac{3}{4}$ (vi) $a, \frac{1}{a}$
7. $A(2, 0), B(0, 1\frac{1}{2}), C(-2, 2)$
8. $\frac{3}{4}, y = \frac{3}{4}x + 3$ (i) -4 (ii) 2.4 units

Exercise 2(b)

1. $a = 40, b = 6$ 2. $P = 15 + 0.24 W, 75$ N
3. $l = 84.5 + 0.53 m$, 84.5 cm, 96.2 cm   4. $l = 250.2 + 0.08T$, 254.2 mm, 19° C
5. $R = 60 + 0.04 V^2$, 140 N/tonne   6. $y = 4.0 - \frac{15}{x}$
7. $a = 1, b = 0.05$, 146 ft

Exercise 2(c)

1. (i) $y = 3x + 7$ (ii) $2y + x = 9$ (iii) $4y = 3x - 6$
   (iv) $2y = 5x - 30$
2. (i) $2y = 3x + 3$ (ii) $2y + 9x = 14$ (iii) $5y = 2x + 22$
   (iv) $y + 3x = -6$
3. (i) $y = 3x + 1$ (ii) $y + 2x = 11$ (iii) $2y = x$
   (iv) $3y + 4x = 8$
4. $(2, 1)$ 5. $(5, 9), 3y + 5x = 52$
6. $(1, 2)$ 7. (i) $3y = 4x + 3, 12y = x + 27$ (ii) $(1, 2\frac{1}{3})$
8. $y + 2x = 1, (\frac{1}{2}, 0)$

Exercise 2(d)

1. (i) $-\frac{1}{4}$ (ii) -3 (iii) 1   (iv) 5   (v) 2   (vi) $-\frac{3}{4}$
2. Parallel (v), perpendicular (ii) and (iii)
3. (i) $3y = x + 17$ (ii) $y + 3x = -1$
4. (i) $3y = 4x + 9$ (ii) $3y = x - 2$
5. $a = 8,\ b = 6$ 6. $4y + 10x = 13,\ (1.3, 0)$
7. $3y = x,\ (1\frac{1}{2}, \frac{1}{2}),\ \frac{1}{2}\sqrt{10}$ 8. $(2.3, 4.1)$
9. (i) $4y + 6x = 11$ (ii) $N(2\frac{1}{2}, -1)$ (iii) 26 sq. units
10. $(1\frac{1}{2}, 2\frac{1}{2})$

Exercise 3(a)

1. (a) 7   (b) $6\frac{1}{2}$ 2. (a) 21   (b) 7
3. (a) $-\frac{1}{12}$ (b) -1 4. (a) 4   (b) 0
5. (a) 4.2   (b) 4.1   (c) 4.01   (d) 4.001

Exercise 3(b)

1. (i) -3 (ii) -0.75 2. (i) 4   (ii) -5
3. (i) 6.1   (ii) 6.01   (iii) 6.001, 6
4. (i) 12.61   (ii) 12.0601   (iii) 12.006, 12
5. (i) -2.857 (ii) -2.985 (iii) $-2.9985, -3$

Exercise 3(c)

1. (i) 6   (ii) 8   (iii) 10   2. 4   3. (i) 6   (ii) 8
4. (i) 7   (ii) 9   5. (i) 12   (ii) 27

Exercise 3(d)

1. (i) $2x - 2$ (ii) $2x + 3$ (iii) $4 - 2x$
2. (i) $6x$ (ii) $4x - 1$ (iii) $5 - 4x$
3. (i) $2x$ (ii) $2x + 3$ (iii) $2 - 6x$
4. (i) 4   (ii) -3 5. (i) $3x^2$ (ii) $6x^2$
6. $-\dfrac{1}{x^2}$ 7. $-\dfrac{2}{x^3}$

Exercise 3(e)

1. (i) $4x$ (ii) $10x$ (iii) $9x^2$ (iv) $-12x^2$
   (v) $-3/x^2$ (vi) 6   (vii) 0   (viii) $-4/x^3$
2. (i) $6x - 2$ (ii) $2x + 5$ (iii) $1 - 1/x^2$ (iv) $3x^2 - 10x$
   (v) 4   (vi) $-6/x^3 - 2x$ (vii) $2/x^2$ (viii) $x + 4/x^3$
   (ix) $\frac{1}{3} - 2x^3$
3. (i) $6x^2 - 2x$ (ii) $-4 + 3x^2$ (iii) $6x - 6/x^3$
   (iv) $2x - 1 + 4/x^2$ (v) $12x^3 - 8x + 7$ (vi) $-2/x^2 + 6/x^3$
   (vii) $2 - 3x^2 + 1/x^2$ (viii) $-1/x^3 + 1/3x^2$

4. (i) $7x^6$ (ii) $21x^6$ (iii) $10x^4$ (iv) $20x^3$
   (v) $-4/x^5$ (vi) $-10/x^6$ (vii) $\frac{1}{3}x^{-\frac{2}{3}}$ (viii) $-\frac{1}{2}x^{-1\frac{1}{2}}$
5. (i) $4x+3$ (ii) $6x^2+2x+2$ (iii) $6x^2+2x+1/x^2$
   (iv) $2/x^2-2/x^3$
6. (i) $1-3/x^2$ (ii) $-2/x^3+1/x^2$ (iii) $1-1/x^2$ (iv) $3+2/x^3$

Exercise 3(f)

1. 5   2. $2\frac{3}{4}$ 3. $(\frac{1}{2}, -2\frac{1}{4})$ 4. 6 and -6
5. $(3,14)$ 6. 7 and -7 7. $(-1,-2)$ and $(6,12)$, -5 and 9
8. $(-3,6)$ and $(\frac{1}{3}, \frac{22}{27})$ 9. $(1,17)$ 10. $1\frac{1}{4}$
11. $(0,8)$, 1, $y=x+8$
12. $(-1,-2)$ and $(-3,-6)$, $y=7x+5$ and $y=7x-27$
13. (i) $y=7x-25$ (ii) $y+2x=6$ (iii) $4y=24x+3$
14. (i) $7y+x=75$ (ii) $2y=x+2$ (iii) $24y+4x=55$
15. (i) $\frac{1}{6}$ (ii) $1\frac{1}{2}$ 16. $A=2, B=-4$

Exercise 3(g)

1. (i) $18\ \text{cm}^3/\text{sec}$ (ii) $16\frac{1}{2}\ \text{cm}^3/\text{sec}$; $11\frac{1}{2}\ \text{cm}^3/\text{sec}$, $23\frac{1}{2}\ \text{cm}^3/\text{sec}$
2. (i) $2.1°\,\text{C}$ (ii) $0.7°\,\text{C/min}$, $0.06°\,\text{C/min}$
   (iii) $2.5°\,\text{C/min}$, $0.16°\,\text{C/min}$, $0.02°\,\text{C/min}$
3. (i) $28\ \text{cm/min}$ (ii) $-36\ \text{cm/min}$, $-12\ \text{cm/min}$
   (iii) $t=4\frac{1}{2}$ (iv) rising at $40\ \text{cm/min}$
4. (i) -16 (ii) $t=1, -15$ (iii) $t=2\frac{2}{3}$, $-400/27$ (iv) $t=3\frac{2}{3}$
5. (i) 15 m, $5\ \text{ms}^{-1}$ (ii) 20 m, $10\ \text{ms}^{-1}$; $2\ \text{ms}^{-1}$, $8\ \text{ms}^{-1}$ $12\ \text{ms}^{-1}$
6. (i) $2\ \text{ms}^{-1}$ (ii) $70\ \text{ms}^{-1}$; $16\ \text{ms}^{-1}$, $56\ \text{ms}^{-1}$, $120\ \text{ms}^{-1}$
7. (i) $2\ \text{ms}^{-1}$ per second   (ii) $8\ \text{ms}^{-2}$, $20\ \text{ms}^{-2}$
8. (i) $12\ \text{ms}^{-1}$, $2\ \text{ms}^{-1}$, $-8\ \text{ms}^{-1}$ (ii) $t=3.2$, 51.2 m   (iii) $32\ \text{ms}^{-1}$
9. (i) $-2.25\ \text{ms}^{-1}$, $3\ \text{ms}^{-1}$, $3.75\ \text{ms}^{-1}$
   (ii) $6.25\ \text{ms}^{-2}$, $0.4\ \text{ms}^{-2}$, $0.05\ \text{ms}^{-2}$ (iii) $t=2.5$ (iv) $4\ \text{ms}^{-1}$
10. (i) $\frac{1}{2}\pi$ sq. units   (ii) 2.4π sq. units.   11. 10π cu. units

Exercise 4(a)

3. (i)   max 4 at $0°$, $360°$; min -4 at $180°$
   (ii)   max 5 at $90°$; min 1 at $270°$
   (iii)   max 4 at $180°$; min -2 at $0°$, $360°$
   (iv)   max 1 at $270°$; min $\frac{1}{3}$ at $90°$
   (v)   max 1 at $0°$, $180°$, $360°$; min 0 at $90°$, $270°$
4. (i) $\sin 60° = \sqrt{3}/2$, $\cos 60° = \frac{1}{2}$, $\tan 60° = \sqrt{3}$
   (ii) $\sin 30° = \frac{1}{2}$, $\cos 30° = \sqrt{3}/2$, $\tan 30° = 1/\sqrt{3}$
5. $\sin 45° = \cos 45° = 1/\sqrt{2}$, $\tan 45° = 1$

Exercise 4(b)

1. (i) 0.8480   (ii) -0.8090 (iii) -3.7320 (iv) 0.5736
   (v) -5.6713 (vi) -0.6428 (vii) 0.7880   (viii) 0.2679
   (ix) -0.3289 (x) -0.4226 (xi) -0.6481 (xii) 0.3600

2. (i) $27°, 153°$ (ii) $38°, 322°$ (iii) $66°, 246°$ (iv) $245.5°, 294.5°$
   (v) $50.8°, 309.2°$ (vi) $163.3°, 343.3°$ (vii) $93.5°, 266.5°$ (viii) $45°, 225°$

4. (i) $\frac{1}{2}$ (ii) $\frac{1}{2}$ (iii) $-\sqrt{3}$ (iv) $-\sqrt{3}/2$
   (v) 1 (vi) $-1/\sqrt{2}$ (vii) $-1/\sqrt{3}$ (viii) $1/\sqrt{2}$
   (ix) $-\frac{1}{2}$

5. (i) $31°, 149°$ (ii) $20°, 200°$ (iii) $60°, 300°$ (iv) $234°, 306°$
   (v) $103.3°, 256.7°$ (vi) $135°, 315°$ (vii) $90°,270°$ (viii) $60°, 240°$

Exercise 4(c)

1. (i) $14.5°, 165.5°$ (ii) $60°, 300°$ (iii) $153.4°, 333.4°$
   (iv) $209.3°, 330.7°$ (v) $101.8°, 258.2°$ (vi) $30°, 210°$
   (vii) $270°$ (viii) $45°, 315°$

2. (i) 2 (ii) $1/\sqrt{3}$ (iii) $2/\sqrt{3}$ (iv) 1
   (v) $-\sqrt{2}$ (vi) -1 (vii) -1 (viii) 0

3. $\frac{5}{4}, \frac{3}{4}$ 4. $\frac{15}{17}, \frac{17}{8}$ 5. $-\frac{24}{25}, -\frac{24}{7}$

6. (i) $\sec\theta$ (ii) 1 (iii) $\csc\theta$ (iv) $\tan\theta$

7. (i) $19.5°, 160.1°$ (ii) $53.1°, 233.1°$ (iii) $26.6°, 206.6°$
   (iv) $60°, 120°, 240°, 300°$ (v) $71.6°, 251.6°$

Exercise 4(d)

1. (i) $\csc^2\theta$ (ii) $\cos\theta$ (iii) $\tan^2\theta$ (iv) $\sin\theta$
2. (i) $\tan\theta$ (ii) $\sin^2\theta$ (iii) $\sec\theta$ (iv) $\sec^2\theta$

Exercise 4(e)

1. (i) $53.1°, 233.1°$ (ii) $45°, 135°, 225°, 315°$
   (iii) $48.2°, 180°, 311.8°$ (iv) $0°, 180°, 210°, 330°, 360°$

2. (i) $51.3°, 231.3°$ (ii) $104°, 284°$ (iii) $90°, 189.6°, 350.4°$
   (iv) $56.3°, 90°, 236.3°, 270°$

3. (i) $71.6°, 135°, 251.6°, 315°$ (ii) $60°, 180°, 300°$ (iii) $14.5°, 165.5°$
   (iv) $30°, 150°, 210°, 330°$ and $60°, 120°, 240°, 300°$

4. (i) $30°, 150°, 270°$ (ii) $19.5°, 160.5°, 210°, 330°$
   (iii) $45°, 135°, 225°, 315°$ (iv) $45°, 63.4°, 225°, 243.4°$

Exercise 4(f)

1. (i) $\csc\theta$ (ii) $\sin^2\theta$ (iii) $\cot^2\theta$ (iv) $\sec\theta$
2. (i) $0°, 71.6°, 180°, 251.6°, 360°$ (ii) $26.6°, 135°, 206.6°, 315°$
   (iii) $60°, 300°$

4. (i) $30°, 150°, 210°, 330°$ (ii) $11.5°, 90°, 168.5°, 270°$
   (iii) $131.8°, 228.2°$ (iv) $60°, 300°$
   (v) $30°, 150°$ (vi) $70.5°, 90°, 270°, 289.5°$
   (vii) $60°, 90°, 120°, 240°, 270°, 300°$ (viii) $30°, 150°$

Exercise 5(a)

1. $12, 22, 6x - 5, -5, 1$
2. $0, 20, 3x^2 - 3, 9, 0$
3. $8\frac{1}{2}, 17\frac{2}{3}, 4t - \dfrac{1}{t^2}, 3, -2$
4. (i) $-\frac{2}{3}, 1$ (ii) $\frac{1}{2}$ 5. $\frac{1}{3}$ or -2
6. (i) all values   (ii) $f(x) > 0$ (iii) $0 \leqslant f(x) \leqslant 1$ (iv) $0 \leqslant f(x) \leqslant 1$
   (v) $f(x) \leqslant 6$ (vi) $0 \leqslant f(x) \leqslant 9$ (vii) $f(x) > 0$ (viii) $0 \leqslant f(x) < 1$
7. (i) $f'(x) = -2$ (ii) $-6 \leqslant f'(x) \leqslant 6$ (iii) $f'(x) \neq 0$
   (iv) $0 < f'(x) \leqslant 1$

Exercise 5(b)

2. (i) $(x + 1)^2 + 4$ (ii) $(x - 3)^2 - 4$ (iii) $(x + \frac{1}{2})^2 - 1\frac{1}{4}$
   (iv) $(x - 2\frac{1}{2})^2 + \frac{3}{4}$
3. (i) $c = 3$ (ii) $c = 2\frac{1}{4}$
4. (i) $2(x - 2)^2 + 1$ (ii) $5(x + 1)^2 - 3$ (iii) $3(x + \frac{1}{3})^2 + \frac{2}{3}$
   (iv) $2(x - \frac{3}{4})^2 - 2\frac{1}{8}$
5. (i) max 7 (ii) min $2\frac{3}{4}$ (iii) max 3 (iv) max $4\frac{1}{4}$
   (v) max $3\frac{4}{5}$ (vi) min $(a^2 - \frac{1}{4}b^2)$

Exercise 5(c)

1. (i) distinct   (ii) imaginary   (iii) distinct   (iv) repeated
   (v) imaginary   (vi) imaginary
2. (i) $x < -3, x > 2$ (ii) $x < \frac{2}{3}, x > 1$ (iii) $-1 < x < 5$
   (iv) $-2 < x < 1\frac{1}{2}$
3. $c = 5\frac{1}{3}$
4. (i) positive   (ii) both   (iii) both   (iv) both
   (v) positive   (vi) negative
5. (i) $1 < x < 3$ (ii) $x \leqslant -2\frac{1}{2}, x \geqslant 1$ (iii) $x < -4, x > 3$
   (iv) $-2 < x < 4$ (v) $x \leqslant 2, x \geqslant 3$ (vi) $-\frac{1}{3} < x < 4$
6. (i) $(3, 9)$ line touches curve   (ii) $-2\frac{1}{4}$
7. (ii) $x < -1\frac{1}{3}$ and $x > 3$ 8. -1 and $6, x = 2\frac{1}{2}, -12\frac{1}{4}$
9. (ii) $x < 1, x > 2$ 10. (i) $-2 < x < \frac{2}{3}$ (ii) $1\frac{1}{3}$

Exercise 5(d)

1. (i) sum -3, product 4 (ii) sum $-\frac{1}{2}$, product $-2\frac{1}{2}$
   (iii) sum $\frac{4}{3}$, product $-\frac{2}{3}$ (iv) sum $\frac{1}{5}$, product $\frac{1}{5}$
   (v) sum $2\frac{1}{2}$, product 3 (vi) sum 1, product 5
   (vii) sum -1, product -1 (viii) sum $-\frac{3}{4}$, product $\frac{1}{4}$
2. (i) 3 (ii) 4 (iii) 5 (iv) 12
3. (i) $\frac{7}{4}$ (ii) -6 (iii) $-\frac{9}{4}$ (iv) 28
4. (i) $-\frac{1}{2}$ (ii) $-2\frac{3}{4}$ (iii) $14\frac{1}{4}$ (iv) $\pm\frac{3}{4}\sqrt{57}$
5. (i) -1 (ii) $-2\frac{1}{3}$ (iii) $\frac{52}{9}$ (iv) $\pm\frac{4}{9}\sqrt{13}$
6. (i) $6\frac{1}{4}$ (ii) $5\frac{1}{4}$
7. $4x^2 - 14x + 9 = 0, (1\frac{3}{4}, \frac{1}{2})$ 8. 9 or -9
9. (i) $x^2 - 2x - 16 = 0$ (ii) $x^2 - 9x + 16 = 0$ (iii) $4x^2 + x - 1 = 0$

10. (i) $3x^2 + 10x + 4 = 0$　(ii) $9x^2 - 19x + 1 = 0$　(iii) $x^2 + 5x + 3 = 0$
11. (i) $x^2 + 12x + 64 = 0$　(ii) $x^2 + 9x + 22 = 0$
    (iii) $4x^2 - x + 4 = 0$
12. (i) $2x^2 - 5 = 0$　(ii) $9x^2 - 28x + 4 = 0$　(iii) $8x^2 + 136x - 27 = 0$

Exercise 5(e)

1. (i) 2　　　(ii) -1.15　　(iii) $-1.3, 0, 2.3$　(iv) 2.45
3. (i) 1, 3　　(ii) none　　　(iii) -1 (repeated)　(iv) $-3, \frac{1}{2}$
   (v) none　(vi) $\frac{1}{4}(1 \pm \sqrt{17})$

Exercise 5(f)

1. (i)　7　(ii) 4　(iii)　0　(iv)　8
   (v) -7　(vi) 2　(vii) $-2\frac{1}{2}$　(viii) 0
2. (i) $a = -3$　(ii) $b = 3$　(iii) $c = 4$
3. (i)　$(x - 3)(x^2 + x + 1)$　　(ii) $(x - 1)(2x + 1)(2x - 3)$
   (iii) $(x - 2)(x + 2)(2x + 1)$　(iv) $(2x - 1)(x^2 + 1)$
   (v) $(x - 4)(x^2 + 4x + 5)$　(vi) $(x + 1)(2x + 1)(3x - 2)$
4. $p = -5, q = 8$
5. (i) $-1, \frac{1}{2}, 1$　　(ii) -2　　(iii) $2, 0.618, -1.618$　　(iv) $2, 2\frac{1}{3}, -2\frac{1}{2}$
6. (i)　$(x - a)(x^2 + ax + a^2)$　(ii) $(x + a)(x^2 - ax + a^2)$
   (iii) $(x - 2)(x^2 + 2x + 4)$ $(x + 1)(x^2 - x + 1)$

Exercise 6(a)

1. (i)　$6x^2 - 10x + 1, 12x - 10$　(ii) $4x + 7, 4$
   (iii) $5 + 1/x^2, -2/x^3$　(iv) $-1/x^2 - 4/x^3, 2/x^3 + 12/x^4$
2. (i) $5x^4$　(ii) 6　(iii) $1 - \frac{1}{2}h$　(iv) $12t^2 - 6$
3. $2x - 3x^2, 2 - 6x, -21, 2$　(i) $0, \frac{2}{3}$　(ii) $x > \frac{1}{3}$
4. (i) decreasing　　(ii) increasing　5. (i) increasing　　(ii) decreasing

Exercise 6(b)

1. (i) min. -11 at $x = 3$　(ii) max. 26 at $x = 4$　(iii) max. $3\frac{1}{4}$ at $x = \frac{1}{2}$
2. (i)　min. $(0, 3)$, max. $(4, 35)$　(ii) min. $(3, -9)$, max. $(-1, 1\frac{2}{3})$
   (iii) min. $(1, -1)$, max. $(-1, 3)$　(iv) min. $(-1, -1)$, max $(\frac{1}{3}, \frac{5}{27})$
4. $x(24 - 2x), 72 \text{ m}^2$　　　5. all sides $12\frac{1}{2}$ cm
6. $x^2(60 - x), x = 40, h = 20$

Exercise 6(c)

1. (i) max. $(\frac{1}{4}, 6\frac{1}{8})$　　(ii) max. $(\frac{1}{3}, \frac{4}{27})$, min. $(1, 0)$
2. min. $(-2, -16)$, max. $(0, 0)$, min. $(2, -16)$
3. (i)　max. $(-3, -6)$, min. $(3, 6)$　(ii) min. $(-1, 2)$, min. $(1, 2)$
   (iii) max. $(-2, -3)$　　　　　　(iv) min. $(-\frac{1}{2}, 3)$
4. max. $(-\sqrt{2}, -4\sqrt{2})$, min $(-1, -6)$, max. $(1, 6)$, min. $(\sqrt{2}, 4\sqrt{2})$
6. (i) $x = 1$　(iii) max. $(2, \frac{1}{4})$

Exercise 6(d)

1. 24 m²
2. $x \approx 6.69$ cm ($\sqrt[3]{300}$), $h \approx 8.93$ cm
3. $4.22 \times 8.44 \times 5.63$ cm
4. $\frac{2}{3} \times 1\frac{2}{3} \times 6\frac{2}{3}$ ft
5. 1.57 ft
6. $r = h = \sqrt{2/\pi} \approx 0.80$ metre (80 cm)
7. $r \approx 3.17$ cm, $h \approx 6.34$ cm
8. 25 cm²
10. $256\pi/3$ cm³
11. $r = h = \sqrt[3]{3000/\pi} \approx 9.85$ cm

Exercise 6(e)

1. inf. (0, 0)
2. min. (1, −3)
3. inf. (0, 0), min. (3, −27)
4. inf. (2, 8)
5. inf. (−1, 1), min. (0, 0)
6. inf. (0, 0), inf. (1, 1)
7. max. (−2, 48), min. (0, 0)
8. max. (−1, 2), inf. (0, 0), min. (1, −2)

Exercise 7(a)

1. 11.9 cm
2. 7.28 m
3. 2.71 m, 6.29 m²
4. 24.65 m, 167.2 m²
5. 5.2 km
6. 26 m
7. 117.2 cm³
8. (i) 8.06 km   (ii) 1.95 km

Exercise 7(b)

1. 7.32 cm
2. 67.9 m
3. 11.0 m
4. 4.74 m
5. 22.6°, 9.43 cm
6. 10.5, 14.2, 17.0 cm
7. 86 m
8. 10.3, 16.3 cm, 78.4 cm²
9. 14.7 km hr⁻¹

Exercise 7(c)

1. 50.7°, 95.7°
2. 42.7°, 99.2°
3. 25.8°, 27.7 cm
4. 62.7° or 117.3°, 8.26 m
5. 44.0°, 52.6°
6. 41.1°, 36.1 m
7. 262 km, 044.4°
8. 65.6°, 114.4°

Exercise 7(d)

1. (i) 19.4°   (ii) 56.3°   (iii) 21.8°
2. (1) 32.0°   (ii) 28.1°   (iii) 41.6°
3. (i) 8 cm   (ii) 24.0°   (iii) 22.9°
4. 16.9 m, 7.7°, 25.7°   5. 43.3 cm, 70.9°
6. (i) 28.1 m   (ii) 195 m   (iii) 8.3°
7. 25.7°   8. 27.7°   9. 53.4°
10. (i) $10\sqrt{3}$ m   (ii) 21.54 m   (iii) 70.9°, 60°
11. 2560 m   12. 4.315 m, 9.02 m, 64.4°

Exercise 8(b)

1. (i) 15   (ii) 13   (iii) 10   (iv) 16
2. (i) 8   (ii) 8   (iii) −3   (iv) 2.2
3. (i) 37   (ii) 100   (iii) 42   (iv) −66
4. (i) 990   (ii) 1100   (iii) 1620
5. (i) 376   (ii) 120   (iii) 1600
6. 1683, 3267
7. (i) 52   (ii) $\frac{2}{3}$ (iii) $\frac{2}{3}$
8. (i) 8   (ii) $\frac{1}{3}$ (iii) 95

328   *Essentials of Pure Mathematics*

Exercise 8(c)

1. (i) 3105   (ii) 2925   (iii) 1820   (iv) −425
2. (i) −5½   (ii) 1½   (iii) 130½
3. 858 km   4. 10
5. (i) 0.5 m   (ii) 2.7 m   (iii) 3.5 m   6. 9
7. 1.1, 0.2, 20   8. 29.3

Exercise 8(d)

1. (i) $60\frac{3}{4}$ (ii) −32/27
2. (i) ±20, ±320, 1280   (ii) 36, 24, $10\frac{2}{3}$
   (iii) 4, $\frac{2}{3}$, $\frac{1}{54}$ (iv) −12.8, −80, 200
3. (i) 10, 8   (ii) 34, 30   (iii) $\frac{13}{72}$, $\frac{1}{6}$ (iv) $\frac{89}{40}$, 2
4. $16\frac{1}{8}$ 5. 5, 315
6. −3, −2   7. $r = 2\frac{1}{2}$ or $-3\frac{1}{2}$
8. q^2/p, q^3/p^2, $p(q/p)^{n-1}$ 9. −1
10. $-58\frac{1}{3}$

Exercise 8(e)

1. (i) 3069   (ii) 98 301   (iii) 3 145 725
2. (i) 648.97   (ii) 4667.2   (iii) 29 547.04
3. (i) 60.396   (ii) 63.797   (iii) 63.989   (iv) 64.000
4. (i) 446.313   (ii) 494.235   (iii) 499.381   (iv) 499.993
5. approximately £1.84 × 10¹⁷
6. (i) 88 574   (ii) 15.6244   7. (i) 10.2 cm   (ii) 104.9 m

Exercise 8(f)

1. Series (i), (iii) and (iv) converge
2. (i) $41\frac{2}{3}$ (ii) 100   (iii) $2\frac{1}{4}$ (iv) 110
   (v) $36\frac{4}{7}$ (vi) $1\frac{1}{8}$ 3. 0.8
4. (i) $\mathrm{cosec}^2\,\theta$ (ii) $\cos^2\theta$, valid for $0 < \theta < 45°$, $135° < \theta < 180°$
5. $r = \frac{1}{3}$ or $\frac{2}{3}$, $a = 18$ or 9   6. $r = \pm\frac{3}{4}$; 4, 3 or 28, −21
7. $ar/(1 - r^2)$, 36   9. 4.4 m

Exercise 8(g)

1. (i) $1 + \frac{1}{2} + \frac{1}{3} + \frac{1}{4} + \frac{1}{5} + \frac{1}{6}$
   (ii) $11 + 14 + 17 + 20 + 23 + 26$
   (iii) $2 + 4 + 8 + 16 + 32$
   (iv) $35 + 48 + 63 + 80 + 99 + 120$
   (v) $108 + 72 + 54 + 36 + 24 + 16 + 10\frac{2}{3}$
   (vi) $\frac{1}{4} - \frac{1}{9} + \frac{1}{16} - \frac{1}{25} + \frac{1}{36}$

2. (i) 120   (ii) 840   (iii) 127   (iv) 4   (v) $\frac{3}{2}(3^n - 1)$ (vi) $\frac{1}{2}an(n+1)$

3. (i) $\sum_{r=1}^{6} r^3$ (ii) $\sum_{r=1}^{10} 2r$ (iii) $\sum_{r=1}^{10} \frac{1}{r^2}$ (iv) $\sum_{r=1}^{9} \frac{r}{r+1}$

(v) $\sum_{r=1}^{14} (3r - 2)$ (vi) $\sum_{r=0}^{\infty} 54(\frac{2}{3})^r$

4. (i) $23 - 3r$ (ii) $r \cdot x^{r-1}$ (iii) $\frac{60}{r}$ (iv) 2^{r-1}

(v) $r \cdot 10^{-r}$ (vi) $-\frac{16}{3}(-\frac{3}{2})^r$

5. (ii) 14   (iii) 12

Exercise 8(h)

1. (i) 650   (ii) 6084   2. 34 370   3. 42 075
4. (i) $n(n+1)$ (ii) $2n^2(n+1)^2$ (iii) n^2 (iv) $n(n+1)^2$
5. (i) 1360   (ii) 5456   (iii) 22 075   (iv) 3850

Exercise 9(a)

1. (i) $3x^2 + c$ (ii) $2x^3 + c$ (iii) $2x^2 - 5x + c$
   (iv) $x^4 - 4x^2 + c$ (v) $x + \frac{1}{2}x^2 + \frac{1}{3}x^3 + c$ (vi) $\frac{1}{2}x^4 + \frac{1}{x} + 3x + c$
2. $y = \frac{3}{2}x^2 - x^3 + c$ 3. $y = \frac{2}{3}x^3 + \frac{1}{2}x^2 - x$
4. $y = \frac{1}{4}x^4 - x^2 - 1\frac{1}{4}$ 5. $y = \frac{1}{3}x^3 - 2x - \frac{1}{x} + 1\frac{1}{3}$
6. $y = \frac{1}{3}x^3 - 5x + 2$ 7. $\frac{1}{3}x^3, \frac{1}{4}x^4, \frac{1}{5}x^5, \frac{1}{9}x^9, \frac{1}{n+1} \cdot x^{n+1}$

8. $\frac{1}{x}, -\frac{1}{x}, \frac{1}{x^2}, -\frac{1}{2x^2}$, yes

Exercise 9(b)

1. (i) $x - x^2 + x^3 + c$ (ii) $\frac{1}{2}x^4 + 2x^3 + \frac{1}{2}x^2 + c$
   (iii) $\frac{1}{7}x^7 + \frac{1}{3}x^6 + c$ (iv) $\frac{5}{2}x^2 + \frac{4}{x} + c$
   (v) $\frac{1}{5}x^5 - \frac{2}{3}x^3 + 3x + c$ (vi) $-\frac{1}{2x^2} - \frac{2}{x} + c$
2. (i) $x - x^2 + \frac{1}{3}x^3 + c$ (ii) $\frac{1}{4}x^4 + x^3 - x^2 - 6x + c$
   (iii) $\frac{1}{2}x^2 + \frac{3}{x} + c$ (iv) $\frac{2}{3}x^3 - 5x - \frac{1}{x} + c$
   (v) $\frac{1}{4}x^4 + \frac{4}{3}x^3 + 2x^2 + c$ (vi) $3x^2 - 4x - \frac{3}{x} + \frac{1}{x^2} + c$
3. (i) $t^3 + 3t^2 + c$ (ii) $s - \frac{4}{s} + c$
   (iii) $ax + \frac{1}{2}x^2 + x + c$ (iv) $\frac{1}{2}a^2 + ax + a + c$
   (v) $\frac{1}{3}ax^3 + \frac{1}{2}bx^2 + cx + d$ (vi) $x^2y + xy^2 + \frac{1}{3}y^3 + c$
4. (i) $\frac{1}{13}x^{13}$ (ii) $-\frac{1}{3x^3}$ (iii) $-\frac{1}{5x^5}$ (iv) $\frac{2}{5}x^{\frac{5}{2}}$ (v) $\frac{2}{3}x^{\frac{3}{2}}$ (vi) $2x^{\frac{1}{2}}$

Exercise 9(c)

1. (i) $2\frac{2}{3}$ (ii) 9   (iii) $6\frac{1}{3}$ 2. (i) 78   (ii) -12 (iii) 90
3. (i) 60   (ii) $41\frac{1}{2}$ (iii) $21\frac{1}{3}$ (iv) 24   4. $1\frac{1}{3}$
5. 33   6. $6\frac{3}{4}$

Exercise 9(d)

1. (i) 20 (ii) 4 (iii) 15 (iv) $37\frac{1}{3}$ 2. (i) $27\frac{1}{2}$ (ii) $10\frac{1}{12}$ (iii) 9 (iv) $12\frac{2}{3}$
3. (i) 32   (ii) $20\frac{5}{6}$ 4. $y = 10 + 3x - x^2$, $57\frac{1}{6}$
5. $11\frac{1}{4}$

Exercise 9(e)

1. $1\frac{1}{3}$ 2. $\frac{4}{27}$ 3. $4\frac{1}{2}$ 4. $21\frac{1}{3}$
5. $11\frac{1}{4}$, 4   6. $5:32$ 7. $5\frac{5}{24}$ 8. $\frac{1}{12}$, $1\frac{1}{3}$
9. $2\frac{2}{3}$

Exercise 9(f)

1. (i) 3 (ii) 10   2. (i) 1 (ii) $1\frac{1}{3}$ (iii) $2\frac{1}{3}$ (iv) 2
3. (i) $\frac{1}{4}$ (ii) 6 (iii) -24 (iv) $4\frac{5}{6}$ 4. (i) 7 (ii) 52

Exercise 9(g)

1. 8π 2. (i) $32\pi/5$ (ii) 6π (iii) 63π (iv) 48π
   (v) $68\pi/3$ (vi) $47\frac{11}{30}\pi$
3. (i) 10π (ii) $14\pi/3$ 4. $5:4$ 5. $16\pi/15$
7. $22\frac{2}{5}\pi$ 8. 24π 9. $32:15$

Exercise 10(a)

1. (i) $(\sqrt{3}-1)/2\sqrt{2}$ (ii) $(1+\sqrt{3})/2\sqrt{2}$
2. $77/85$, $36/85$, $77/36$ 3. $13/14$, $-3\sqrt{3}/14$
4. (i) 1   (ii) $1/\sqrt{2}$ (iii) $\sqrt{3}/2$ (iv) $\frac{1}{2}$
5. (i) $\cos x$ (ii) $-\cos x$ 6. $24/25$, $7/25$, $24/7$
7. (i) $56/65$, $33/65$ (ii) $323/325$, $-36/325$

Exercise 10(b)

1. (i) $(\sqrt{3}-1)/2\sqrt{2}$ (ii) $(\sqrt{3}+1)/2\sqrt{2}$ 2. $7\sqrt{5}/27$, $22/27$, $7\sqrt{5}/22$
3. $-13/85$, $85/84$, $-84/13$ 4. $\frac{1}{3}$, $R = 2S$
5. (i) $\cos x$ (ii) $-\cos x$ 11. $45°$, $225°$

Exercise 10(c)

1. $19/17$, $23/11$ 3. $(1+\sqrt{3})/(1-\sqrt{3})$ 4. $12/5$, $-46/9$ 5. $\frac{1}{5}$
7. (i) $\sqrt{3}$ (ii) $1/\sqrt{3}$ 8. (i) $1/3$ (ii) $7/6$ (iii) $9/7$

Exercise 10(d)

1. (i) $\sin 20°$ (ii) $\cos 80°$ (iii) $\frac{1}{2}\sin 2x$ (iv) $\cos 6\theta$
2. $40/9$, $-236/115$ 3. (i) $31/49$ (ii) $-17/25$
4. $15/17$, $-8/17$, $-15/8$ 5. (i) $24/25$, $7/25$ (ii) $117/125$, $-44/125$
6. $2/\sqrt{5}$, $\frac{1}{2}$ 7. $1/\sqrt{26}$, $1/5$, $37/55$

Exercise 10(e)

6. $30°$, $90°$, $150°$, $270°$ 7. $60°$, $180°$, $300°$
8. $0°$, $76.0°$, $180°$, $256.0°$ 9. $26.6°$, $153.4°$, $206.6°$, $333.4°$
10. $48.6°$, $131.4°$, $270°$ 11. $0°$, $109.5°$, $250.5°$
12. $26.6°$, $153.4°$, $206.6°$, $333.4°$ 13. $0°$, $40.9°$, $139.1°$, $180°$, $220.9°$, $319.1°$
14. $45°$, $90°$, $135°$, $270°$ 15. $30°$, $150°$, $180°$

Exercise 11(a)

1. (i) $1 + 7x + 21x^2 + 35x^3 + 35x^4 + 21x^5 + 7x^6 + x^7$
   (ii) $1 + 8x + 28x^2 + 56x^3 + 70x^4 + 56x^5 + 28x^6 + 8x^7 + x^8$
2. (i) $1 + 3x + 3x^2 + x^3$, $1 - 3x + 3x^2 - x^3$
   (ii) $1 \pm 6x + 15x^2 \pm 20x^3 + 15x^4 \pm 6x^5 + x^6$
3. (i) $1 + 8a + 24a^2 + 32a^3 + 16a^4$
   (ii) $1 - 9b + 27b^2 - 27b^3$
   (iii) $1 - 20x + 160x^2 - 640x^3 + 1280x^4 - 1024x^5$
   (iv) $1 + 12y + 60y^2 + 160y^3 + 240y^4 + 192y^5 + 64y^6$
   (v) $1 + a + a^2/3 + a^3/27$
   (vi) $1 - 5b/2 + 5b^2/2 - 5b^3/4 + 5b^4/16 - b^5/32$
4. (i) $1 + 30r + 375r^2 + 2500r^3$
   (ii) $1 + 4s + 7s^2 + 7s^3$
   (iii) $1 - 30a + 360a^2 - 2160a^3$
   (iv) $1 - 0.7b + 0.21b^2 - 0.035b^3$
5. (i) 10 (ii) -35 (iii) 108 (iv) $3/125$
6. (i) $1 + 3x^2 + 3x^4 + x^6$ (ii) $1 - 4x^2 + 6x^4 - 4x^6 + x^8$
7. (ii) $41 - 29\sqrt{2}$

Exercise 11(b)

1. (i) $a^6 + 6a^5b + 15a^4b^2 + 20a^3b^3 + 15a^2b^4 + 6ab^5 + b^6$
   (ii) $a^7 + 7a^6b + 21a^5b^2 + 35a^4b^3 + 35a^3b^4 + 21a^2b^5 + 7ab^6 + b^7$
   (iii) $a^3 - 3a^2b + 3ab^2 - b^3$ (iv) $a^4 - 4a^3b + 6a^2b^2 - 4ab^3 + b^4$
2. (i) $a^3 + 6a^2b + 12ab^2 + 8b^3$
   (ii) $81x^4 - 108x^3y + 54x^2y^2 - 12xy^3 + y^4$
   (iii) $32 + 240p + 720p^2 + 1080p^3 + 810p^4 + 243p^5$
   (iv) $27r^3 - 108r^2s + 144rs^2 - 64s^3$
   (v) $64r^6 - 96r^5s + 60r^4s^2 - 20r^3s^3 + 15r^2s^4/4 - 3rs^5/8 + s^6/64$

(vi) $128q^7 - 448q^6 + 672q^5 - 560q^4 + 280q^3 - 84q^2 + 14q - 1$
(vii) $x^4 + 4x^2 + 6 + 4/x^2 + 1/x^4$
(viii) $x^{10} - 5x^7 + 10x^4 - 10x + 5/x^2 - 1/x^5$

3. (i) 240   (ii) −20   (iii) 720   (iv) 2835   4. (i) 24   (ii) 15
5. (i) $1 + 6x + 21x^2 + 50x^3$ (ii) $16 + 32x - 8x^2 - 40x^3$

Exercise 11(c)

2. (i) $1 - 10x + 45x^2 - 120x^3$ (ii) $a^8 + 8a^7b + 28a^6b^2 + 56a^5b^3$
3. $1 + 9x + 36x^2 + 84x^3 + 126x^4 + \ldots$, 1.09369
4. $1 - 13x + 78x^2 - 286x^3 + 715x^4 - \ldots$, 0.87752
5. (i) $1 - 27b + 324b^2 - 2268b^3$
   (ii) $1 + 6x + 33x^2/2 + 55x^3/2$
   (iii) $a^{14} + 28a^{13}b + 364a^{12}b^2 + 2912a^{11}b^3$
   (iv) $x^{20} - 20x^{18} + 190x^{16} - 1140x^{14}$
6. (i) 560, 4368   (ii) $\frac{55}{4}, \frac{165}{8}$ 7. (i) $55a^8b^4/9$ (ii) $-1001x^5$
8. $1 + 15x + 102x^2 + 408x^3 + \ldots$

Exercise 11(d)

1. (i) $1 + x/2 - x^2/8 + x^3/16 - 5x^4/128$
   (ii) $1 - x + x^2 - x^3 + x^4$
   (iii) $1 + 5x/2 + 15x^2/8 + 5x^3/16 - 5x^4/128$
   (iv) $1 - 3x + 6x^2 - 10x^3 + 15x^4$
   (v) $1 + 4x + 10x^2 + 20x^3 + 35x^4$
   (vi) $1 + x/3 + 2x^2/9 + 14x^3/81 + 35x^4/243$
3. (i) $1 - 2x/3 - x^2/9 - 4x^3/81$
   (ii) $1 - 2x + 5x^2/2 - 5x^3/2$
   (iii) $1 + x - 3x^2/2 + 7x^3/2$
   (iv) $1 + 3x + 9x^2 + 27x^3$
   (v) $1 - 6x + 24x^2 - 80x^3$
   (vi) $1 - x^2/2 + 3x^4/8 - 5x^6/16$
4. (i) $1 - x - 4x^2 - 6x^3$
   (ii) $1 + 3x + 8x^2 + 20x^3$

Exercise 11(e)

1. (i) $-1 < x < 1$ (ii) $-2 < x < 2$ (iii) $-\frac{1}{4} < x < \frac{1}{4}$
   (iv) $-\frac{1}{3} < x < \frac{1}{3}$ (v) $-\frac{1}{2} < x < \frac{1}{2}$ (vi) $-1 < x < 1$
2. (i) $-\frac{1}{4} < x < \frac{1}{4}$ (ii) $-\frac{1}{2} < x < \frac{1}{2}$
3. $1 + 2x + 3x^2 + 4x^3 + \ldots$, 1.0060271
4. (i) 1.0392(3)   (ii) 5.1962   (iii) 10.0995
5. $1 + x - x^2 + \frac{5}{3}x^3 - \ldots$ (i) 1.0196   (ii) 2.0198
6. $1 - \frac{1}{2}x - \frac{1}{8}x^2 - \frac{1}{16}x^3 - \ldots$ (i) 1.4142   (ii) 3.3166
7. (i) $1 - \frac{1}{4}x^2 - \frac{1}{4}x^3 \ (-2 < x < 2)$
   (ii) $2 - 3x + 10x^2 - 34x^3 \ (-\frac{1}{4} < x < \frac{1}{4})$
8. 7.1414

Exercise 12(a)

1. Powers of 10 are
   (i) 1.5682, 2.3316, 0.6928, 3.7199, 0.2625, 1.9989
   (ii) -0.0757, -1.2832, -3.0605, -0.9702, -0.6021, -1.6990
2. (i) 50.12, 347.5, 4.92, 133400, 1.202
   (ii) 0.00794, 0.0851, 0.189, 0.993, 0.0000204
3. (i) 0.7185, 1.7185, 2.7185, 3.7185
   (ii) 0.5403, 2.5403, 4.5403, 6.5403
   (iii) 1.2000, 0.2000, -0.8000, -1.8000
6. (i) 2471   (ii) 0.9376   (iii) 7.987   (iv) 3.996   (v) 12.06
   (vi) 5.623   (vii) 0.8383   (viii) 1.561

Exercise 12(b)

1. (i) 4   (ii) 6   (iii) -2 (iv) $\frac{1}{2}$ (v) -3
2. (i) 2   (ii) 3   (iii) -1 (iv) $\frac{1}{4}$ (v) $-1\frac{1}{2}$
3. (i) 3   (ii) 5   (iii) 0   (iv) -4 (v) $1\frac{1}{2}$
4. (i) 2   (ii) 3   (iii) 4   (iv) 7   (v) -3 (vi) 2
   (vii) $\frac{1}{2}$ (viii) $-\frac{1}{2}$ (ix) $\frac{2}{3}$
5. (i) 2 and $\frac{1}{2}$ (ii) 3 and $\frac{1}{3}$ (iii) $1\frac{1}{2}$ and $\frac{2}{3}$
6. (i) 8   (ii) $\frac{1}{9}$ (iii) 49   (iv) 3   (v) 32   (vi) $\sqrt{2}$
   (vii) 4   (viii) -4 (ix) 4

7. 16   8. (ii) 625, 5, $\sqrt{5}$

Exercise 12(c)

1. (i) $\log 30$ (ii) $\log 36$ (iii) $\log 5$ (iv) $\log 4$ (v) $\log 8$
   (vi) $\log 8$ (vii) $\log 20$ (viii) $\log 2$
2. (i) $\log a + \log b + \log c$ (ii) $\log a + \log b - \log c$ (iii) $\frac{1}{3}\log a$
   (iv) $\log a + 3\log b$ (v) $\frac{1}{2}\log b - \frac{1}{2}\log c$ (vi) $-\log c$
3. (i) $\log_2 21$ (ii) $\log_5 8$ (iii) $\log 16$ (iv) $\log_2 5$ (v) $\log 3$
   (vi) $\log_3 10$ (vii) $\log_{10} 2$ (viii) $\log 12$
4. (i) $\log a = 3\log b$ (ii) $\log a = 2\log b - \log c$
   (iii) $\log a + \log b + \log c = 0$ (iv) $\log a = \frac{1}{2}\log b + \frac{1}{2}\log c$
   (v) $\log a = -\log b$ (vi) $\log a = c\log b$
5. 1.1761, 1.3980, 1.6532, 1.8751, 0.8751, -0.4771, -0.2219, 0.2552
6. 0.60206, 0.90309, 1.30103, 0.69897, 1.39794, 0.39794, 0.09691, 0.20412
7. (i) 2   (ii) 2   (iii) 1   (iv) 0   (v) $\log(x-1)$ (vi) $2\log a$
   (vii) 0   (viii) $2\frac{1}{2}$
8. (i) $2b$ (ii) $b+1$ (iii) $\frac{1}{2}b$ (iv) $2-2b$
9. 0.301, 1.204, 1.505, 1.398, 0.699, 2.097, 1.903
10. (i) $x=2$, $y=4$ (ii) $x=3$, $y=\frac{1}{3}$ or $x=6$, $y=1\frac{1}{3}$
11. 0.23855, -0.06245, -0.3010, -0.1505

Exercise 12(d)

1. (i) £2750   (ii) £3025   (iii) £3327.50   (iv) £3660.25

2. (i) £1554   (ii) £2013   (iii) £2841   3. 14   4. £93.40
5. (i) £5041   (ii) £5081   6. £759.19, £905.35   7. (i) 7   (ii) 10
8. (i) £11 790   (ii) £11 559   (iii) £11 304.90   (iv) £10 718
9. (i) £611   (ii) £803   (iii) £765   10. £2260

Exercise 12(e)

1. (i) 1.29   (ii) 2.67   (iii) 1.18   (iv) -4.42
2. (i) 2 or -1 (ii) 0.602   (iii) 0 or 0.631
3. (i) 2.807   (ii) 1.585   (iii) 0.693   (iv) 1.626   4. 3, 4, 2; $\frac{1}{3}, \frac{1}{4}, \frac{1}{2}$
5. 1.43, 0.43, 2.33   6. 2 or $\sqrt{2}$ 7. 1.66, 0.301, 3.32, 1.11, 2.22
8. 2.008   9. yz 10. $\frac{1}{r} + \frac{1}{s}$ or $\frac{r+s}{rs}, \frac{rs}{r+s}$

Exercise 12(f)

1. $a = 4, n = 1\frac{1}{2}$ 2. $H \approx 300/r^2$ 3. $y \approx 5(1.2)^x$ 4. $m \approx 500(0.8)^t$
5. $P = 0.2d^{1.5}$, 1425×10^6 km   6. $k = 0.04, n = 3$

Exercise 13(a)

1. (i) ± 3.16 (ii) $32°, 290°$ 2. (i) ± 1.41 (ii) $20°, 250°$

Exercise 13(b)

1. $\sqrt{2} \sin(x - 45°)$, $+\sqrt{2}$ at $x = 135°$, $-\sqrt{2}$ at $x = 315°$
2. (i) $\sqrt{5} \sin(x + 26.6°)$, $\sqrt{5}$ at $x = 63.4°$
   (ii) $5 \sin(x + 36.9°)$, 5 at $x = 53.1°$
3. (i) $\sqrt{17} \cos(x + 14.0°)$, $-\sqrt{17}$ at $x = 166.0°$
   (ii) $2 \cos(x + 60°)$, -2 at $x = 120°$
4. $\sqrt{29} \cos(x - 68.2°)$, $158.2°$ and $338.2°$
5. (i) ± 13 (ii) $\pm \sqrt{2}$ (iii) ± 3 (iv) $\pm 5\sqrt{2}$

Exercise 13(c)

1. (i) $32.4°, 290.8°$ (ii) $19.9°, 250.1°$
2. (i) $119.5°, 346.7°$ (ii) $116.9°, 341.3°$
   (iii) $204.6°, 351.7°$ (iv) $0°, 90°, 180°, 323.2°, 360°$
3. (i) $114.3°, 335.7°$ (ii) $74.3°, 167.7°$
   (iii) $67.4°, 180°$ (iv) $23.2°, 45°, 203.2°, 225°$
4. (i) $40.4°, 117.0°$ (ii) $40.4° < x < 117°$ 5. $83.1° < x < 203.1°$
6. (i) $30°, 210°$ (ii) $120°, 300°$ (iii) $150°, 270°$;
   $120° < x < 150°$ and $270° < x < 300°$

Exercise 13(d)

1. (i) $2 \sin 25° \cos 5°$ (ii) $2 \cos 45° \cos 20°$
   (iii) $2 \cos 3A \sin A$ (iv) $-2 \sin 4A \sin A$

(v) $2 \cos \frac{5}{2}B \cos \frac{1}{2}B$ (vi) $-2 \cos 4B \sin 2B$

(vii) $2 \sin(\alpha + \beta) \cos(\alpha - \beta)$ (viii) $2 \cos \alpha \cos \beta$

2. (i) $(\sqrt{3} - 1)/2\sqrt{2}$ (ii) $(\sqrt{3} + 1)/2\sqrt{2}$

3. (i) $2 \cos x$ (ii) $\tan \frac{1}{2}\theta$ (iii) $\cot \frac{1}{2}B$ (iv) $2 \sin \phi$

7. (i) $30°, 90°, 150°$ (ii) $0°, 22\frac{1}{2}°, 67\frac{1}{2}°, 112\frac{1}{2}°, 157\frac{1}{2}°, 180°$

   (iii) $0°, 120°, 180°$ (iv) $15°, 75°, 90°$

8. (i) $0°, 90°, 120°, 180°$ (ii) $30°, 60°, 90°, 120°, 150°$

10. (ii) $\cos 5A = 16 \cos^5 A - 20 \cos^3 A + 5 \cos A$

Exercise 13(e)

1. (i) $30°, 120°, 270°, 720°, 22\frac{1}{2}°, 126°$ (ii) $114.6°, 85.9°, 19.1°, 36.1°$

2. (i) $\frac{1}{4}\pi, \frac{3}{4}\pi, \frac{1}{3}\pi, \frac{1}{12}\pi, \frac{1}{5}\pi, \frac{5}{9}\pi$ (ii) $0.145, 1.34, 1.90, 3.71$

3. $\frac{1}{2}, 1, -\frac{1}{2}, -1, \sqrt{3}, -1$

4. $0.9659, 0.5878, -0.8391, 0.5646, -0.2272, -1.7098$

5. (i) 12.2 cm, 61 cm^2 (ii) 4.8 cm, 14.4 cm^2

6. 8 cm, 56 cm^2 7. 54 cm^2, 11.1 cm   8. 4.8 cm, 1.042^r, $59.7°$

9. 10.85 cm^2, 8.75 cm^2 10. 1.35^r, 20.8 cm   11. 47.75, 2 ms^{-1}

12. (i) 12 cm   (ii) 96 cm^2 (iii) 1.287^r; 32.7 cm^2, 25.7 cm

Exercise 13(f)

2. $1, 1, 3, 2, 0$

Exercise 14(b)

1. (i) $3 \cos x$ (ii) $2 \sec^2 x$ (iii) $-\frac{1}{2} \sin x$

   (iv) $\cos x + \sin x$ (v) $1 - 5 \sec^2 x$ (vi) $-3 \sin x - 2 \cos x$

   (vii) $\frac{2}{3} \cos x + \frac{1}{3} \sec^2 x$ (viii) $\sec^2 x$ (ix) $-\sec^2 x$

2. (i) $1, \frac{1}{2}$ (ii) $-\frac{1}{2}\sqrt{3}, 0$ (iii) $2, 4$ (iv) 3 (v) $2\frac{1}{3}$ (vi) 2

3. (i) $-5 \sin \theta, -5 \cos \theta$

   (ii) $3 \cos \theta + 4 \sin \theta, -3 \sin \theta + 4 \cos \theta$

   (iii) $-\sin \theta - \cos \theta, -\cos \theta + \sin \theta$

4. (i) $3\pi/2$ (ii) $\pi/3, 2\pi/3, 4\pi/3, 5\pi/3$ (iii) $1.37^r, 4.91^r$ (iv) $0.41^r, 2.73^r$

5. min. $(\frac{1}{3}\pi, \frac{1}{3}\pi - \sqrt{3})$, max. $(\frac{5}{3}\pi, \frac{5}{3}\pi + \sqrt{3})$

6. (i) $\sqrt{5}$ at $x = 1.11$ (ii) $\sqrt{34}$ at $x = 5.74$

8. max. $(\frac{1}{4}\pi, \frac{1}{2}\pi - 1)$, min. $(\frac{3}{4}\pi, \frac{3}{2}\pi + 1)$

Exercise 14(c)

1. (i) $-4 \cos x + c$ (ii) $\frac{1}{3} \sin x + c$

   (iii) $2 \tan x + c$ (iv) $-3 \cos x - 2 \sin x + c$

   (v) $\frac{1}{2}x^2 - 5 \cos x + c$ (vi) $\frac{1}{2} \sin x + \frac{1}{2} \cos x + c$

   (vii) $-\cos x + c$ (viii) $-\cos x + \sin x + c$

   (ix) $\frac{1}{2} \tan x + c$

2. (i) $\frac{1}{2}$ (ii) $2\sqrt{2} - 1$ (iii) $\frac{1}{3}\pi + 1$ (iv) $\sqrt{3}$

3. (i) $\pi + 1$ (ii) $3\sqrt{2}$ 4. (i) π (ii) $2\pi(\sqrt{3} - 1)$ (iii) $\pi(1 - \frac{1}{4}\pi)$

5. (i) $2/\pi$ (ii) $(\pi + 4)/\pi$ (iii) $3/\pi$

Exercise 14(d)

1. (i) $8x(x^2+3)^3$ (ii) $-21(1-3x)^6$
   (iii) $3(x-5)^2$ (iv) $2(3x^2-1)(x^3-x)$
   (v) $3\cos x(1+\sin x)^2$ (vi) $2(1+\sin x)(x-\cos x)$
2. (i) $-4/(2x+1)^3$ (ii) $-3/(3x-5)^2$
   (iii) $12/(1-4x)^4$ (iv) $1/(2x+1)^{\frac{1}{2}}$
   (v) $2x/(3x^2-2)^{\frac{2}{3}}$ (vi) $-2/(4x-1)^{1\frac{1}{2}}$
3. (i) $3\cos 3x$ (ii) $2\sec^2 2x$
   (iii) $-\frac{1}{2}\sin\frac{1}{2}x$ (iv) $-5\sin 5x$
   (v) $4\cos 4x + 2\sin 2x$ (vi) $6\cos 2x$
   (vii) $2\sec^2 4x$ (viii) $3\cos\frac{1}{2}x$
   (ix) $-6\sin 3x + 3\sin x$
4. (i) 54 (ii) $-\frac{2}{9}$ (iii) 4 (iv) $2\frac{1}{2}$
5. $2\cos 2x + 2\sin x$ 6. $\min(\frac{1}{6}\pi, \frac{1}{6}\pi - \frac{1}{2}\sqrt{3})$, $\max(\frac{5}{6}\pi, \frac{5}{6}\pi + \frac{1}{2}\sqrt{3})$
7. $27y + 2x = 13$ 8. $r=1$ (min) at $\frac{1}{2}\pi$, $r=1\frac{1}{2}$ (max) at $\frac{1}{6}\pi, \frac{5}{6}\pi$

Exercise 14(e)

1. (i) $-2\cos x.\sin x$ (ii) $3\sin^2 x.\cos x$
   (iii) $2\tan x.\sec^2 x$ (iv) $5\sin^4 x.\cos x$
   (v) $-2\cos^3 x.\sin x$ (vi) $6\sin x.\cos x$
   (vii) $-\sin(x+\frac{1}{2}\pi)$ (viii) $2\cos(2x-\alpha)$
   (ix) $\frac{1}{2}\sec^2(\frac{1}{2}x+\frac{1}{4}\pi)$
2. (i) $4\sin 2x.\cos 2x$ (ii) $-\cos\frac{1}{2}x.\sin\frac{1}{2}x$
   (iii) $12\tan^2 4x.\sec^2 4x$ (iv) $-2\cos(x-\alpha).\sin(x-\alpha)$
   (v) $24\sin^3 3x.\cos 3x$ (vi) $1\frac{1}{2}\tan\frac{1}{4}x.\sec^2\frac{1}{4}x$
   (vii) $5\sin(\frac{1}{2}x-\alpha).\cos(\frac{1}{2}-\alpha)$ (viii) $\dfrac{\cos x}{2\sqrt{\sin x}}$

   (ix) $\dfrac{\sec^2 x}{2\sqrt{\tan x}}$
3. $9\sin^2 x.\cos x - 3\cos x$ 6. $2\sec^2 x(1+3\tan^2 x)$
7. $0, \frac{1}{4}\pi, \frac{1}{2}\pi, \pi, \frac{5}{4}\pi, \frac{3}{2}\pi, 2\pi$
8. max. $(\frac{1}{6}\pi, \frac{1}{4})$, min. $(\frac{1}{2}\pi, 0)$, max. $(\frac{5}{6}\pi, \frac{1}{4})$, min. $(\frac{3}{2}\pi, -2)$

Exercise 14(f)

1. (i) $\frac{1}{2}\sin 2x + c$ (ii) $-\frac{1}{3}\cos 3x + c$
   (iii) $2\sin\frac{1}{2}x + c$ (iv) $\frac{1}{4}\tan 4x + c$
   (v) $-\frac{1}{2}\cos 4x + c$ (vi) $8\tan\frac{1}{2}x + c$
   (vii) $-\frac{3}{2}\cos\frac{1}{3}x + c$ (viii) $-\frac{1}{2}\cos(2x-\frac{1}{2}\pi) + c$
   (ix) $\frac{1}{10}\sin(5x+1) + c$
2. (i) $\frac{1}{2}\sqrt{3}$ (ii) $\pi + \frac{3}{2}\sqrt{3}$ (iii) $\sqrt{2}$ (iv) $R(1-\cos 2\alpha)$
3. $\frac{3}{4}\pi + \frac{1}{2}$ 4. $\frac{1}{6}\pi(3\sqrt{3}-\pi)$
5. (i) $\frac{3}{4}\sqrt{3}-1$ (ii) $\frac{3}{2}-\frac{3}{4}\sqrt{3}$
6. (i) $-\frac{1}{4}\cos 4x - \frac{1}{2}\cos 2x + c$ (ii) $-\frac{1}{4}\cos 2x - \frac{1}{2}\cos x + c$
7. (i) $\frac{2}{5}\sin 5x + 2\sin x + c$ (ii) $\frac{1}{6}\sin 3x - \frac{1}{14}\sin 7x + c$

Exercise 14(g)

1. (i) $\frac{1}{4}\sin^4 x + c$ (ii) $-\frac{1}{3}\cos^3 x + c$
   (iii) $\frac{1}{2}\sin^2 x$ or $-\frac{1}{2}\cos^2 x$ or $-\frac{1}{4}\cos 2x$ (iv) $\frac{1}{9}\sin^3 3x + c$
2. (i) $\frac{1}{2}x + \frac{1}{4}\sin 2x + c$ (ii) $-\cos x + \frac{1}{3}\cos^3 x + c$
   (iii) $\frac{1}{2}x - \frac{1}{2}\sin x + c$ (iv) $\frac{1}{2}\sin 2x - \frac{1}{6}\sin^3 2x + c$
3. $\frac{1}{2}$, $1/\sqrt{2}$ 4. $\frac{1}{8}\pi(\pi + 2)$
5. (i) $x + c$ (ii) $\frac{1}{2}\sin 2x + c$ (iii) $\frac{1}{3}(1 + \sin x)^3 + c$
   (iv) $\frac{3}{2}x - 2\cos x - \frac{1}{4}\sin 2x + c$ (v) $-\frac{1}{2}\cos^4 x + c$
   (vi) $\frac{2}{3}(\sin x)^{\frac{3}{2}} + c$ (vii) $\frac{1}{8}x - \frac{1}{32}\sin 4x + c$ (viii) $\frac{1}{3}\sin^3 x - \frac{1}{5}\sin^5 x + c$

Exercise 15(a)

1. (i) $x > 3$ (ii) $x > \frac{1}{2}$ (iii) $x \leqslant 2$ (iv) $x > -3\frac{1}{2}$
2. (i) $0 < x < 4$ (ii) $x < -5, x > 4$
   (iii) $x \leqslant -\frac{1}{3}, x \geqslant 2$ (iv) $-2 \leqslant x \leqslant 1\frac{1}{2}$
   (v) $-\frac{3}{4} < x < 1$ (vi) $x < -3, x > -1$
3. (i) $x < -\frac{1}{2}, 0 < x < \frac{1}{2}$ (ii) $x = 0, x \geqslant 3$
   (iii) $-2 \leqslant x \leqslant -1, x \geqslant 3$ (iv) $x < -1, -\frac{1}{2} < x < 1$
4. (i) 2, 8   (ii) 6, 24   (iii) 2, $\frac{1}{4}$
6. (i) $x < -2, x > 1\frac{1}{3}$ (ii) $-\frac{1}{5} < x < 1$
   (iii) $-10 < x < -2$ (iv) $2 < |x| < \sqrt{14}$
   (v) $|x| > 2$ (vi) $x < -1, x > 3$
7. $x < \frac{1}{4}, x > 1\frac{1}{2}$

Exercise 15(b)

1. $-\frac{1}{2} < x < 0, x > 3$ 2. $x < 3, x > 4$ 3. $-\frac{1}{2} \leqslant x < 4$
4. $x < -\frac{2}{3}, 0 < x < 1$ 5. $-2 < x < 1, x > 2$ 6. $x \leqslant -1, x = 2$
7. $0 < x < 2$ 8. $\frac{3}{4} < x < 1\frac{1}{2}$ 9. $2 < x < 4\frac{2}{3}$
10. $x < 0, 2 < x < 4$ 11. $0° < x < 30°, 150° < x < 180°$
12. $45° < x < 90°, 180° < x < 225°, 270° < x < 360°$

Exercise 15(c)

1. $x < -3, -3 < x < 0$ 2. $x < 0$ and $x > 1$
3. $-2 < x < \frac{1}{2}$ and $x > 2$ 5. $0 < f(x) \leqslant 1$

Exercise 15(d)

1. $-4 < f(x) < 0$ 2. $\frac{1}{6} < f(x) \leqslant 1$
3. $f(x) < 1$ 4. $0 < f(x) \leqslant 1$
5. (i) $f(x) \leqslant 1, f(x) \geqslant 4$ 7. $f(x) \leqslant -9, f(x) \geqslant -1$

Exercise 15(e)

1. (i) equilateral triangle, $3\sqrt{3}$ (ii) parallelogram, $18\sqrt{3}$

3. $(0, 3)$, $(2, 2\sqrt{3})$, $(\sqrt{2}, -\sqrt{2})$, $(-5, 0)$, $(-1\frac{1}{2}, -\frac{1}{2}\sqrt{3})$, $(-4.16, 9.09)$
4. $(6, -\frac{1}{2}\pi)$, $(\sqrt{2}, \frac{1}{4}\pi)$, $(2, \pi)$, $(5, 0.927)$, $(13, -1.966)$, $(2, -\frac{1}{3}\pi)$

Exercise 15(f)

1. (i) $\theta = \alpha$ (ii) $r = 5\sec\theta$ (iii) $r = 4\cosec\theta$
2. (i) $r = 2a\cos\theta$ (ii) $r = 2a\sin\theta$ (iii) $4ar\cos\theta = r^2 + 3a^2$
3. (i) $r = 3\cosec\theta$ (ii) $\theta = \pm\frac{1}{2}\pi$
   (iii) $r = 2$ (iv) $r^2 = 4\sec 2\theta$
   (v) $r = 4a\cot\theta\cdot\cosec\theta$ (vi) $r = 6\sin\theta$
4. (i) $y = -x$ (ii) $x^2 + y^2 - 2y = 0$
   (iii) $(x^2 + y^2 - ax)^2 = a^2(x^2 + y^2)$ (iv) $xy = \frac{1}{2}$
   (v) $x^2y^2 + y^4 = a^2x^2$ (vi) $y^2 = 1 - 2x$
8. (iii) distances are 1.6, $\sqrt{5}$, $-c/\sqrt{a^2 + b^2}$ units

Exercise 16(a)

1. (i) $x^2\cos x + 2x\cdot\sin x$ (ii) $12x(3x - 1)^3 + (3x - 1)^4$
   (iii) $2\cos^2 x - 4x\cdot\cos x\cdot\sin x$ (iv) $(2 + 3x)/2\sqrt{1 + x}$
   (v) $\dfrac{2}{x^2}\cdot\sec^2 2x - \dfrac{2}{x^3}\cdot\tan 2x$ (vi) $2\sin x\cos^2 x - \sin^3 x$
2. (i) $x\cdot\sec^2 x + \tan x$ (ii) $3(2x - 3)^2(x + 1)^2 + 4(2x - 3)(x + 1)^3$
   (iii) $-(\sin x)/x - (\cos x)/x^2$ (iv) $2\cos 2x\cos 3x - 3\sin 2x\sin 3x$
   (v) $(2x^2 + x + 1)/\sqrt{1 + x^2}$ (vi) $3\cot x - 3x\cdot\cosec^2 x$
3. (i) $-\frac{1}{3}, \frac{5}{6}, 2$ (ii) 1   (iii) $\frac{1}{2}\pi, \frac{3}{2}\pi$ and $\pi/6, 5\pi/6, 7\pi/6, 11\pi/6$
4. (i) $(6x - x^3)\cos x - 6x^2\sin x$
   (ii) $2(2x + 1)^4 + 32x(2x + 1)^3 + 48x^2(2x + 1)^2$
   (iii) $-10\sin x\cos 3x - 6\cos x\sin 3x$
5. (i) $(\pi + 1)^2$ (ii) $-\frac{1}{2}\pi$ (iii) $-11/500$
6. inf. $(-1, 0)$, max $(1/5, 3456/3125)$, min $(1, 0)$

Exercise 16(b)

1. $6y\dfrac{dy}{dx}$, $6\dfrac{dy}{dx}$, $3y^2\dfrac{dy}{dx}$, $\dfrac{-2}{y^3}\cdot\dfrac{dy}{dx}$, $\sec^2 y\cdot\dfrac{dy}{dx}$,
   $2x\dfrac{dy}{dx} + 2y$, $x^2\dfrac{dy}{dx} + 2xy$, $\dfrac{1}{y} - \dfrac{x}{y^2}\cdot\dfrac{dy}{dx}$
2. (i) $4x/y$ (ii) $2x/(4y - 3)$ (iii) $(3y - 4x)/(2y - 3x)$
   (iv) $-y^2/x$ (v) $(1 - 2xy)/(x^2 + 2y)$ (vi) $2\sin x/3\cos y$
3. (i) $48/11$ (ii) -74 (iii) $-5/6, -7/6$
4. $x = -2$ and $x = 3$, $3y + 5x = 15$, $2y + 5x = -10$
5. $(1, 3)$ and $(-\frac{2}{5}, \frac{1}{5})$, $-3/2$ and $-13/11$

Exercise 16(c)

1. (i) $4/y - 16x^2/y^3$ (ii) $2/(4y - 3) - 16x^2/(4y - 3)^3$

2. (i) $-1, \frac{2}{3}$ (ii) $-\frac{2}{3}$ and $\frac{10}{27}$ at $(0, 2)$, $\frac{2}{3}$ and $-\frac{10}{27}$ at $(0, -1)$

3. (i) max. $(0, -2)$, min. $(0, 2)$ (ii) max. $(3, 3)$, min. $(3, -1\frac{1}{2})$

   (iii) max. $(1, 1)$, min. $(-1, -1)$ (iv) max. $(1, -2)$, min. $(-\frac{3}{5}, \frac{6}{5})$

Exercise 16(d)

1. (i) $15.7 \text{ cm}^2/\text{sec}$ (ii) $31.4 \text{ cm}^2/\text{sec}$
2. (i) $181 \text{ cm}^2/\text{sec}$ (ii) $1086 \text{ cm}^3/\text{sec}$
3. -0.125 cm/sec 4. 11.8 cm/sec
5. (i) 0.0477 cm/sec (ii) 0.144 cm/sec
6. (i) 0.106 cm/sec (ii) 0.075 cm/sec
7. $4\pi h^3/27 \text{ cm}^3$ (i) 0.318 cm/sec (ii) 1.273 cm/sec
8. 160 litres   (i) 1.25 cm/sec (ii) 0.625 cm/sec
9. 6.25 cm/sec 10. $12 \text{ cm}^2/\text{sec}$
11. (i) 1 cm/sec (ii) 2 cm/sec (iii) 4 cm/sec
12. (i) 1.6 cm/sec (ii) 2 cm/sec (iii) 2.5 cm/sec
14. (i) 4.90 mm/sec (ii) 0.10 mm/sec
15. (i) 6.4 cm/sec (ii) 40 cm/sec 16. 0.101 rad/sec

Exercise 16(e)

1. (i) $\dfrac{1-x^2}{(x^2+1)^2}$ (ii) $\dfrac{\cos x}{(1+\sin x)^2}$

   (iii) $\dfrac{3x^2-4x-3}{(3x-2)^2}$ (iv) $\dfrac{\sin x - \cos x - x\cos x}{\sin^2 x}$

   (v) $\dfrac{-1-2x}{(2x-1)^3}$ (vi) $\dfrac{\cos x - \sin x - 1}{(1-\cos x)^2}$

   (vii) $\dfrac{-3(1+x)\sin 3x - 2\cos 3x}{(1+x)^3}$ (viii) $\dfrac{2(x\sec^2 x - \tan x)}{(x-\tan x)^2}$

   (ix) $\dfrac{1}{(x^2+1)^{1\frac{1}{2}}}$

2. (i) $-\dfrac{1}{x^2} - \dfrac{2}{x^3}$ (ii) $\dfrac{1}{x}\sec^2 x - \dfrac{1}{x^2}\tan x$

   (iii) $\dfrac{-6}{(3x+1)^3}$ (iv) $\dfrac{\sin x - x\cos x}{\sin^2 x}$

   (v) $\dfrac{-1}{(x-1)^2}$ (vi) $2\sec^2 x$

   (vii) $\dfrac{-(1-\sin x)}{(x+\cos x)^2}$ (viii) $\dfrac{2x(\cos x + x\sin x)}{\cos^3 x}$

   (ix) $\dfrac{3}{x^2}\cdot\cos 3x - \dfrac{2}{x^3}\cdot\sin 3x$ (x) $\dfrac{2}{x^2}$

   (xi) $2\tan x . \sec^2 x$ (xii) $\dfrac{6-4x-x^2}{x^2(x-3)^2}$

3. $\sec^2 x$, $\sec x . \tan x$, $-\operatorname{cosec}^2 x$, $-\cot x . \operatorname{cosec} x$

4. $n . \tan x . \sec^n x$

5. $\dfrac{-8(x-2)}{(x+1)^4}$, $\dfrac{24(x-3)}{(x+1)^5}$, $\dfrac{-96(x-4)}{(x+1)^6}$, $\dfrac{-4(-1)^n . n!(x-n)}{(x+1)^{n+2}}$

6. (i) $\tan x(\cos x + \sec x)$ (ii) $2 \tan x . \sec^2 x$

   (iii) $(1 + \sin^2 x)/\cos^3 x$ (iv) $-4 \cot 2x . \operatorname{cosec} 2x$

7. (i) $2y + x = -1$ (ii) $y + 2x = 1$

8. (i) max. $(-2, -4)$, min. $(0, 0)$ (ii) max. $(1, -1)$, min. $(2, -\frac{1}{2})$

9. (i) $x \cos 2x + \frac{1}{2} \sin 2x$ (ii) $6x(x^2 - 1)^2$

   (iii) $\dfrac{\sin x + x \cos x + x^2 \cos x}{(1+x)^2}$ (iv) $\dfrac{1 + 2x^2 + x^3}{(1+x)^2(1+x^2)}$

10. (i) $x = +\sqrt{3}$, $x = -\sqrt{3}$ (ii) $y = x$

    (iii) max. $(-3, -4\frac{1}{2})$, inf. $(0, 0)$, min. $(3, 4\frac{1}{2})$

Exercise 17(a)

1. $x^2 + y^2 = 9$ 2. $xy = 4$ 3. $y^2 = 8x + 16$ 4. $6y = 4x - 11$

5. $8x^2 + 8y^2 - 12x - 22y + 5 = 0$ 6. $x^2 + 4x + y^2 - 10y = 7$

7. $x = 2y - 4$ and $x = 4 - 2y$ 8. $4x^2 - 8x + 3y^2 - 24y + 40 = 0$

9. $x^2 + y^2 - 6x - 6y + 13 = 0$ 10. $y^2 = 4ax$ 11. $x^2 + y^2 = 13$

12. $y = \frac{3}{4}x + 3$ and $y = \frac{3}{4}x - 3$ 13. $y^2 = 12x - 12$

14. $32x^2 + 36y^2 = 45$

Exercise 17(b)

1. (i) $x^2 + y^2 = 49$ (ii) $x^2 - 6x + y^2 - 2y - 6 = 0$

   (iii) $x^2 - 8x + y^2 + 2y + 13 = 0$ (iv) $x^2 - 2ax + y^2 - 2ay - 2a^2 = 0$

2. $x^2 + 6x + y^2 - 10y + 9 = 0$, $(0, 1)$ and $(0, 9)$

3. $x^2 - 8x + y^2 - 6y = 0$, $(8, 0)$ and $(0, 6)$

4. (i) centre $(0, 0)$, radius 4 (ii) centre $(2, 1)$, radius 3

   (iii) centre $(-4, 5)$, radius 6 (iv) centre $(-6, 0)$, radius 7

   (v) centre $(-1\frac{1}{2}, \frac{1}{2})$, radius $\sqrt{2}$ (vi) centre $(-1, 1\frac{1}{3})$, radius $1\frac{2}{3}$

5. $x^2 - 2x + y^2 - 6y = 15$, $x^2 - 2x + y^2 + 6y = 15$ 6. $(0, -1)$, 2 units

7. $(-2, -4)$ and $(1, 2)$, $(-\frac{1}{2}, -1)$ 8. (i) 4 units (ii) 4 units

9. (i) $x^2 + y^2 - 16x + 28 = 0$ (ii) $x^2 + y^2 - 16x - 336 = 0$

10. $(2, 1)$ and $(6, 3)$ 12. $4y + 3x = 12$, $(4, 0)$

13. $x^2 + y^2 - 8x - 6\frac{1}{2}y + 16 = 0$, $x^2 + y^2 + 4x - 6\frac{1}{2}y + 4 = 0$

14. $(3, 2\frac{1}{4})$, $(0, 2\frac{1}{2})$

Exercise 17(c)

1. (i) 3 (ii) $\sqrt{10}$ (iii) $4\sqrt{2}$ (iv) $1/\sqrt{3}$ (v) 0 (vi) $3\sqrt{5}$

2. B and C 4. $\frac{1}{2}$ unit

5. (i) $x^2 + y^2 - 2x - 6y - 8 = 0$ (ii) $x^2 + y^2 - y = 0$

6. 12 units 7. $2y + 4x = 1$, $(\frac{1}{2}, -\frac{1}{2})$

8. $5y - 12x = 20$, $5y - 12x = -6$

Exercise 17(d)

1. $(-4, 2)$ and $(7, 2)$, $-\frac{11}{3}$ and $\frac{11}{3}$ 2. (i) $y + 3x = 14$ (ii) $10y = 14x - 21$
3. (i) $3y = -4x - 8$ (ii) $4y = 3x - 19$ 4. $2y = 3x + 4$, $(2, 5)$
5. (i) $2x^2 + 2y^2 + 3x - y = 15$ (ii) $x^2 + y^2 - 2x - 2y = 3$
6. (i) $x^2 + y^2 - 10x - 10y + 33 = 0$ (ii) $x^2 + y^2 - x - 6y + 3 = 0$
7. reflection in (i) y-axis   (ii) x-axis   (iii) $y = -x$
8. (ii) $a^2 = 4c$ 9. $x^2 + y^2 - 3x - 7y + 2 = 0$
10. $x^2 + y^2 - 5x + y - 12 = 0$, $(0, 3)$ and $(0, -4)$
11. $2x^2 + 2y^2 + x + 3y - 11 = 0$ 12. $8y = 6x + 9$
13. $m = 2$ or $\frac{2}{11}$, $y = 2x$ and $y = \frac{2}{11}x$
14. $m = -3$ or $\frac{13}{9}$, $y = -3x + 7$ and $9y = 13x + 63$

Exercise 18(b)

1. (i) $1/x$ (ii) $3/x$ (iii) $1/(x - 5)$
   (iv) $-1/x$ (v) $3/(3x + 1)$ (vi) $2x/(x^2 - 1)$
   (vii) $-\tan x$ (viii) $-2/(7 - 2x)$ (ix) $\cos x/(1 + \sin x)$

2. (i) 0.2 (ii) 0.217 (iii) 0.4 (iv) $\sqrt{3}$

3. (i) $\sec^2 x/\tan x$ (ii) $2/(3 + x)$ (iii) $2 \cot x$
   (iv) $\tan x$ (v) $1/2(x + 1)$ (vi) $(x^2 - 1)/(x^3 + x)$

4. $|x| > \sqrt{3}$, $x = 3$
5. (i) $1 + \ln x$, $1/x$ (ii) $x + 2x \cdot \ln x$, $3 + 2 \ln x$
6. (i) 2 (ii) $e^{-\frac{1}{2}} \approx 0.606$ (iii) $(1/e, -1/e)$ min.
7. (ii) $2/(1 - x^2)$, $2 \operatorname{cosec} x$, $(1 + x - x^2)/(1 + x^2)(1 - 2x)$
8. (i) $1/2xy$ (ii) $(1 + y^2)/2y$ (iii) $y/x(y - 1)$

Exercise 18(c)

1. (i) $5 \ln x + c$ (ii) $\frac{1}{3} \ln x + c$
   (iii) $-1/2x + c$ (iv) $\sin x + c$
   (v) $x - 2 \ln x + c$ (vi) $x + 2 \ln x - 1/x + c$

2. (i) $\ln (x - 3) + c$ (ii) $-1/(x - 3) + c$
   (iii) $\frac{1}{2} \ln (2x + 1) + c$ (iv) $-\ln (4 - x) + c$
   (v) $-\frac{1}{5} \ln (1 - 5x) + c$ (vi) $\frac{3}{7} \ln (7x + 1) + c$
3. (i) $\ln (x^2 + 1) + c$ (ii) $\frac{3}{2} \ln (x^2 + 1) + c$
   (iii) $-3 \ln (4 - x^2) + c$ (iv) $\frac{1}{6} \ln (3x^2 - 5) + c$
   (v) $\frac{1}{2} \ln (x^2 + 4x + 1) + c$ (vi) $\frac{1}{4} \ln (x^4 - 1) + c$
4. (i) $3 \ln (2 + \sin x) + c$ (ii) $-\ln (\cos x) + c$
   (iii) $\ln (1 + \tan x) + c$ (iv) $\ln (\cos x + \sin x) + c$
   (v) $\ln (1 + \sin^2 x) + c$ (vi) $\ln (\ln x) + c$
5. (i) $4 \ln 3 - 4$ (ii) $\frac{1}{3} \ln 4$
   (iii) $\frac{1}{3} \ln (28/9)$ (iv) $-\frac{1}{2} \ln 7$
   (v) $\frac{1}{2} \ln (4/3)$ (vi) $\ln 2$
6. (i) $2 \ln (3/2)$ (ii) $\ln 2$

Exercise 18(d) (constants of integration omitted)

1. $x + 3\ln(x - 3)$ 2. $\frac{1}{2}x - \frac{1}{4}\ln(2x + 1)$
3. $x - 3\ln(x + 2)$ 4. $-x - \ln(1 - x)$
5. $\frac{1}{3}x - \frac{1}{9}\ln(3x - 2)$ 6. $-\frac{1}{2}x + \frac{5}{4}\ln(2x - 3)$
7. $\frac{1}{2}x^2 + x + \ln(x - 1)$ 8. $\frac{1}{2}x^2 - 3x + 6\ln(x + 2)$
9. $\frac{1}{2}x^2 - x - 2\ln(x + 1)$ 10. $1 + \frac{1}{4}\ln 5$
11. $9\ln(3/2) - 2$ 12. $10\ln 3 - 4$

Exercise 18(e)

1. (i) 2.7, 1, 0.37   (ii) -1.85, 1.15
2. (i) 1.253   (ii) 0.597   (iii) ± 1.665 (iv) 2.394
   (v) 0 or 0.693   (vi) 0.288
3. (i) $10^x \cdot \ln 10$ (ii) $-2^x \cdot \ln 2$ (iii) e^x (iv) $-e^{-x}$
   (v) $2x \cdot e^{x^2}$ (vi) $(1 + \ln x)x^x$

Exercise 18(f)

1. (i) $3e^x$ (ii) $4e^{4x}$ (iii) $-e^{-x}$
   (iv) $e^x - e^{-x}$ (v) $-\frac{1}{2}e^{-\frac{1}{2}x}$ (vi) $-12e^{-3x}$
   (vii) e^x (viii) $\frac{1}{2}e^{\frac{1}{2}x}$ (ix) $2e^{2x} - 2e^{-2x}$
2. (i) 1   (ii) 3   (iii) 2
3. (i) $\frac{1}{2}e^{2x} + c$ (ii) $-\frac{1}{4}e^{-4x} + c$ (iii) $\frac{1}{3}(e - 1)$
   (iv) $2(e^2 - 1)$ (v) $x + e^{-x} + c$ (vi) $\frac{1}{2}e^{2x} + 2x - \frac{1}{2}e^{-2x} + c$
5. $(1 + x)e^x$, $(2 + x)e^x$, $(3 + x)e^x$, $(n + x)e^x$
6. min. $(0, 0)$, max. $(2, 4/e^2)$
7. (i) $x - e^{-x} + c$ (ii) $\ln(1 + e^x) + c$ (iii) $\ln(e^x + e^{-x}) + c$
8. (i) $-e^{-x}$ (ii) $e^x/(1 + e^x)^2$ (iii) $4/(e^x + e^{-x})^2$
9. $(\ln 2, 2)$, area $= \ln 2$ 10. $\pi(\ln 3 - \frac{8}{9})$

Exercise 18(g)

1. (i) $1 + 3x + \dfrac{9x^2}{2} + \dfrac{9x^3}{2} + \dfrac{27x^4}{8}$ (ii) $1 - 2x + 2x^2 - \dfrac{4x^3}{3} + \dfrac{2x^4}{3}$

   (iii) $1 + \dfrac{x}{2} + \dfrac{x^2}{8} + \dfrac{x^3}{48} + \dfrac{x^4}{384}$ (iv) $1 + x^2 + \dfrac{x^4}{4} + \dfrac{x^6}{6} + \dfrac{x^8}{24}$

   (v) $1 + 2x + 2x^2 + \dfrac{4x^3}{3} + \dfrac{2x^4}{3}$ (vi) $1 - \dfrac{1}{x} + \dfrac{1}{2x^2} - \dfrac{1}{6x^3} + \dfrac{1}{24x^4}$

2. (i)   1.6487   (ii) 0.3679   (iii) 0.7165
3. (i) $x - \dfrac{x^2}{2!} + \dfrac{x^3}{3!} - \dfrac{x^4}{4!} + \dfrac{x^5}{5!}$ (ii) $1 - \dfrac{x^2}{2} + \dfrac{x^3}{3} - \dfrac{x^4}{8} + \dfrac{x^5}{30}$

   (iii) $1 + \dfrac{x^2}{2!} + \dfrac{x^4}{4!} + \dfrac{x^6}{6!} + \dfrac{x^8}{8!}$ (iv) $2 + 2x - \dfrac{2x^3}{3} - \dfrac{5x^4}{12} - \dfrac{3x^5}{20}$

(v) $1 + x - \dfrac{x^2}{2} - \dfrac{x^3}{6} + \dfrac{5x^4}{24}$

(vi) $2\left[x + \dfrac{x^3}{3!} + \dfrac{x^5}{5!} + \dfrac{x^7}{7!} + \dfrac{x^9}{9!} \right]$

6. (i) $-x - \dfrac{x^2}{2} - \dfrac{x^3}{3} - \dfrac{x^4}{4} - \dfrac{x^5}{5}$

(ii) $2x - 2x^2 + \dfrac{8x^3}{3} - 4x^4 + \dfrac{32x^5}{5}$

(iii) $\dfrac{1}{2}\left[x - \dfrac{x^2}{2} + \dfrac{x^3}{3} - \dfrac{x^4}{4} + \dfrac{x^5}{5} \right]$

(iv) $x^2 - \dfrac{x^4}{2} + \dfrac{x^6}{3} - \dfrac{x^8}{4} + \dfrac{x^{10}}{5}$

8. (i) $x + \dfrac{3x^2}{2} + \dfrac{x^3}{3} - \dfrac{x^4}{4}$

(ii) $-x + \dfrac{x^2}{2} + \dfrac{x^3}{6} + \dfrac{x^4}{12}$

(iii) $x - \dfrac{3x^2}{2} + \dfrac{4x^3}{3} - x^4$

9. 4.6347, 4.6540   10. 3.93183

Exercise 19(a)

1. $x = y^2 - 4y$, $\frac{1}{4}$ and $-\frac{1}{4}$ 2. $y = x(x+2)^2$, $3t^2 - 4t$, $y = 7x + 18$

4. $y^2 = (x+3)(x-1)^2$, $(0, \sqrt{3})$ and $(0, -\sqrt{3})$, $x = -1\frac{2}{3}$

5. (i) $-1/4t^3$ (ii) $-4t^3/(t^2-1)^3$

6. (i) $x^2 + y^2 = 16$ (ii) $(x-1)^2 + y^2 = 1$ (iii) $(x-3)^2 + (y+1)^2 = 4$

7. (i) $\dfrac{x^2}{16} + \dfrac{y^2}{9} = 1$ (ii) $\dfrac{x^2}{a^2} + \dfrac{y^2}{b^2} = 1$

8. $(\frac{1}{2}, \frac{1}{2}\sqrt{3})$ and $(1, 0)$, 1 unit.   10. $3y = x + 9$, $-2y = x + 4$

11. $t^2y + x = 2t$, $9y + x = 6$, $y + x = -2$

Exercise 19(b)

2. (i) $(0, 2)$, $(1, 2)$, $y = 2$, $x = -1$

(ii) $(2, -1)$, $(7, -1)$, $y = -1$, $x = -3$

(iii) $(-1, 3)$, $(2, 3)$, $y = 3$, $x = -4$

(iv) $(0, \frac{1}{2})$, $(0, 2\frac{1}{2})$, $x = 0$, $y = -1\frac{1}{2}$

3. (i) $y^2 = 10x$ (ii) $y^2 = -12x$ (iii) $x^2 = 24y$

(iv) $(y-3)^2 = 16x$ (v) $(y-2)^2 = 4(x-1)$

4. (i) $y^2 = 18x$ (ii) $y^2 = \dfrac{16}{3}x$ (iii) $x^2 = 18y$

5. (i) 2   (ii) $-\frac{1}{4}$ (iii) $\frac{1}{4}$

6. $(\frac{1}{2}, -2)$ and $(4\frac{1}{2}, 6)$, $y + 2x = -1$ and $3y - 2x = 9$.

7. (i) $3y = 4x - 4$, $(\frac{1}{4}, -1)$ 8. $(a, 2a)$, $(a, -2a)$, $y - x = a$, $y + x = -a$

9. $3y - x = 13\frac{1}{2}$ 10. $2y = 5x - 11$

Exercise 19(c)

1. (i) $(4t^2, 8t)$ (ii) $(\frac{1}{2}t^2, t)$ (iii) $(2t, t^2)$

(iv) $(-2t^2, 4t)$ (v) $(3t, -\frac{3}{2}t^2)$ (vi) $(-\frac{1}{4}t^2, \frac{1}{2}t)$

2. (i) $y^2 = 16x$ (ii) $y^2 = 4x$ (iii) $x^2 = 4y$

(iv) $y^2 = 24x$ (v) $y^2 = -24x$ (vi) $x^2 = -12y$

3. 16   4. (i) $\frac{1}{2}$ (ii) $-\frac{2}{3}$ (iii) $-\frac{1}{2}$ 5. $(2, -4)$ and $(50/9, 20/3)$

6. $(\frac{1}{3}, 2)$ 7. $4y = 3x - 6$, $t = -\frac{1}{3}$

8. (i) $2y = 4x + 5$ (ii) $3y = x + 99$ (iii) $ty = x + t^2$

9. $-y = 2x + 4$, $3y = 2x + 36$ 10. $5y = 4x + 12$ 11. $y^2 = 20x$

Exercise 19(e)

1. (i) $y^2 = ax$ (ii) $y^2 = 8ax$ 3. $y^2 = ax - a^2$

4. $y^2 = 8ax + 8a^2$ 5. $y^2 = 9ax/2$

8. (i) $(x - 1)^2 + y^2 = \frac{1}{4}$ (ii) $(2x - 2)^2 + y^2 = 1$

10. (ii) $y^2 = 2ax + 4a^2$

Exercise 20(a)

1. (i) $\pm 3i$ (ii) $\pm 10i$ (iii) $\pm \sqrt{7}i$ (iv) $\pm \frac{1}{2}i$

2. (i) $\pm 5i$ (ii) $\pm 4i$ (iii) $\pm \frac{3}{2}i$ (iv) 0 or $\pm 2i$

3. (i) -1 (ii) -4 (iii) -16 (iv) 1

   (v) -1 (vi) $-i$ (vii) $-8i$ (viii) $-i$

   (ix) $8i$ (x) 0 (xi) -1 (xii) $-2i$

4. (i) $x = \pm 2$ or $\pm 2i$ (ii) ± 3 or $\pm 3i$

Exercise 20(b)

1. (i) rational (ii) rational (iii) irrational (iv) imaginary (v) complex

   (vi) rational   (vii) 1 rational and 2 irrational

   (viii) 1 rational and 2 imaginary

2. (i) $3 - 5i$ (ii) $-2 + 7i$ (iii) $\sqrt{2} - \sqrt{3}i$

   (iv) $-3i - 1$ (v) $-2i$ (vi) $\cos\theta - i\sin\theta$

3. (i) $\pm 3i$ (ii) $-4 \pm 3i$ (iii) $\frac{1}{2} \pm \frac{1}{2}\sqrt{3}i$ (iv) $\frac{3}{4} + \frac{1}{4}\sqrt{7}i$

4. (i) $2, -2 \pm \sqrt{3}i$ (ii) $1, -\frac{1}{3} \pm \frac{1}{3}\sqrt{2}i$ (iii) $3, \frac{1}{4}(-3 \pm \sqrt{17})$ (iv) $\frac{1}{2}, \pm i$

5. $-1, \frac{1}{2} \pm \frac{1}{2}\sqrt{3}i$

6. (i) ± 1 and ± 2 (ii) ± 1 and $\pm 2i$ (iii) $0, 1, -1 \pm i$

   (iv) $0, -1, \frac{1}{2} \pm \frac{1}{2}\sqrt{7}i$

Exercise 20(c)

1. (i) $7 - 4i$ (ii) $1 - 6i$ (iii) $17 - 11i$

   (iv) $(7 - 19i)/10$ (v) $(7 + 19i)/41$ (vi) $(3 - i)/10$

2. (i) $10 - 2i, 29 + 2i$ (ii) $7 + 2i, 3 + 21i$

   (iii) $10, 34$ (iv) $3 + 2\sqrt{3}i, -1 + 3\sqrt{3}i$

3. (i) $(1 + 2i)/5$ (ii) $(-3 + 21i)/50$ (iii) $(8 + 15i)/17$ (iv) $(5 + \sqrt{3}i)/7$

4. (i) $12 - 16i$ (ii) $(3 + 4i)/100$ (iii) $-46 + 9i$ (iv) $-7 + 24i$

5. (i) $-2 + 5i$ (ii) $(57 + 46i)/5$

6. (i) $3 - 4i, -4$ (ii) $-2i, 3$ (iii) $3 + 2i, -6, k = 78$

7. (i) $x = \frac{2}{29}, y = \frac{5}{29}$ (ii) $x = 16, y = 30$

8. (i) $3 - i$ and $-3 + i$ i.e. $\pm(3 - i)$ (ii) $\pm(4 - 3i)$

9. (i) $(x_1 + x_2) + (y_1 + y_2)i$ (ii) $(x_1 x_2 - y_1 y_2) + (x_1 y_2 + x_2 y_1)i$

(iii) $\dfrac{(x_1 x_2 + y_1 y_2) + (x_2 y_1 - x_1 y_2)i}{(x_2{}^2 + y_2{}^2)}$

10. (i) $3 - 3i$ (ii) $3 + 3i$ (iii) $-6 + 13i$
    (iv) $-6 - 13i$ (v) $3 + 3i$ (vi) $-6 - 13i$

13. (i) $(x^2 - y^2) + 2xyi$ (ii) $x^2 + y^2$ (iii) $\dfrac{x - yi}{(x^2 + y^2)}$ (iv) $4xyi$

Exercise 20(d)

1. (i) $\sqrt{26}, 0.20^r$; $2\sqrt{5}, 2.03^r$; $\sqrt{10}, 1.25^r$
3. (i) $5, 0.64r$ (ii) $4, \frac{1}{2}\pi$ (iii) $\sqrt{2}, -\frac{1}{4}\pi$
   (iv) $2, \frac{2}{3}\pi$ (v) $5\sqrt{2}, -\frac{3}{4}\pi$ (vi) $4\sqrt{3}, -\frac{1}{6}\pi$
4. (i) $-2\sqrt{2} + 2\sqrt{2}i$ (ii) $5\sqrt{3} - 5i$ (iii) $-2i$
   (iv) $\sqrt{5} + 2\sqrt{5}i$ (or $-\sqrt{5} - 2\sqrt{5}i$)
6. (i) $6, 2, 12$ then $3, 2, 6$ (ii) $\frac{2}{3}\pi, \frac{1}{6}\pi, \frac{5}{6}\pi$ then $\frac{1}{2}\pi, -\frac{1}{4}\pi, \frac{1}{4}\pi$
7. $3, \frac{1}{2}\pi$ then $1\frac{1}{2}, \frac{3}{4}\pi$
8. (i) $1, -\frac{1}{2} \pm \frac{1}{2}\sqrt{3}i$ arguments $0, \frac{2}{3}\pi$ and $-\frac{2}{3}\pi$
   (ii) $1, -1, i, -i$ arguments $0, \pi, \frac{1}{2}\pi$ and $-\frac{1}{2}\pi$
   (iii) $0, \pm\frac{2}{5}\pi, \pm\frac{4}{5}\pi$

Exercise 20(e)

1. (i) $9, 165°$; $4, 75°$ (ii) $2\frac{1}{4}i$ (iii) 216
2. (i) $20, 60°$; $100, 150°$; $5, 90°$; $0.2, -90°$ (ii) $5i, -0.2i$
3. (i) $4\sqrt{2}, 5\pi/12$ (ii) $1/\sqrt{2}, 11\pi/12$ (iii) $8, -\frac{1}{2}\pi$
4. (i) $\sqrt{2}, \frac{1}{4}\pi$ (ii) $z^2 = 2i, z^3 = -2 + 2i, z^4 = -4$
   (iii) $8, z^8 = 16$
5. $|z| = 2, \arg(z) = \frac{1}{4}\pi$ or $-\frac{3}{4}\pi, \pm(\sqrt{2} + \sqrt{2}i)$
6. $\pm(-1 + \sqrt{3}i)$

Exercise 20(f)

1. (i) $x^2 + y^2 = 4$ (ii) $y = 0$ (iii) $y = x$ (for $x > 0$)
2. (i) $x^2 + (y - 2)^2 = 9$ (ii) $(x - 3)^2 + (y - 2)^2 = 16$
4. (i) $x^2 + y^2 = 25$ (ii) $(x - 3)^2 + y^2 = 25$
   (iii) $(x - 3)^2 + (y + 1)^2 = 25$
6. (i) $x = -1$ (ii) $4x - 2y = 3$; $z = -1 - 3\frac{1}{2}i$

Exercise 21(a) (constants of integration omitted)

1. (i) $x\sin x + \cos x$ (ii) $\frac{1}{9}\sin 3x - \frac{1}{3}x.\cos 3x$
   (iii) $\frac{1}{3}x^3 \ln x - \frac{1}{9}x^3$ (iv) $xe^x - e^x$
   (v) $-\frac{1}{x}\ln x - \frac{1}{x}$ (vi) $2x.\sin \frac{1}{2}x + 4\cos \frac{1}{2}x$
2. (i) π (ii) $1 - (3/e^2)$ (iii) $2\ln 2 - \frac{3}{4}$
3. $x\ln x - x$

4. (i) $\frac{1}{8}\sin 2x - \frac{1}{4}x.\cos 2x$ (ii) $x^2 e^x - 2xe^x + 2e^x$

   (iii) $x\tan x + \ln(\cos x)$ (iv) $x^2.\sin x + 2x.\cos x - 2\sin x$

   (v) $\frac{1}{4}x.\sin 2x + \frac{1}{8}\cos 2x + \frac{1}{4}x^2$ (vi) $\frac{1}{2}(\ln x)^2$

5. (i) $\frac{1}{8}e - \frac{1}{4}$ (ii) $\frac{1}{16}\pi^2 - \frac{1}{4}\pi + \frac{1}{2}$ (iii) $\frac{1}{4}e^2 + \frac{11}{6}$

6. (i) $\frac{1}{2}e^x(\cos x + \sin x)$ (ii) $-\frac{1}{2}e^{-x}(\cos x + \sin x)$

   (iii) $\frac{1}{13}e^{3x}(2\sin 2x + 3\cos 2x)$

Exercise 21(b)

1. $26/3$ 2. $68/15$ 3. $1/108$ 4. $1\frac{1}{2} + 2\ln 2$

5. $184/105$ 6. $2 - 2\ln\left(\frac{3}{2}\right)$ 7. $\frac{1}{4}\sqrt{3}$ 8. $1 - \frac{1}{4}\pi$

9. $\dfrac{1}{4}\ln(2x - 3) - \dfrac{3}{4(2x - 3)} + c$ 10. $\dfrac{1}{3}(x - 1)\sqrt{2x + 1} + c$

11. $-2\cos\sqrt{x} + c$ 12. $\frac{1}{2}(\ln x)^2 + c$

13. $\frac{2}{15}(3x - 2)(x + 1)^{\frac{3}{2}} + c$ 14. $2\ln(1 + \sqrt{x}) + c$

15. $\arccos x - \frac{1}{x}\sqrt{1 - x^2} + c$ 16. $-\frac{1}{3}(x^2 + 2)\sqrt{1 - x^2} + c$

Exercise 21(c)

1. $\pi/2$ 2. $\pi/12$ 3. π 4. $\pi/6\sqrt{3}$ 5. $\pi/6$ 6. $\pi/12$

7. $\pi/12$ 8. $\arctan(e) - \frac{1}{4}\pi$

Exercise 21(d)

1. $\dfrac{3}{(x + 2)} - \dfrac{1}{(x - 1)}$ 2. $\dfrac{1}{(x + 1)} + \dfrac{1}{(x - 1)}$

3. $\dfrac{2}{x} - \dfrac{1}{(x + 2)}$ 4. $\dfrac{2}{(x + 2)} - \dfrac{3}{(2x - 1)}$

5. $2 + \dfrac{5}{x} - \dfrac{3}{(x - 1)}$ 6. $\dfrac{3}{(3x - 1)} - \dfrac{1}{(x + 2)}$

7. $\dfrac{2}{(x + 1)} - \dfrac{3}{(3x - 2)}$ 8. $1 + \dfrac{3}{(x + 2)} - \dfrac{2}{(x + 1)}$

9. $\ln\left[(x + 3)^2(x - 1)\right] + c$ 10. $\ln\left[2x^2 - x - 3\right] + c$

11. $\dfrac{1}{2}\ln\left[\dfrac{x - 1}{x + 1}\right] + c$ 12. $\ln\left[(x - 3)^3(x + 2)^2\right] + c$

13. $\frac{1}{2}\ln 3$ 14. $2 + \ln\left(\frac{5}{3}\right)$

15. $x + \ln\left[(x - 2)^3(x - 1)\right] + c$ 16. $\frac{1}{3}\ln\left[x(x - 3)^2\right] + c$

17. $\ln\left[\dfrac{\sqrt{x} - 1}{\sqrt{x} + 1}\right]$ 18. $x - \ln(e^x + 1) + c$

19. $\frac{1}{3}\ln\left(\frac{9}{8}\right)$ 20. $2 + \ln\left(\frac{3}{2}\right)$

Exercise 21(e)

1. $\dfrac{1}{(x + 3)} - \dfrac{2}{(x + 3)^2}$ 2. $\dfrac{2x + 1}{(x^2 + 2)} - \dfrac{2}{x}$

3. $\dfrac{1}{2(2x-3)}+\dfrac{1}{2(2x-3)^2}$ 4. $\dfrac{x}{(5+x^2)}+\dfrac{1}{(1-x)}$

5. $\dfrac{1}{2}\ln\left[\dfrac{x^2}{x^2+1}\right]+c$ 6. $\dfrac{1}{(1-x)}+\ln(1-x)+c$

7. $\dfrac{1}{2}\ln\left[\dfrac{(x-2)^2}{x^2+3}\right]+c$ 8. $\ln\left[\dfrac{x^2}{x^2+x+1}\right]+c$

9. $2\ln\left(\dfrac{3}{2}\right)-\dfrac{1}{2}$ 10. $\dfrac{1}{4}\pi-\dfrac{1}{2}\ln 2$

11. $x+\dfrac{1}{(x-2)}-\ln(x-2)+c$ 12. $\dfrac{1}{2}\ln\left[\dfrac{4+x^2}{(1-x)^2}\right]+\arctan\left(\dfrac{x}{2}\right)+c$

13. (i) $\dfrac{2}{x^3}-\dfrac{2}{(x+1)^3},\quad -\dfrac{6}{x^4}+\dfrac{6}{(x+1)^4}$

(ii) $\dfrac{4}{(x-2)^3}-\dfrac{24}{(2x-1)^3},\quad -\dfrac{12}{(x-2)^4}+\dfrac{144}{(x-2)^4}$

(iii) $\dfrac{2}{(x-2)^3}+\dfrac{1}{(x+1)^3}-\dfrac{3}{(x-1)^3},\quad -\dfrac{6}{(x-2)^4}-\dfrac{3}{(x+1)^4}+\dfrac{9}{(x-1)^4}$

14. $\dfrac{(n+1)!}{(1-x)^{n+2}}-\dfrac{n!}{(1-x)^{n+1}}$ or $\dfrac{n!(n+x)}{(1-x)^{n+2}}$

15. $x-2x^2+7x^3-20x^4+\ldots,\quad -\frac{1}{3}<x<\frac{1}{3}$

16. $1-3x+7x^2-15x^3+31x^4-\ldots$

17. $a=b=1,\ c=d=e=f=2,\ 0<|x|<1$

Exercise 21(f) (constants of integration omitted)

1. $2x^2+4x+\ln x$ 2. $\frac{1}{2}\tan 2\theta$ 3. $\frac{1}{2}\sin 2\theta$

4. $\dfrac{-1}{4(2x-3)^2}$ 5. $\frac{1}{2}x-\frac{1}{4}\ln(1+2x)$ 6. $\frac{1}{3}(x^2+1)^{\frac{3}{2}}$

7. $\frac{1}{2}\theta+\frac{1}{8}\sin 4\theta$ 8. $-\frac{1}{10}\cos 5\theta-\frac{1}{2}\cos\theta$ 9. $\frac{1}{4}\sin 2x-\frac{1}{2}x\cos 2x$

10. $2x^{\frac{1}{2}}-\frac{2}{3}x^{\frac{3}{2}}$ 11. $-\frac{1}{3}\cos^3\theta$ 12. $\frac{4}{3}\sin^3\theta-\frac{4}{5}\sin^5\theta$

13. $\frac{1}{2}x^2+3x+9\ln(x-3)$ 14. $x+6\ln(x-3)-\dfrac{9}{(x-3)}$

15. $\frac{1}{15}(3x-1)(1+2x)^{\frac{3}{2}}$ 16. $\dfrac{-1}{(1+e^x)}$ 17. $\frac{1}{2}\ln(1+\sin 2\theta)$

18. $\frac{1}{2}\tan\theta$ 19. $\frac{1}{6}\ln[(2x-1)(x+1)^2]$ 20. $\frac{1}{3}\ln(x^3-3x+1)$

21. $\arcsin\left(\frac{x}{2}\right)$ 22. $-(x^2+2x+2)e^{-x}$ 23. $\sec\theta$

24. $\frac{1}{8}\theta-\frac{1}{32}\sin 4\theta$ 25. $\frac{2}{3}(\ln x)^{\frac{3}{2}}$

26. $\frac{2}{15}\sqrt{1+x}(3x^2-4x+8)$ 27. $\ln\left[\dfrac{(x+3)^2}{x+2}\right]$

28. $\frac{1}{2}\ln[(x+1)(x+3)]$ 29. $\frac{1}{4}\ln\left[\dfrac{x^4-1}{x^4}\right]$ 30. $\frac{1}{4}\ln\left[\dfrac{x^2-1}{x^2+1}\right]$

Exercise 22(a)

1. (i) 24   (ii) 17 160   2. (i) 720   (ii) 120   3. 72, 432

4. 5040   5. 729   6. 120   7. (i) 6720   (ii) 3360   8. 3840
9. 80, 32   10. 72   11. 360, 120
12. (i) 360   (ii) 6720   (iii) 1260   (iv) 302 400   13. 1680, 1560
14. 136   15. (i) 24   (ii) 192   (iii) 24   16. 1440

Exercise 22(b)

1. 35, 126, 15, 252, 220, 2002   2. 56   3. 924   4. approx. 1.2×10^9
5. 1820   6. 728   7. (i) 15   (ii) 360   8. 7200   9. 29
10. 810   11. 203   12. (i) 34 650   (ii) 11 550
13. (i) 420   (ii) 595   (iii) 561
14. 792, 56   15. 1050, 24
16. (i) $^{48}C_{13}$ (ii) $4 \times {}^{48}C_{12}$ (iii) $^{4}C_2 \times {}^{48}C_{11}$ (iv) $2 \times {}^{26}C_{13}$
    (v) $4 \times {}^{39}C_{13}$
17. 4845, 2380   18. (i) 21   (ii) 140   (iii) 210; 44 520
19. 1296, 204

Exercise 22(c)

1. (i) 220   (ii) 126   (iii) 190   3. (i) $2^{10} - 1 = 1023$ (ii) $2^n - 1$

Exercise 22(d)

1. $y = Ae^{x^2}$ 2. $y^2 = A(1 + x^2)$ 3. $y^2 = x + \ln(x - 1) + c$

4. $y = Axe^{x^2}$ 5. $y = \dfrac{2}{(1 - x^2)}$ 6. $y^2 + x^2 = 1$

7. $y = \frac{1}{x} - 1$ 8. $y = \dfrac{1}{(x - 2)(x + 1)}$ 9. $y = x^3$

11. $S = \dfrac{10S_0}{(10 - t)}$ 12. $V = V_0(1 - \frac{1}{4}t)^2$

15. (i) $y = 2e^x - x - 1$ (ii) $y = \tan(x + \frac{1}{4}\pi) - x$
16. (i) $y^2 = x^2(1 + 2\ln x)$ (ii) $y = x \ln x/(1 + \ln x)$

Exercise 22(e)

1. (i) $\sec^2 x \cdot \delta x$ (ii) $e^x \cdot \delta x$ (iii) $-2 \sin 2x \cdot \delta x$ (iv) $-\dfrac{1}{x^2} \cdot \delta x$
   (v) $\sin 2x \cdot \delta x$ (vi) $\cot x \cdot \delta x$
2. $2\pi r \cdot \delta r$, 0.31 cm^2 3. $4\pi r^2 \cdot \delta r$, 22.6 cm^3
4. (i) 1.035   (ii) 0.713   (iii) 0.4924   (iv) 2.773

Exercise 22(f)

1. (i) 1.791   (ii) 1.549   2. (i) 1.516   (ii) 2.926   (iii) 1.763
3. (i) 1.146   (ii) 1.466   (iii) 0.453   (iv) 1.910

Index